GW00381394

Operational Research Analysis and Applications

Operational Research:
Analysis and Applications

Michael Wilkes
Senior Lecturer in Economics
School of Social Sciences
University of Birmingham

McGRAW-HILL BOOK COMPANY

London • New York • St Louis • San Francisco • Auckland
Bogotá • Guatemala • Hamburg • Lisbon • Madrid • Mexico
Montreal • New Delhi • Panama • Paris • San Juan • São Paulo
Singapore • Sydney • Tokyo • Toronto

Published by
McGRAW-HILL Book Company (UK) Limited
Maidenhead · Berkshire · England

British Library Cataloguing in Publication Data

Wilkes, Michael
    Operational research: analysis and applications.
    1. Management. Operations research
    I. Title
    658.4'034 .

    ISBN 0-07-707210-3

Library of Congress Cataloging-in-Publication Data

Wilkes, Michael
    Operational research: analysis and applications/Michael Wilkes.
    p.   cm.
    Includes bibliographies and index.
    ISBN 0-07-707210-3
    1. Operations research.   I. Title.
    T57.6.W638   1989
    658.4'034—dc20

                   89-32845

Copyright © 1989 Michael Wilkes. All rights reserved.
No part of this publication may be reproduced, stored in a
retrieval system, or transmitted, in any form or by any
means, electronic, mechanical, photocopying, recording, or
otherwise, without the prior permission of the author and
McGraw-Hill Book Company (UK) Limited.
1234 IP 8909
Typeset, printed and bound by Interprint Ltd (Malta)

CONTENTS

PREFACE

Operational research—the scientific approach to organizational problems—is a subject that is at once highly relevant and intellectually stimulating. Many of the techniques are not difficult to grasp and have become widely used. Many more, if presented in an appropriate way, can be made accessible to a wide audience. This is one of the prime objectives of *Operational Research: Analysis and Applications*. Formalisms have been eliminated and extensive use is made of worked examples to convey the essential points. An important feature of the book is the wide range of topics and sub-topics covered.

A modular approach to the subject is adopted with most chapters being self-contained. This allows for the topics to be selected which are most appropriate to particular courses or half-courses. Nevertheless, careful attention has been given to the linkage between topics and an overall view of the subject is contained in Chapter One.

A theme throughout is the use of sensitivity analysis (what happens to the solution when problem parameters change). Sensitivity analysis is not only a most practical way to handle data uncertainties and present results but also a way of developing insight into the structure of the models. To be of maximum value in practice, operational research techniques must convey as much management information as possible. Within an effective organization, it is the task of management to vary restricting parameters. A clear understanding of sensitivity analysis is therefore essential.

It is also important to appreciate the role played by computers both in the application of operational research methods to practical situations and in the development of the subject as a whole. Appropriate reference is made throughout the text to the use of both mainframe and micro-computers in operational research.

The exercise section begins with a revision exercise covering the key points developed in the chapter. The answers to the revision exercises can be found within the text and the successful completion of the revision exercise represents a learning objective for the narrative part of the material. The revision exercise is followed by numerical exercises corresponding to the examples in the text and the technical areas covered. These numerical exercises are complemented by questions from past examination papers of professional accountancy bodies. The solution guides give answers to the numerical questions and an operational research perspective on the accountancy examination questions. Each chapter ends with references, where used, and a brief list of further reading.

In each topic, all the questions commonly posed by students should be covered within the text and the examples used have been constructed to maximize pedagogical value. The treatment of linear programming has been divided into two chapters. Chapter Two covers the essentials of the topic without the use of the simplex method. Chapter Three explains the simplex method and applies it to both maximization and minimization problems. It is suggested that Chapter Two by itself would be suitable for inclusion in an introductory half-course at first-year polytechnic or university level.

A suggested introductory half-course could consist of:

Introduction
Linear programming (non-simplex)
Transportation problems
Critical path method
Stock control
Queueing theory
Statistical replacement methods
Simulation

Naturally, selectivity is possible as to the sections of each chapter employed depending on the depth of the coverage required. *Operational Research: analysis and applications* as a whole would represent the basis of an introductory full course. Again, the sectionalized and progressive structure within each chapter allows suitable variation of emphasis as desired and as time permits.

Operational research is an absorbing subject of enormous practical utility. It provides a powerful insight into model structures and the potential performance of systems. A study of OR should prove to be both productive and pleasant and it is hoped that the accessible style of this book will succeed in conveying this.

Operational Research: Analysis and Applications is a development of the earlier McGraw-Hill text *Elements of Operational Research* published in 1980 and users of this should find themselves very much at home with this latest book.

I should like to thank Julie Ganner of McGraw-Hill for eliciting much helpful feedback and for demonstrating that cost minimization can be made a practical reality. My thanks also to Vivienne Wilkes for assistance in manuscript preparation; to John Morris of the Economics Department at the University of Birmingham for permission to reproduce computer programs; to the various professional accounting bodies for permission to reproduce questions; to an anonymous reviewer for helpful and detailed comments and to students over the years who have helped in the development of this particular approach to operational research.

Michael Wilkes

INTRODUCTION

1-1 OPERATIONAL RESEARCH

Operational research (also known as operations research, operational management and management science) applies mathematical and logical methods to improve efficiency and help solve managerial problems in business and administration. Operational research (OR) approaches problems in a scientific way and so involves measurement, the construction of models and testing. The name 'operational research' originated in England at the time of the Second World War to describe scientific studies of military operations, but an increasingly systematic approach to practical management in industry had been developing gradually since the Industrial Revolution. After the War, operational research methods, particularly linear programming, were seen to have an enormous range of applications in business and industry, increasingly made possible by parallel developments in computing.

It is as well to begin with a working definition of the subject. It is not easy to give a precise explanation of the philosophy of OR, but one of the most useful definitions is the following:

> Operational Research is a scientific approach to the management of systems usually involving the allocation of scarce resources. A quantitative model of the system is developed with the objectives of prediction, control or optimization.

There are a number of key terms in the definition. We shall now consider the most important of these.

OR is the first of all a style of *approach* of business and organizational problems. It does not attempt to supplant existing decision-making procedures

1

but to improve them. A *scientific* approach means that data gathering and measurement and testing will be involved. A mathematical model that is *quantitative* will link the variables of the system and will express organizational objectives in terms of these controllable variables. The model is *developed*, i.e. it not necessarily 100 per cent correct first time. It must be tested and modified as necessary.

The fact that *scarce resources* need to be allocated between alternative and, therefore, competing uses, highlights the economizing nature of most OR problems. The word 'economize' is here used in its true sense: 'to make *best* use of', not in the widely misconceived sense of minimal usage. Economical usage of a resource is characterized by efficiency.

As an ideal, the entire *system* under study is modelled with a view to improving the effectiveness of the system as a whole. This recognizes that the interactions between the parts of a system can be as important as the parts themselves. However, it is quite legitimate to study sub-systems provided the interactions are weak or are otherwise taken into account when management is assessing the output of the model. A full systems approach is an ideal that may not always be practical but the wider organizational context of an OR model should always be borne in mind.

The objective of *prediction* is essentially passive and may take the form of estimated values of key performance indicators or parameters of the system. *Control* is a more ambitious objective where influence is exercised over the performance of the system by altering its parameters or structure. The control may result in an 'improved' or 'satisfactory' level of performance. The most ambitious objective of all, though not always a realistic one, is *optimization* where the variables are set at ideal values to produce (for example) a minimum of cost or a maximum of profit.

Operational research in use is frequently an interdisciplinary endeavour that may involve managers, economists, engineers, mathematicians, computer programmers, sales and personnel staff, etc. It is a style of approach to managerial problems amenable to logical analysis. In fact, a number of conditions need to be satisfied before a problem exists that is suitable for OR methods; Daellenbach and George (1978) list five.

Firstly, there must be a *decision maker*. The decision maker may be an individual, the board of directors, or even a computer.

Second, the decision maker must have an *objective* or objectives. Turning a perception—'we're not doing well enough'—into a specific goal is an important part of an OR exercise.

Third, the decision maker must have at least two *alternative courses of action*. If this is not the case, the decision maker faces a *fact*, rather than a *problem*.

Fourth, there must be some degree of doubt as to which course of action is best—otherwise, we are again faced with a 'non-problem'.

Finally, there must be an environment to which the problem pertains—for example, a firm.

When these conditions are fulfilled, an OR approach can be used to provide a quantitative basis for decision making.

1-2 MODELS IN OR

The OR ideal is a model of the complete system under study: for example, the firm. The essence of the systems approach is to take fully into account the interactions between all parts of a system and optimize overall. Separate analysis of and optimization on the constituent parts carried out independently may produce a far from optimal result. For example, ideal equipment utilization on the shop floor may result in more production than can be disposed of by the sales-force, more inventory than can be stored, problems with personnel in terms of hours worked, and so on.

However, there are many occasions in practice when an OR study *must* focus on one aspect of an enterprise because that is the remit given. And there are many occasions when there are relatively few implications for other parts of the system. For example, the introduction of more efficient vehicle maintenance procedures would be unlikely to have dramatic consequences elsewhere in the organization. Practical judgements have to be made and care taken about what is to be included in the model.

A *normative* model (often based on mathematical programming) seeks an ideal set of mutually consistent decisions in all the sub-problem areas (the 'parts' of the system). There is a specified goal to be optimized. Where the 'system' is the enterprise as a whole, such a normative model is called a *corporate model*. Less ambitiously, a normative model can be constructed for one aspect of the firm's operations. *Simulating* models are *positive* in that they are based on actual accountancy practice. Simulating models show 'scenarios'— the results that would follow given courses of action under specified assumptions about the future. Thus, for example, a simulation model might project balance sheets consequent upon a particular decision to invest, with a variety of assumptions about currency rates of exchange, inflation and taxation policy. In such a case, the simulation model may be little more than a series of interconnected accounting identities.

OR models, whether normative or positive, are mathematical statements of the relationships between all the important factors of a problem. The model is an abstraction that should *include* the salient features of a situation and *exclude* all else. The output of the model should consistently compare well with the performance of the actual system. If it does not, something important has been left out; for example, a significant linkage has been wrongly described or poor quality data has been fed in.

An OR model is not intended to be a comprehensive description of reality. In a sence, the model should be minimalist. The aim is to have the simplest structure possible, encompassing the essential characteristics of a system. Phillips, Ravindran and Solberg (1976) offer ten principles of model building:

1. Do not build a complicated model when a simple one will suffice.

2. Beware of moulding the problem to fit the technique.
3. Exercise great care in 'solving' the model (do not make mathematical slips).
4. Confirm the appropriateness of a model before implementing decisions.
5. A model should not be mistaken for the real thing.
6. Do not try to make a model do that for which it was not intended.
7. Beware of overselling a model.
8. The construction and development of the model itself yields many benefits.
9. GIGO (garbage in, garbage out). A model's value is no better than its data.
10. Models cannot replace decision makers.

The acid test of the value of a model building OR approach is that it should result in significant improvements on what would otherwise have been done. Perfection is not a requirement. It should always be remembered that the quantitative approach is an *aid* to decision making and not a substitute for the exercise of sound judgement or the acceptance of responsibility.

1-3 THE PHASES OF AN OR STUDY

Once the decision is taken that an operational research approach to a problem is worthwhile, there are six main phases of an OR study. These are:

1. The definition of the problem
2. The construction and reconstruction of the model
3. Data gathering
4. 'Solving' the model
5. Testing the solution for reasonableness (validation)
6. Implementation.

The flow diagram in Fig. 1-1 illustrates the relationship between the phases. Problem definition begins with the recognition that there *is* a problem and sets out a verbal description of the factors involved. This will include making vaguely perceived objectives more specific and identifying the restrictions on courses of action available. Also at this stage, a judgement needs to be made as to whether or not the OR approach will be worth the costs likely to be involved.

Once the problem is defined some of the data requirements will have been identified and construction of the mathematical model can begin. As construction of the model progresses, it may become clear that further data is required and, as the information available comes to the attention of the model builders, greater scope may be seen and the model adjusted accordingly. Thus, data gathering and model construction are interactive. The model constructed may be a formal, normative model (as in linear programing) or a representation of the essential logical structure of the system (as in simulation).

The 'solution' phase for a normative model should identify the best values

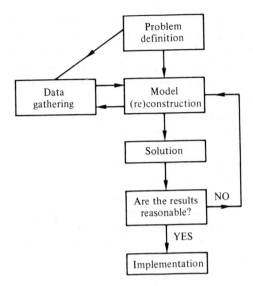

Figure 1-1 The phases of an OR study

of variables under the decision maker's control, for example, output levels, and should state the range of values of key parameters for which the solution is optimal (sensitivity analysis).

In a simulating model, the 'solution' might be the projection of profit and loss accounts, key system parameters or the probability distribution of net present values.

The validation phase gauges the reasonableness of the results. If the output of the model is not acceptable or is totally unrealistic, it may be that important relationships have been wrongly specified in the model or left out altogether. Therefore, the model may have to be reconstructed. The model may be solved using test data or real historical data if available.

Implementation usually means putting together detailed operating instructions to staff or the introduction of automated procedures. The managerial changes call for close liaison with management so that vital practicalities are not overlooked. The new arrangements may be phased in over a period of time, particularly if new capital equipment is called for, or if there are many staff changes.

1-4 OPERATIONAL RESEARCH AND COMPUTERS

The take-up and development of operational research models in business and industry, and the general acceptance of the management science approach, have been closely associated with the rapid and sustained growth of computing power and the progressive reductions in computing costs.

All of the major computing companies offer software packages for the main operational research techniques. Prime examples are linear programming, stock control forecasting, and simulation. Computers are particularly likely to be of value in situations where there is a large volume of data to handle, where the mathematical model has many equations and variables, where the solution procedure is very long or where there are uncertainties that can be characterized by probability distributions.

Nowadays, there is also an increasing number of practical micro-computer applications of operational research methods and an expanding range of user-friendly software. Problems can now be solved on micro-computers which, 20 years ago, would have required mainframe computing capacity. Hence the range and size of organizations that can usefully apply management science techniques has expanded dramatically.

This progress shows every sign of continuing indefinitely. In terms of sheer size, modern mainframe computers can solve problems with thousands of equations and variables—large enough for most practical applications! Specialist computer languages have been written as computer simulation methods have developed and complex problems beyond the reach of formal analytical methods can now be addressed.

The advent of low-cost high-power computing has brought about enormous changes of managerial philosophy and corresponding opportunities for the use and development of operational research methods. Much of the theoretical progress in OR methods, for example, the development of the simplex method for linear programming, occurred in the United States, and the most intensive use of computers in management has occurred in Japan. However, it is interesting to note that operational research as such originated in England, as did Charles Babbage's 'analytical engine' and George Boole's algebra, both so essential to computer design.

There remains considerable further scope for the use of computers and the application and understanding of operational research methods as managerial awareness of the logical and quantifiable nature of problems grows, and they have the means and instruments available for their solution.

EXERCISES

1-1 *Revision exercise*
Use the textbook as necessary to ensure that you are able to answer the following questions:
   (i) What is OR alternatively known as?
   (ii) Briefly explain the three objectives of prediction, control and optimization.
   (iii) What conditions need to be satisfied for an OR approach to be useful?
   (iv) Set out the stages likely to be involved in most OR studies in practice and explain what you understand by them.

1-2 Compare and contrast the following definitions of operational research:

OR is the application of the methods of science to complex problems arising in the direction and management of large systems of men, machines, materials and money in industry, business, government and defence. The distinctive approach is to develop a scientific model of the system, incorporating measurements of factors such as chance and risk, with which to predict and compare the outcomes of alternative decisions, strategies or controls. The purpose is to help management determine its policy and actions scientifically.

(Operational Research Society of Great Britain)

Operations Research is concerned with scientifically deciding how to best design and operate man-machine systems, usually requiring the allocation of scarce resources.

(Operations Research Society of America)

1-3 What is meant by 'model building' in an operational research context?

Solution guides

1-2 These two definitions are important as they emanate from two of the largest agencies in the subject area. Note first of all that they are not identical. The UK definition is longer but omits the US reference to the allocation of scarce resources. Key words are 'scientific approach', 'model', 'system', 'measurement', 'predict' and 'scarce resources'. Notice that the UK definition contains no reference to optimization. The US definition includes the word 'best' which may be included in a general sense but may also refer to the use of normative models. The UK definition specifically includes 'prediction' as an objective and the comparison of 'the outcomes of alternative decisions' strongly suggests the use of simulating rather than normative models. The UK definition rightly draws attention to the purpose of OR as an *aid* to managerial decision making, rather than a replacement for it.

1-3 Model building in an OR context means the construction of a mathematical model. This may well be preceded by a verbal 'model' of the problem—a comprehensive description of objectives, limitations, linkages and courses of action open to the decision maker. A normative mathematical model identifies the decision variables, or instruments, and expresses the objective and constraints in terms of the decision variables (see Chapter Two). The model will be quantitative and significant data gathering will be required. Ideally, the model should be of the complete system under study. In practice, the model may relate to part of the enterprise but significant consequences for the profitability or feasibility of other parts of the enterprise must be taken into account. Simulating models are intended to project the behaviour and consequences of the system under study. The results of changes in parameter values or changes in structure can be deduced.

OR models are always mathematical statements of the relationships between all the *important* factors in a problem. They are not 'iconic', in the sense of being a detailed replica of the system. The models always involve abstraction and are an aid to, rather than substitute for, managerial decision making. The model building approach must meet the criterion of improving current practice in the organization—it does not have to result in perfect solutions.

REFERENCES

Daellenbach, H. G., and George, J. A. (1978), *Introduction to Operations Research Techniques*, Allyn and Bacon.
Phillips, D. T., Ravindran, A., Solberg, J. (1976), *Operations Research: Principles and Practice*, Wiley.

FURTHER READING

Beer, S. (1966), *Decision and Control*, Wiley. The classic text on operational research.
Littlechild, S. C. (1977), *Operational Research for Managers*, Philip Allan. Contains chapters on history and OR methodology.

Monks, J. G. (1982), *Operations Management: Theory and Problems*, McGraw-Hill. Contains two chapters on historical development, definitions and methodology of OR.

Ranyard, J. C. (1988), 'A History of OR and Computing', *Journal of the Operational Research Society*, Vol. 39, No. 12. A concise history covering both mainframe and micro-computers.

Waddington, C. H. (1973), *OR in World War Two* Paul Elek Scientific Books. Early military history of modern OR.

TWO

LINEAR PROGRAMMING—
INTRODUCTION AND GRAPHICAL METHOD

2-1 BACKGROUND

Linear programming (LP) is one of the most widely used quantitative management techniques. Developed mainly since the Second World War, the method first found use in solving military logistical problems. The commercial potential of the technique was soon recognized with agriculture providing one of the earliest applications. Producing (at least cost) an animal-feed mix with given minimum nutrient contents was seen to be a linear programming problem. Other early uses were found in the petro-chemical industry and the use of the method then spread rapidly. Just some of the many industries currently using linear programming are: oil refining; steel making; food processing; paper making; brick manufacture; electrical goods.

A general description of an LP problem sounds very similar to a definition of the static economizing problem, viz., the problem of the optimal allocation of scarce resources between alternative uses within an all-linear framework. Indeed some writers describe LP as the *general allocation* problem. Among many other uses some problems addressed by LP are:

1. *Production planning* deciding what goods to produce and how much of each
2. *Production scheduling* deciding which jobs should go on which machines in what order.

9

3. *Transportation arrangements* how to ship goods to customers at least cost.
4. *Assignment problems* matching people to jobs, work to machines or contracts to bidders.
5. *Investment planning* selecting the best projects on a limited budget.
6. *Overall corporate planning* LP models that can encompass the whole company.

2-2 PROBLEM FORMULATION

Two of the earliest phases of an OR study are problem definition and data gathering. To see an illustration of these phases in the context of linear programming, consider a situation where OR consultants are called in to discuss a problem with the management of 'Azed Enterprises'. Management may feel that the company is 'not doing well enough' or that it 'could be more profitable'. Other factors, such as turnover, growth and share of market, may in practice be considerations. One of the first tasks, having located the decision makers, is to focus on an objective, or, in general, objectives. Let us suppose that it is in due course agreed that the problem is 'lack of profit' and that this is due partly to the fact that the company presently relies exclusively on one product—the Omega—of which it makes 300 units per day. Production is limited by labour supply at 900 hours per day.

However, the marketing director has, in a recent study, identified a niche for an upmarket version of the production the 'Alpha' model—with potential maximum sales of 180 units. The Alpha model would retail to a different market sector and have no affect on Omega sales. It is decided that the OR study should identify the most profitable production levels of the two models bearing in mind the limited availability of labour time and the fact that shortage of materials may also be a consideration. The financial director and production manager are briefed to provide relevant figures relating to resource consumption, prices and costs. The production manager reports as follows:

Resources: Maximum available daily supply of labour: 900 hours. Might bc increased by overtime working if sufficient inducement offered— possibility to be investigated in course of OR study.

Suppliers of a key material have been contacted and in total no more than 800 units (kilogram) are available per day at present price levels. Further units could only be obtained at a premium price.

The principal remaining factor in the production process is machining time.

The resource consumption data *per unit produced* of each model are:

	x_1 Alpha model	x_2 Omega model	Cost ($£$)
Materials (kg)	4	1	3
Labour (hours)	2	3	5
Machining time (hours)	$\frac{1}{2}$	$\frac{1}{2}$	6

Sell £31? £25

At this point, the financial director's report notes that the cost of materials is £3 per unit, labour is paid £5 per hour and machine time is costed at £6 per hour. Overheads (unallocated) amount to £500 per day. The *unit variable cost* of producing the Omega model is thus:

1 kg materials @ £3 + 3 hours labour @ £5 + $\frac{1}{2}$ hr machining @ £6 = £21.

For the Alpha model the unit variable cost would be: 4 kg materials @ £3 + 2 hours labour @ £5 + $\frac{1}{2}$ hr machining @ £6 = £25. Competitive conditions leave little scope for discretion in terms of selling prices. The Omega sells at £26 per unit while the Alpha price is settled at £31 per unit.

In summary form:

A $12x_1 + 10x_1 + 3x_1 = 25$
O $3x_2 + 15x_2 + 3x_2 = 21$

	Alpha model	Omega model x_2
Unit variable cost (£)	25	21
Selling price (£)	31	26

π £6   £5   Max:- $6x_1 + 5x_2$

The OR team are now ready to proceed with model construction. A number of key questions are identified. The first is:

Constraints:- $2x_1 + 3x_2 \leq 900$ hrs labo.

$4x_1 + 1x_2 \leq 800$ kg mat.

Q$_1$: What are the *decision variables?*

$x_1 \leq 180$ $x_2 \leq 300$ $x_1 \geq 0, \; x_2 \geq 0$

Decision variables are those elements within a problem over which the decision maker has at least some control. Sometimes the decision variables are called *instruments*. For instance, a farmer's decision variables might be the acreages to plant with wheat or barley, an investor's decision variables might be the number of shares to buy in certain companies. Azed's decision variables are the production figures for the two products. Let x_1 and x_2 be the number of units made of the Alpha and Omega models respectively. (In reality there are many more decision variables than two, and LP problems with over a thousand variables are routinely solved.)

The next question relates to the objective identified by the company.

Q$_2$: What is the *objective?*

Initial discussions identified this as 'profit' although there was some disagreement as to how this should be computed for the OR exercise. Some staff felt that overheads should be loaded into the unit cost data for the products but the OR team advised against this approach on the grounds that any such allocations of overhead are a matter of judgement and would, therefore, introduce an arbitrary element into the solution of the problem. The OR team maintained that the best way to provide for the fixed overheads of £500 was to make as big an excess of revenue over variable costs as possible.

It was agreed, therefore, that production levels would be decided on the basis on the excess of revenue over variable costs but that this framework need not be adopted in matters of report. This decided, it was then necessary to *express the objective in terms of the decision variables.* The excess of unit revenue (price) over unit variable cost respectively £(31–25) = £6 for the Alpha model and £(26 – 21) = £5 for the Omega model. Thus, for x_1 Alphas made in any production plan, an excess of revenue over variable costs of £$6x_1$ would be made and if x_2 units of the Omega model are produced this contributes £$5x_2$. The total excess of revenue over costs—which we shall here refer to as profit—is thus given by:

$$\pi = 6x_1 + 5x_2$$

This is the *objective function*–which it is the decision makers' objective to maximize.

The next question relates to the limitations on the decision makers' choices:

Q₃: What are the *constraints?*

The model builder must be specific about the restrictions on the choice of values of the decision variables. In mathematical form these restrictions are called constraints.

Here these relate to the use of the potentially scarce resources: labour and materials. In other contexts the farmer's scarce resource is land; the investor's is cash (or credit). Consider the materials constraint. As a first step we can write:

$$\text{Total materials used in production} \leqslant 800$$

where the sign $\leqslant$ is read 'less than or equal to'.

From the data given we note that *each* unit of the Alpha product requires 4 kg of material giving a requirement of $4x_1$ kg if x_1 Alphas are made. Also each unit of the Omega product requires 1 kg of material, thus calling for x_2 hours altogether. A production plan is a pair of values of x_1 and x_2 so the amount of materials called for by any plan is $4x_1 + x_2$ in total. Thus we can write:

$$4x_1 + x_2 \leqslant 800$$

In a similar fashion, each unit of Alpha made requires 2 labour hours while each Omega calls for 3 labour hours. Hence the labour time requirement of a production plan is $2x_1 + 3x_2$ where, clearly:

$$2x_1 + 3x_2 \leqslant 900$$

In addition, the sales department has put limits to the amounts of the two goods that can be sold at the stated prices.

Daily production of Alphas must not exceed 180 units. Daily production of Omegas must be less than or equal to 320 units. These are expressed as *upper bound* constraints:

$$x_1 \leqslant 180$$
$$x_2 \leqslant 320$$

The full range of constraints will also normally include *lower bounds* on the decision variables. Unless otherwise specified (for example, due to contractual arrangements) these lower bounds will be zero and are written as:

$$x_1 \geqslant 0$$
$$x_2 \geqslant 0$$

These are called *sign requirements* or *non-negativity constraints*.

Having answered the three key questions, the mathematical model can now be set out in full. It is to choose a pair of values of x_1 and x_2 (the daily production levels) so as to:

			Constraint number
Maximize	$\pi =$	$6x_1 + 5x_2$	
subject to		$4x_1 + x_2 \leqslant 800$	(1)
		$2x_1 + 3x_2 \leqslant 900$	(2)
		$x_1 \qquad\ \leqslant 180$	(3)
		$x_2 \leqslant 320$	(4)
and where		$x_1 \geqslant 0 \quad$ and $\quad x_2 \geqslant 0$	

Handwritten annotations:
$(200, 0)$ $(0, 800)$
$4x_1 + x_2 = 800$
$4x_1 + 6x_2 = 1800$
$-5x_2 = -1000$
$x_2 = 200$
$x_1 = 150$
$(450, 0)(0, 300)$
(180)
(320)

This completes the construction of the mathematical model. The next phase is the *solution* of the problem—a standard linear programming problem involving the maximization (or minimization) of a linear function subject to linear inequality restrictions and sign restricted variables.

2-3 GRAPHICAL SOLUTION OF LP PROBLEMS

LP problems involving two variables and several constraints, or two constraints and several variables, can be solved graphically. Larger problems use an *algorithmic* approach—usually the simplex method or one of its variants. This will be described in Chapter Three. Mainframe computers can handle LP problems involving thousands of variables and contraints. It will nevertheless prove instructive to examine a simple solution procedure involving diagrams and elementary linear algebra. Let us start with constraint (1). First draw in the line corresponding to the equation part of the constraint, viz., $4x_1 + x_2 = 800$. This cuts the axes at $x_1 = 200$ and $x_2 = 800$ as shown in Fig. 2-1. Clearly it would be permissible to have $4x_1 + x_2 = 700$ which would give a new line of *the same slope* cutting the axes at 175 and 700 respectively. Thus all points on or below the original line are allowed as indicated by the hatched region in Fig. 2-1. Notice that there is nothing in this constraint that excludes negative values of the decision variables. Figure 2-2 shows the results of adding the remaining constraints and sign requirements in a similar fashion. In each case, take the equality part of the constraint, draw in the straight line that this produces, then identify which side of the line is permitted. The final result is that only points in the polygon OABCD satisfy *all* the constraints and the sign requirements. Those parts of the constraint lines outside of the axes have been

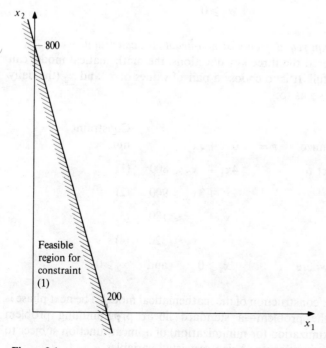

Figure 2-1

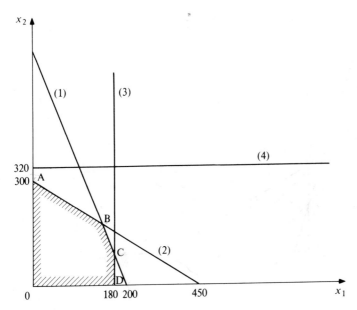

Figure 2-2

suppressed. Note that there is nothing different in character about the sign requirements. For $x_1 \geqslant 0$ we could equally well have written $-x_1 + 0x_2 \leqslant 0$ which as an equality identifies the vertical (x_2) axis and points on or to the right of this line are allowable. Notice also that constraint (4) is *redundant*. At all times one or other of the remaining restrictions sets tighter limits than does constraint (4). Constraint (4) can be left out of the problem although the constraint may become relevant at a later stage of analysis if parameter values such as resource availabilities are varied.

The boundary and interior of OABCD is called the *feasible region, feasible production set, production possibility set* or *opportunity set*. The coordinates of each point in the feasible region give a pair of production levels for the two products and is sometimes called a *production plan*. It is much easier to determine from the diagram which production plans are feasible than it is to do so using the constraints in algebraic form.

To determine which point in the feasible region is best, the objective function must be introduced. Consider the firm's original production plan at point A where $x_1 = 0$ and $x_2 = 300$. These values, when substituted into the objective function, give $\pi = 6(0) + 5(300) = 1500$ so that 1500 in contributions is made at A. What other values of x_1 and x_2 would give 1500 profit? Clearly, if we reduced x_2 by six units this would reduce the total profit by 30, but this could be made up by raising production of x_1 by five units. Thus the point $x_1 = 5$, $x_2 = 294$ also gives a profit of 1500. Continuing with this process of substitution at the rate of six units of x_2 for five of x_1 would maintain profit at

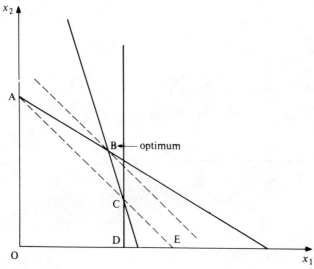

Figure 2-3

1500 and bring us eventually to the point $x_1 = 250, x_2 = 0$ on the x_1 axis. This is point E shown in Fig. 2-3. All of the points on the line AE represent production levels giving the same (1500) profit. Such a line is a *contour* of the profit surface lying above the x_1, x_2 'plane'. It is a contour in just the same sense as the contours of hills on an Ordnance Survey map. Not all points on the $\pi = 1500$ contour are feasible but many are within OABCD. The company could earn its current level of profit by joint production of both Omega and Alpha models. However, 1500 was no more than a convenient *trial value* of the objective function to find the slope of the contours. This is 6/5 in absolute terms (i.e. ignoring sign) and all contours will have this value of slope.

The next point to note is that the further 'out' (upwards and to the right) a contour lies, the greater profit to which it corresponds. For instance, £1800 would result from x_1 and x_2 values lying along a line joining 360 on the x_2 axis with 300 on the x_1 axis. Again not all points on such a line would be in the feasible region, but *some* are.

The best overall production plan—the optimum—is represented by a point in the feasible region that is on the *highest* contour. This is point B, the coordinates of which are the optimal values of x_1 and x_2. From a well-drawn diagram these values could be read off the axes, but this is not recommended. There is no guarantee that the optimal values will be convenient numbers, and the degree of approximation may not be good enough. Rather we shall use the diagram to see where the optimum lies and then solve algebraically for the values of x_1 and x_2. In particular, we determine from the diagram which constraints *intersect* at the optimum. These *binding* constraints—and only these—will be satisfied as strict equalities. These equations can then be solved in a simple fashion for the precise values of x_1 and x_2. Thus in the present case we have constraints (1) and (2) intersecting at B so that

$$4x_1 + x_2 = 800 \quad (1) \times 3$$
$$2x_1 + 3x_2 = 900 \quad (2)$$

[handwritten annotations:] $12x_1 + 3x_2 = 2400 \; +x_2 = 800$; $2x_1 + 3x_2 = 900$

$12x_1 + 3x_2 = 2400$
$2x_1 + 3x_2 = 900$
$10x_1 = 1500 \quad x_1 = 150$

To solve these equations multiply (2) by two and subtract (1) from the result to eliminate x_1.

This operation produces:

[handwritten:] $\therefore x_2 ; 4(150) + x_2 = 800$
$\therefore x_2 = 200 ; \quad x_2 = (4 \times 150) + x_2 = 800$

$$(2) \times 2 = 4x_1 + 6x_2 = 1800$$
$$(1) \qquad 4x_1 + \;x_2 = \;\;800$$
$$\overline{\qquad\qquad\qquad\qquad}$$
$$5x_2 = 1000$$
$$\therefore \quad x_2 = \;\;200$$

[handwritten:] $= 600 + x_2 = 800$
$x_2 = 200$

Substitution of $x_2 = 200$ into either (1) of (2) gives $x_1 = 150$. Putting these values of the x's into the objective function results in

$$\pi = 6(150) + 5(200) = 1900$$

So the optimum production plan would be for the company to manufacture 150 Alphas and 200 Omegas per day and thus secure a maximum daily profit of £1900. Any other feasible plan will have less profit. Point B is the *only* point in the feasible region which lies on the 1900 profit contour. All of the other points in the region lie on lower-valued contours.

The management of Azed must now decide whether this result is valid—does the output of the model represent a realistic possibility? Clearly, a result suggesting a negative production level would be invalid, but so too would the result achieved above, if sales staff could initially handle only 100 Alpha models per day or if it turned out that a further resource constraint had in fact been overlooked. In these circumstances, the model output would be rejected as invalid and the mathematical model re-cast accordingly.

If the result is regarded as valid, the new production plan must be implemented. Our highly simplified model has not included costs associated with the introduction of a new product or the consequences of changing existing production levels. These can, of course, be included in a larger study.

Let us return to the original problem and summarize the steps involved in the graphical solution procedure. Having obtained a comprehensive verbal description of the problem:

1. Express the problem algebraically.
2. Draw a diagram, showing the constraints and identifying the feasible region.

3. Draw in a specimen contour of the objective function.
4. Identify the position of the optimum on the diagram and determine which constraints intersect at this position.
5. Solve these constraints as equalities to obtain the optimal values of the decision variables.

2-4 RESOURCE UTILIZATION

Azed's optimal production plan called for the manufacture of 150 Alphas and 200 Omegas. As it so happened, this plan called for the full utilization of scarce resources. Prior to the advent of linear programming, an operating 'rule of thumb' for production management was to ensure full use of available resources and to deduce the production levels that would follow. This method will not generally produce the best profit position for the firm and it should not be assumed that resources available in limited supply should always be fully used. To illustrate this point, suppose that in Azed's original problem the resource availabilities and sales limits were as previously determined but that the unit profit figures were £12 for the Alpha model and £2 for the Omega model. The objective function would then have been

$$\pi = 12x_1 + 2x_2$$

The production plan giving full use of resources would still be $x_1 = 150$, $x_2 = 200$, resulting in a profit figure of $\pi = 2200$. This, however, is not optimal, as is seen in Fig. 2-4. The highest objective function contour that has a point in

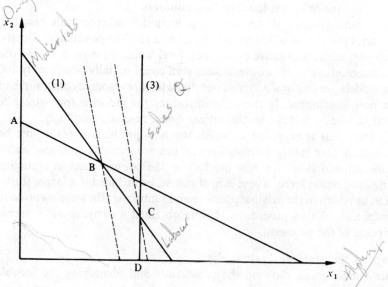

Figure 2-4

common with the feasible region is at point C. The constraints intersecting at C which therefore hold as strict equalities are constraints (3) and (1). Thus multiplying constraint (3) by 4 and subtracting from constraint (1) gives:

$$(1) \qquad 4x_1 + x_2 = 800$$

$$(3) \times 4 \qquad 4x_1 \qquad = 720$$

$$\overline{\qquad\qquad x_2 = \ 80} \qquad \therefore x_1 = 180$$

Thus $x_2 = 80$, $x_1 = 180$ and $\pi = 2320$. Although an accounting profit is shown if the firm remained at point B with the original production plan, there would be a lost opportunity to make an additional profit of £120. Notice that the optimum plan of $x_2 = 80$ and $x_1 = 180$ calls for full use of available materials but requires only $2(180) + 3(80) = 600$ labour hours, leaving 300 hours not called upon. In practice it may be that a certain level of resource usage is required as a minimum—if so, a new constraint must be added in. This is just the sort of model revision that can occur in the validation phase of an OR study.

2-5 SENSITIVITY ANALYSIS

(i) The objective function

In section 2-4, we saw that the choice of production plan could depend upon the values taken by the objective function coefficients. In practice, these may change as costs, market prices exchange rates and competitive conditions vary and it would be a poor OR technique that could say nothing about changes in problem parameters. After all, it is management's *job* to secure improved margins and remove production bottlenecks. Other changes may be externally determined, for example, by exchange rate variations affecting materials costs, or compressing margins on products sold in foreign markets.

    Sensitivity analysis (sometimes called post-optimality analysis) determines maximum ranges of variation for system parameters for which the optimum solution remains both optimal and feasible. Sensitivity analysis also answers specific questions such as 'would it still be worth producing the Omega model if unit profit fell to £2?' Let us consider this question and suppose that profit on the Omega product *did* fall to £2. Should production be cut back or even stopped altogether and the released resources put to work in making Alphas? The answer in fact is no. There should be no changes at all. The reason for this result can most easily be seen geometrically. Look again at point B in Fig. 2-3. You will see that point B will be on the highest contour, and thus be optimal, provided that the slope of the contours remains between the slopes of constraints (1) and (2). Constraint (1) can be re-written as:

$$x_2 = 800 - 4x_1$$

in which the slope is readily seen to be -4. Similarly constraint (2) can be written as:

$$x_2 = 300 - \frac{2}{3}x_1$$

in which the slope is clearly seen to be $-2/3$. The slope of the constraint lines is always minus the ratio of the coefficients of x_1 and x_2 in the constraint. In a similar fashion the slope of the objective function contours is minus the ratio of the coefficients of x_1 and x_2 in the objective function and originally is $-6/5$. Point B will be optimal so long as:

$$\frac{2}{3} \leqslant \frac{6}{5} \leqslant 4$$

Now in general let the profit per unit of Omega be π_2 instead of 5, point B will remain optimal provided that

$$\frac{2}{3} \leqslant \frac{6}{\pi_2} \leqslant 4$$

If π_2 was such that a strict equality held at one end of the range (say $\pi_2 = 9$) then the contours would be parallel to constraint (2) and the optimum would be *non-unique*, anywhere along the line segment AB being just as good as anywhere else. The value of 9 in fact defines the *upper bound* on π_2. It cannot be more than this (given the original values of the other parameters) if B is to remain optimal. The other extreme gives the *lower bound* on π_2:

$$\frac{6}{\pi_2} \leqslant 4 \quad \therefore \pi_2 \geqslant 1.5$$

so that point B will remain optimal provided that π_2 is in the range given by:

$$1.5 \leqslant \pi_2 \leqslant 9$$

This is the *tolerance interval* for the parameter π_2. Thus there is room for variability in the original unit profit figure for Omega. Since £2 falls within this range we conclude that the optimum remains unchanged.

The tolerance interval for the unit profit figure of the Alpha model (π_1) can be found in a similar fashion. Point B will remain optimal provided that:

$$\frac{2}{3} \leqslant \frac{\pi_1}{5} \leqslant 4$$

That is:

$$\frac{10}{3} \leqslant \pi_1 \leqslant 20$$

which is the required tolerance interval.

Underlying forces such as inflation can affect the profitability of the two products simultaneously. In this case, a *joint* sensitivity analysis can be carried out. The first thing to observe is that the slope of the contour depends only on the *relative* sizes of π_1 and π_2 so that equal proportionate changes in both contribution figures make no difference to the optimal plan, although of course the contribution made will be changed by the same proportion. More generally, if we take the slope condition for optimality of B:

$$\frac{2}{3} \leqslant \frac{\pi_1}{\pi_2} \leqslant 4$$

the first part of this condition, $2/3 \leqslant \pi_1/\pi_2$, can be re-written as $\pi_2 \leqslant 1.5\pi_1$ and the second part, $\pi_1/\pi_2 \leqslant 4$, can be re-expressed as $\pi_2 \geqslant 0.25\pi_1$. So, for optimality of B all that is required is that:

$$0.25\pi_1 \leqslant \pi_2 \leqslant 1.5\pi_1$$

Insertion of the original value of π_1 into this relationship will produce the original tolerance interval for π_2. Similarly, the insertion of the original value of π_2 produces the individual range of π_1.

The results of the joint sensitivity analysis are shown in Fig. 2-5. As long as

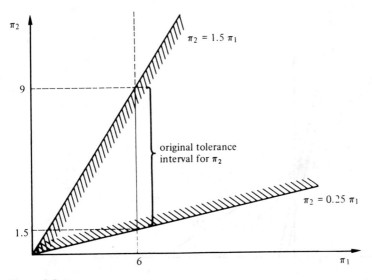

Figure 2-5

the values of π_1 and π_2 fall within the shaded region the original plan remains optimal. When π_1 takes the value of 6 the original tolerance interval for π_2 energes as a line segment in the diagram. The results of the single parameter analysis thus appear as special cases of the more general two parameter results.

2-6 SENSITIVITY ANALYSIS

(ii) Dual values

The main principle of sensitivity analysis—that of obtaining tolerance intervals—can be usefully applied to the resource availability levels, upper bounds on sales and, in fact, any coefficients on the right-hand side (RHS) of the original inequality constraints.

Changes in the objective function coefficients changed the slope of the objective function contours and could therefore change the position of the optimum to another point in the feasible region. Changes in the RHS elements—for example, the amount of materials available—change the feasible region by movement of the constraint lines relative to the origin.

The first step in the analysis is to establish the changes in production levels brought about by the use of more materials with the same labour hours. Having determined the new optimal levels of production, the increase in profit can be identified. This will set a limit to the amount worth paying to bring about the increase in materials. These maximum amounts are called *dual values*, *shadow prices* or *marginal values* and are a most important and useful outcome of the LP method.

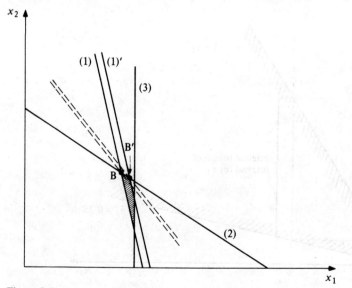

Figure 2-6

Consider then the problem of establishing the dual or marginal value for materials. First, let us see what happens graphically as more material becomes available. The consequence is shown in Fig. 2-6. Constraint line (1) moves outwards to (1)′ and the point B 'slides down' constraint (2) to B′. The shaded area is added onto the feasible region. All the old choices are still available—in particular the old optimum at B is still feasible—but there are now some additional possibilities as shown by the points in the shaded region. It is evident that the objective function contour through B′ is higher than that through B. So that if there had been no change in prices of resources, more profit would be made at B′ than at B. Notice that at B′, x_1 has increased while x_2 had decreased relative to B. More is not produced of both products. There has to be a change in balance in the production plan to accommodate the change in the balance of the resources.

Now compute the new levels of x_1 and x_2 at B′:

$$(2) \times 2 \quad 4x_1 + 6x_2 = 1800$$
$$(1)' \quad 4x_1 + x_2 = 801$$
$$\overline{ 5x_2 = 999}$$
$$\therefore \quad x_2 = 199.8$$

The decimal part of a unit is meaningful in the context of this exercise as we are evaluating the consequence *per unit* of resource increase in order to establish a marginal value. In practice, any consequent change in the level of a resource such as materials would of course be of a more substantial native. By substitution into (1)′, $x_1 = 150.3$ so that the new level of profit is:

$$\pi' = 6(150.3) + 5(199.8) = 1900.8$$

The extra unit of material *if used in the optimal fashion* will produce an extra £0.8 profit. This increase is *directly attributable* to the extra unit of material and is called the *dual value* of the resource. The increase of £0.8 depends upon obtaining the extra unit of material *at the original price* which was included in the unit variable cost figure. So, if one more unit of material is obtained at the original price the contribution rises by 0.8. Also, if we get one more unit of material at the original price *plus* 50p we make an $80 - 50 = 30$p increase in profit. If we had to pay £1 over the odds to secure the extra unit there would be a *fall* of 20p in contribution. It is therefore *not* worth paying a £1 premium for the first or any subsequent units of material. The maximum increase worth paying is the dual value.

The fact that we have dealt with a tiny, impractical change in the constraint level makes no difference to the general result. Perhaps the smallest practical increase would be 10 units. If 810 kg were available then $x_1 = 153$,

$x_2 = 198$ and $\pi = 1908$, a *rate* of increase of π of 0.8 per unit of material. Finally suppose that the premium was less than 0.8. How many more units of material would it be worth buying? We note that the level of x_1 is being increased by 0.3 as material availability increases by 1. This increase cannot take x_1 beyond 180 (due to constraint (3)). Thus since x_1 must not increase by more than 30 materials should not increase by more than 100 kg.

Now consider the dual value of labour. With 901 units the equations to solve become:

$$(2)' \times 2 \quad 4x_1 + 6x_2 = 1802$$
$$4x_1 + x_2 = 800$$
$$\overline{\quad 5x_2 = 1002}$$
$$\therefore \quad x_2 = 200.4 \text{ and so } x_1 = 149.9$$

The new level of π is:

$$\pi' = 6(149.9) + 5(200.4) = 1901.4$$

so that the dual value of labour is £1.40. This is the maximum premium that could be paid over the basic rate without depressing profits. Thus if the basic rate had been £7.50 per hour then the maximum overtime wage rate would be £8.90.

Sometimes the description *shadow price* is used instead of dual or marginal value. There is no uniformity of interpretation of this term. For instance, in the case of labour hours, the shadow price could be used in the sense of either the marginal increase in profit of £1.40 or the full maximum of £8.90. We shall employ the latter interpretation here. Note that both senses are the same if the original resources are cost free. The dual value can also be described as the *profit producing potential* of a further unit of resource obtained at the original price and put to best use. So dual values are of great use in determining the maximum prices worth paying to relax a constraint and to evaluate specific proposals for extra resources.

There is a further use to which the dual values can be put. The firm may have the technical capacity to produce a number of products not presently included in its production plan. For example, suppose that plans for a possible *third* product, the 'Beta' model, have been prepared by the technical division. Each unit of Beta made would need 3 kg of material and four hours of working time. The accounting department has estimated unit cost at £46.50 while the sales department say that competitive conditions would set the selling price at £54 per unit. Should the Beta model be produced? On the face of it, the third product looks attractive since it makes a unit profit of £7.50, higher than either of the existing products. But this is not the sole deciding factor. We found that further units of materials and labour would increase profit by 0.8 and 1.4

respectively. Since the problem is entirely linear, *reducing* the materials availability by one unit would *cut* profit by 0.8. Similarly one hour less labour would reduce profit by 1.4. To make one unit of the third product would reduce the materials availability (for Alpha and Omega) by 3 and the labour available by 4. So that the lost profit from Alpha and Omega production is

$$3(0.8) + 4(1.4) = £8$$

but the Beta model only replaces this with £7.50 which is not good enough. Another way of putting it is to say that the profit producing potential tied up in the manufacture of one unit of the third product exceeds its own ability to contribute. There would be an *opportunity loss* of £0.50 on each unit made. Any further product would only increase profit if the dual value of the resources tied up in its production was less than its unit profit.

Notice the dual value of resources in the Alpha and Omega models. We have for the Alpha:

$$4(0.8) + 2(1.4) = 6$$

and for the Omega:

$$1(0.8) + 3(1.4) = 5$$

The dual values of resources precisely equal the unit profits. This is always true for products that are produced at the optimum. It is simply re-stating that there is no opportunity loss on producing the products that it is best to produce. If the dual value of resources was *less* than the unit profit for some product then the optimum would not have been reached—an opportunity profit would exist.

2-7 A FURTHER EXAMPLE

A company is drawing up production plans for the coming year. Four products are producible with the following data:

Product	1	2	3	4
Amount per unit:				
selling price	£90	£74	£174	£177
cost of materials	17	25	19	11
labour hours: grade A	10	6	—	—
grade B	—	—	10	20
grade C	—	—	12	6
other variable costs	£6	£7	£5	£6

Fixed overheads of the firm amount to £35 500 per annum. Each grade of labour is paid £5.00 per hour but existing agreements mean that an employee in one grade cannot be used to undertake the work of another grade. The annual supply of each grade is limited to the following maxima: Grade A, 9000 hours; grade B, 14 500 hours; and grade C, 12 000 hours. There is no effective limitation on the volume of sales of any product. The company's objective is profits maximization. Management requires detailed information in four respects:

1. The product mix which will maximize profit for the year
2. The minimum price at which the sale of product (1) would be worth while
3. The amount by which profit could be increased if the supply of grade A labour was increased
4. To what extent profits could be increased if a revised agreement between management and unions resulted in Grades B and C labour being fully interchangeable.

It is clear that the decision variables will be x_1, x_2, x_3, and x_4, the amounts made of each product. The objective is profits maximization and for this we need to know the unit profit of each product. This is selling price less unit variable cost. On x_1 the unit variable cost is £17 for materials plus 10 grade A hours at £5.00 plus other variable costs of £6, i.e. £73. This results in a unit profit of £90 − £73 = £17. For the other products we obtain:

$$\text{unit profit on } x_2 = 74 - (25 + 6 \times 5 + 7) = 12$$

$$\text{unit profit on } x_3 = 174 - (19 + 10 \times 5 + 12 \times 5 + 5) = 40$$

$$\text{unit profit on } x_4 = 177 - (11 + 20 \times 5 + 6 \times 5 + 6) = 30$$

so that the total profit made will be:

$$\pi = 17x_1 + 12x_2 + 40x_3 + 30x_4 - 35\,500$$

There are three constraints; these can be written as:

$$10x_1 + 6x_2 \leqslant 9000$$

$$10x_3 + 20x_4 \leqslant 14\,500$$

$$12x_3 + 6x_4 \leqslant 12\,000$$

To which sign requirements must be added. The problem is one in four structural (x) variables but it *can* be solved graphically. This is because of the special structure of the constraints. The scarce resources needed by x_1 and x_2 (i.e., grade A labour) are quite separate from those needed by x_3 and x_4 (grades

B and C labour). Products (1) and (2) do not compete for scarce resources with products three and four—the constraint set is *partitioned*. This means that the whole problem should be split into two *sub-problems*; the first sub-problem involves x_1 and x_2 only and the second involves x_3 and x_4 only. These problems can be considered separately. So first of all:

$$\text{Maximize} \quad \pi(1, 2) = 17x_1 + 12x_2$$

$$\text{subject to} \quad 10x_1 + 6x_2 \leqslant 9000$$

$$x_1 \geqslant 0, x_2 \geqslant 0$$

This is a one-constraint problem which is graphed in Fig. 2-7. The feasible region is the shaded OAB for which A is optimal. At A $x_1 = 0$, $x_2 = 1500$ and $\pi(1, 2) = £18\,000$, so that x_1 should not at present be produced, but all labour of grade A should be used on the second product to yield a maximum contribution to profits of £18 000. Now for the second sub-problem. This is

$$\text{Maximize} \quad \pi(3, 4) = 40x_3 + 30x_4$$

$$\text{subject to} \quad 10x_3 + 20x_4 \leqslant 14\,500$$

$$12x_3 + 6x_4 \leqslant 12\,000$$

$$x_3 \geqslant 0, x_4 \geqslant 0$$

The slope of the objective function contours, 40/30, falls between the slopes of the two constraints (10/20 and 12/6) so that the point of intersection of the constraint lines is optimal. Solving the constraints as equations gives

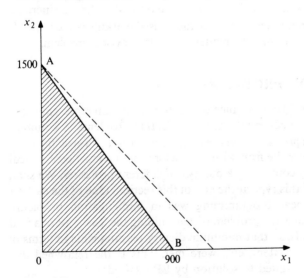

Figure 2-7

$x_3 = 850$ and $x_4 = 300$; so that $\pi(3, 4) = 40 \times 850 + 30 \times 300 = 43\,000$. Thus total profit made is:

$$\pi = 18\,000 + 43\,000 - 35\,500 = 25\,500$$

The manufacture of product one will be *just* worth while when as much profit can be made as from the manufacture of product (2), i.e., £18 000. This would correspond to the objective function contours in Fig. 2-7 being parallel to the constraint line. Clearly for point B to be as good as point A, 900 units of x_1 must give 18 000 profit i.e., the unit profit must be £20. Given the same costs this will result from a price of £93 since the opportunity loss is at present £3.

We are required to determine the dual value of grade A labour. If one more hour was available *at the going rate of* £5, then an extra 1/6 of a unit of x_2 could be produced giving an increased profit of $12 \times 1/6 = £2$. In other words, if an extra hour of grade A labour was available at the original price profit would increase by £2. Evidently if the extra hour can be obtained for less than $£5 + £2 = £7$ some extra profit will remain. The maximum overtime wage rate for grade A labour is thus £7. The reader may wish to verify that the maximum overtime wage rates for labour of types B and C are £5.66 and £7.77 respectively.

Now consider the question of the value to management of revised working agreements so that grades B and C labour are interchangeable. The second sub-problem now, in effect, has the single constraint:

$$22x_3 + 26x_4 \leqslant 26\,500$$

Thus, the maximum now has $x_3 = 1204.\overline{54} x_4 = 0$ and $\pi = 48\,181.\overline{81}$, an increase of profit of $5181.\overline{81}$ per annum as a result of the revised working agreements. It is suggested as an exercise that the reader graph the revised problem.

2-8 MINIMIZATION PROBLEMS

Linear programming problems in which the objective function represents cost, time, or a resource to be conserved, are *minimization* problems. A common example is that of *batch production* where a firm is in receipt of a specific order for its product and where the firm wishes to determine the most economical means of production by combining a number of different processes. We shall consider an example of this type at the end of this section. One of the earliest commercial uses of linear programming was in minimization problems. A minimization problem is the problem of determining the least cost of a feed mix of a number of foods, so that minimum dietary requirements in terms of calorific value, vitamin content, etc., were met. This is the renowned *diet problem* which is ideally suited to solution by LP methods.

A simple example illustrates the solution of LP minimization problems by the graphical method.

Consider the problem:

$$\text{Minimize } F = 3x_1 + 5x_2$$

$$\text{subject to} \quad x_1 + 4x_2 \geqslant 60$$

$$2x_1 + x_2 \geqslant 50$$

$$x \geqslant 0, x_2 \geqslant 0$$

Notice that with an objective function to be minimized the constraints are typically of a 'greater than or equal to' variety. Where the x's have positive coefficients in the constraints there must be at least one $\geqslant$ inequality or else the origin (all x's zero) will be selected.

In terms of the solution procedure, only a minor variation to the graphical method is necessary for application to minimization problems. Once the objective function and constraints have been set out algebraically, a graph of the problem is produced exactly as for maximization problems but the point in the feasible region that is sought is that on the *lowest* objective function contour. The specimen contour is moved as close to the origin as is possible (the origin will not usually be part of the feasible region in minimization problems). This done, the constraints intersecting at the optimal point identified on the diagram are identified and solved algebraically as equations.

A graph of the problem is shown in Fig. 2-8. Note that the feasible region is on the outside of the constraint lines and is bounded only from below by the

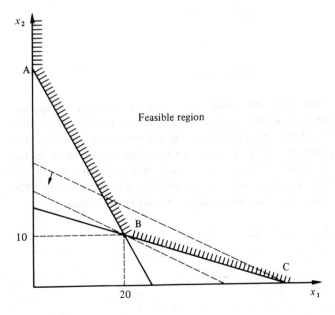

Figure 2-8

axes and line segments AB and BC. A specimen contour has been drawn through point C where $x_2 = 0$, $x_1 = 60$ and where the objective function therefore takes the value $F = 180$. However, it is clearly possible to get closer to the origin and achieve a lower value of F. This is done at point B where $x_1 = 20$, $x_2 = 10$ and $F = 110$, which is the minimum achievable. Sensitivity analysis can follow in the usual way. So long as the slope of the objective function contours remains between the slopes of the constraints, then point B will remain optimal. If the coefficients of x_1 and x_2 in the objective function are altered so that the contours become steeper than either constraint (x_1 coefficient increasing substantially relative to that of x_2) then Point A would become optimal.

Consider the tolerance interval for the coefficient of x_1 (call this C_1). For point B to remain optimal:

$$\frac{1}{4} \leqslant \frac{C_1}{5} \leqslant 2$$

which re-arranges to produce the tolerance interval:

$$1.25 \leqslant C_1 \leqslant 10$$

The tolerance interval on C_2 (the objective function coefficient of x_2) results from the requirement that:

$$\frac{1}{4} \leqslant \frac{3}{C_2} \leqslant 2$$

So that:

$$1.5 \leqslant C_2 \leqslant 12$$

As with maximization problems, dual values can be determined for the constraint levels. The main point to note is that an increase in either constraint level will increase the objective function but this will represent a *worsening* in the position as the objective is to minimize rather than maximimize. In the context of a $\geqslant$ inequality 'relaxation' of a constraint corresponds to a *reduction* in the right-hand side value. In the case of the first constraint if the 60 became 61 the new values at the optimum would be such that:

$$2x_1 + 8x_2 = 122$$
$$\underline{2x_1 + x_2 = 50}$$
$$7x_2 = 72$$
$$\therefore \quad x_2 = 10\tfrac{2}{7} \quad x_1 = 19\tfrac{6}{7} \quad F = 111$$

So that the dual value of the right-hand side of the first constraint is 1. A reduction to 59 in the level of constraint (1) will result in a reduction (i.e. improvement) of the objective function by one unit. It turns out that the dual value of the right-hand side of the second constraint is also one so that a reduction here to 49 units would mean that the lowest achievable value of F was 109.

As a further example of a minimization problem, suppose that a firm can produce a single product in two processes. Two resources are needed for production, the amounts required per unit of output in each process being:

	Unit production in:	
	Process One	Process Two
Resource One	3	2
Resource Two	2	3

So that each unit of output made in Process One requires three units of Resource One and two units of Resource Two. The firm can buy up to 260 units of Resource One at £20 per unit and up to 300 units of Resource Two at £10 per unit. All other costs are fixed. The firm wishes to determine the best means by which to achieve an output level of 100 units and what the cost of further units would then be. The firm is also concerned that Resource Two might jump in price to £30 per unit and wishes to determine what would then be the best quantity to produce in each process.

The first step in the present problem is to determine the unit variable cost for each production process. Let x_1 and x_2 represent the amounts made of the uniform product in each of the two processes respectively.

For process one each unit made requires three units of resource one at £20 and two units of resource two at £10. Thus, since all other costs are fixed, the unit variable cost for x_1 is:

$$c_1 = 3 \times 20 + 2 \times 10 = 80$$

and c_2, the unit variable cost of x_2, is similarly obtained as:

$$c_2 = 2 \times 20 + 3 \times 10 = 70$$

Thus the objective will be to:

$$\text{minimize } c = c_1 x_1 + c_2 x_2 = 80x_1 + 70x_2$$

Now there are *three* constraints. From the resource limits we have:

$$3x_1 + 2x_2 \leqslant 260 \tag{1}$$

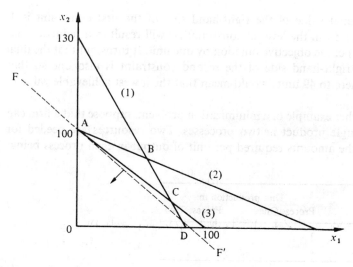

Figure 2-9

and

$$2x_1 + 3x_2 \leqslant 300 \qquad (2)$$

but there is also the requirement that 100 units be made overall. So:

$$x_1 + x_2 = 100 \qquad (3)$$

The problem is graphed in Fig. 2-9. The feasible 'region' is the line segment AC, although presumably, if it wished, the firm could produce *more* than 100 units and operate within ABC. The optimal solution is the point on AC which is on the *lowest* objective function contour. This is point A and the contour FF' is the £7000 cost contour. The coordinates of point A can now be obtained in the usual way or alternatively as follows. Simply note that since production in the x_2 process is cheaper, as much as possible will always be produced in this process. For a required output level of 100 units, it is *just* possible to produce this all in Process Two. However, suppose that a further unit is required—how would 101 units of producton be achieved and what would be the cost of the extra unit? We now have:

$$x_1 + x_2 = 101$$

so that:

$$x_1 = 101 - x_2$$

substituting into the first constraint gives:

$$3(101 - x_2) + 2x_2 \leqslant 260$$
$$\therefore \qquad x_2 \geqslant 43$$

substitution into the second constraint produces:

$$2(101 - x_2) + 3x_2 \leqslant 300$$
$$\therefore \qquad x_2 \leqslant 98$$

Since the second process is the cheaper, the firm will produce as much as possible in it so that $x_2 = 98$, $x_1 = 3$, cost $= £7100$. The additional unit has thus cost £100—more than the cost in either of the processes individually. This is because output in Process Two had to be *reduced* to release the resources needed to obtain the extra unit of output overall. Each additional unit of output has a *marginal cost* of £100 up to the maximum overall output achievable of 112. (This can be confirmed by maximizing total output $x_1 + x_2$ subject to the two resource constraints.)

Finally, if the cost of Resource Two rose to £30 the unit cost figures would become $C_1 = £120$ and $C_2 = £130$. So as much as possible should be produced in the first process. In terms of Fig. 2-9 the best position is at point C where $x_1 = 60$ and $x_2 = 40$.

2-9 CONCLUSIONS

Linear programming is a most important quantitative management technique. It has been of surpassing value in manufacturing industry. All computer companies offer a range of LP packages suitable for a wide range of problems from shop-floor production to overall corporate modelling.

Usable management techniques must take *something* for granted. Every device that is used from advanced mathematical programming or statistics at one extreme, to business experience and raw hunch at the other, will make assumptions. A model is supposed to simplify reality. If it does not simplify it is not a model. However, when using a technique it is wise to be aware of the main assumptions that are made. In the case of linear programming these are:

1. *All data known and constant.* This means that there are no unknowns, no random variables, and no dynamic variables (values changing with time). It means that prices of outputs and factors are constant and unaffected by output or usage. It means that the firm knows its objective and can measure it. There can be no interdependencies between prices themselves or prices and outputs. Technical coefficients, the amounts of resources needed per unit of each x, are given. Economies or diseconomies of scale are not allowed in the basic model.

Finally the assumption means that management has predetermined the possible range of activities.

2. *No fixed charges.* A 'fixed charge' is a *set-up cost*; it is only incurred if an x variable is raised from zero level. It is a lump sum that does not depend on the size of x, only that x is positive. For instance, to start a production run of a product, machinery may have to be re-set. The re-set costs are not incurred if the product is not made.

3. *Divisibility.* It is assumed that fractional values of the x's are meaningful. In cases where this is not so the LP format can often be preserved. Clearly, the effect of rounding down $x_2 = 200.1$ to $x_2 = 200$ is negligible in practical terms; units of measure can be changed (machines to machine hours) or the time period altered (4.25 units per week becomes 17 per month). The solution procedure is so efficient it is always best to retain the LP format if possible.

4. *Boundedness.* There must be linear restrictions on the choice of values of the x's such that the objective function cannot become infinite. In practice these restrictions take the form of linear inequality constraints, each involving some or all of the x's and sign requirements. In general, it must be ensured that all of the x's are bounded from below and from above.

There will of course be occasions when not all of the above provisions are met in the first instance but as was seen in the case of divisibility requirements, many of the non-linearities of the real world can be approximated by linear functions. Sensitivity analysis is most important and is a practical way of taking uncertainties into account. *Any* problem which has the character of maximization subject to constraint is a programming problem of some sort. All significant economic and business problems involve constraints and in most cases best, rather than merely adequate arrangements are sought. It is not surprising therefore that linear programming and its derivative methods have found such widespread usage in practice.

EXERCISES

2-1 Revision exercise

Use the textbook as necessary to ensure that you are able to answer the following questions.

(i) In what areas of a firm's activities might linear programming prove to be a useful technique?

(ii) What essential questions need to be answered when setting a problem in linear programming form?

(iii) Set out the steps involved in the graphical solution procedure and show how the method can be applied to both maximization and minimization problems of suitable size.

(iv) Explain the value of sensitivity analysis in linear programming problems and show how dual values are useful in identifying the price worth paying to relax constraints.

(v) List the assumptions underlying LP, and explain why not all the assumptions need be precisely satisfied for the technique to be of value.

2-2 The Latin Manufacturing Company can make two products. Each of the products requires time on a 'cutting' machine and a 'finishing' machine. Relevant data are:

	Product	
	Prima	Seconda
Cutting hours (per unit)	2	1
Finishing hours (per unit)	3	3
Unit cost (£)	28	25
Selling price (£)	34	29
Maximum sales (units per week)	200	200

The number of cutting hours available per week is 390 and the number of finishing hours available per week is 810. No other resources are in limited supply, but the costs of these resources have been allowed for in the unit cost figures.

(a) How much should be produced of each product in order to achieve Latin's objective of maximization of profit?

(b) Find the dual values (shadow prices) of the scarce resources at the optimum.

(c) A possible third product has a unit profit of £5 and would require two hours cutting and two hours finishing. Should Latin make this product?

(d) Determine the maximum range of variation in the unit profit figures for the original solution to remain optimal.

2-3 Use the graphical method to solve the following linear programming problem:

$$\text{Maximize } F = \quad 35x_1 + 25x_2$$
$$4x_1 + \ 3x_2 \leqslant 92$$
$$x_1 + \ \ x_2 \leqslant 38$$
$$x_1 \qquad \ \leqslant 20$$
$$x_2 \leqslant 20$$
$$x_1 \geqslant 0, x_2 \geqslant 0$$

2-4 Acme Ltd currently manufacture two products, the De Luxe and the Grande. Relevant financial and sales data and consumption of scarce resources are:

	De Luxe	Grande
Machine hours (per unit)	1	2.5
Labour hours (per unit)	4	3
Selling price (£)	30	39
Unit cost (£)	26	27
Maximum sales (units per day)	40	30

Each day there are up to 85 machine hours and 200 labour hours available. Acme's objective is the maximization of profit.

(a) What should be the daily production of each good?

(b) An extra one hour per day of machine time could be made available at a premium of £5 above the current price. Would this be worth having?

(c) Within what range of values must the unit profit figure for the De Luxe model lie for the original solution to remain optimal?

2-5 Excell Ltd can manufacture four products. Only three resources are limited in supply. Each product does not require every type of scarce resource. Resource consumption (per unit produced) and financial details for the products are:

	Product			
	A	B	C	D
Packaging labour (hours per unit)	2	5	—	—
Machine time (hours per unit)	4	1	—	—
Skilled labour (hours per unit)	—	—	3	4
Selling price (£)	25	27	25	24
Unit cost	22	18	20	16

Each month, the resource availabilities are:

Resource	Hours available
Packaging labour	8000
Machine time	4000
Skilled labour	6000

(a) Determine the monthly production levels that would maximize profits.

(b) *Ceteris paribus*, what is the minimum selling price at which the sale of product B would be worth while?

(c) If the current skilled wage rate is £3 per hour, what is the maximum *overtime* wage rate that the company would find it worth while to pay?

2-6 Jewel Enterprises at present manufacture a range of four products. Relevant data are:

	Product			
	A	B	C	D
Current production	1000	900	750	250
Selling price (£)	40	38	35	32
Unit cost (£)	26	14	20	12
Machine hours (per unit)	1	1	1.5	0.5
Materials (per unit)	1.5	2.5	1	2

The two resources, machine hours and materials, are the only ones in limited supply and are currently fully used. A linear programming study revealed that the dual values of the scarce resources were £4 and £9 respectively.

(a) Determine the profits maximizing production levels and the opportunity loss on the present arrangement.

(b) Other data unchanged, at what selling prices would the unattractive products become worth while?

2-7 A linear programming model is to be used for selecting the best mix of the possible products A, B, C, D, and E. The following information is available:

(i)

	Per unit of product				
	A £	B £	C £	D £	E £
Selling price	48	42	38	31	27
Costs:					
Materials	15	14	16	15	16
Direct labour	18	16	6	4	4
Fixed overheads*	9	8	3	2	2
Total costs	42	38	25	21	22
Net profit	6	4	13	10	5

*Based on 50 per cent of direct labour cost.

(ii) Expected maximum unit demand per week for each product at prices indicated:

A	B	C	D	E
1500	1200	900	600	600

(iii) Cost of materials includes a special component which is in short supply; it costs £3 a unit. Only 5800 units will be available to the company during the year. The number of units of the special component needed for a unit of each product is:

A	B	C	D	E
1	1	3	4	5

(iv) Labour is paid at a rate of £1.50 per hour and only 20 000 hours will be available in a week.

(v) Management has ruled that expenditure on materials must not exceed a sum of £30 000.

(vi) All other resources are freely available in sufficient quantities for planned needs.

Required:

(a) Formulate a linear programming model stating clearly the criterion you use. (You are not expected to produce a numerical solution to your model.)

(b) Describe the problems likely to be encountered in the application of linear programming to determine the 'best' product mix.

(Chartered Association of Certified Accountants)

2-8 A company has an assured market for any quantities of two products, which are processed on one machine and then finished by hand. The products are not complementary and may be produced independently in varying quantities. Planned output is 600 units per week of each product, a combination chosen because it fully utilizes machine and labour capacities. Maximum utilization is the rule-of-thumb strategy used by the management as most likely to yield maximum profit. Machine capacity is 1200 units per week of either product or a combination of the two; no time is lost in changing over from one product to the other. Machine operators cannot be discharged and their wages are included in fixed overheads. Finishing-labour supply is limited to 2400 direct hours per week. Finishing labour is a fixed cost in the short run as no other work is available if machine output is delayed for any reason. Standard product costs and selling prices are as follows:

Standard product costs:	Product A £	Product B £
Materials	2	2
Finishing labour: £3 per hour	9	3
Fixed overhead: 1/3 labour cost	3	1
	14	6
Selling price	16	8

Last week the factory manager scheduled production of only 500 units of each product, as an overhaul of the machine, which would reduce available machine capacity to 1000 units, was unavoidable. As a result, the finishing staff was idle for most of one day while the operators carried out the overhaul.

You are required:
(a) using graphical methods, to show
  (i) whether the normal rule-of-thumb strategy optimizes contribution to profit, and if not what strategy would do this;
  (ii) how many units of each product would have optimized contribution to profit during the overhaul; and
(b) to calculate
  (i) standard net profit under the optimum strategy you recommend in (a) (i);
  (ii) how much, if any, contribution to profit was lost by the factory manager's decision on product mix during the overhaul.

(Institute of Chartered Accountants in England and Wales)

2-9 Solve the following minimization LP problem:

$$\text{Minimize } F = 7x_1 + 3x_2$$

$$\text{Subject to: } \quad x_1 + 2x_2 \geqslant 55$$

$$4x_1 + x_2 \geqslant 80$$

$$x_1 \geqslant 0, \ x_2 \geqslant 0$$

Find the tolerance intervals for the objective function coefficients and the dual values associated with the right-hand sides of the constraints.

Solution guides

2-2 Let the decision variables x_1 and x_2 represent the quantities produced of the Prima and Seconda models respectively. The objective of the company is profit maximization and the unit profits on the two goods are $34 - 28 = 6$ and $29 - 25 = 4$ respectively, hence the objective function will be:

$$\pi = 6x_1 + 4x_2$$

The constraints relate to the numbers of cutting and finishing hours used and the sales limits which give upper bounds on x_1 and x_2. The two resource constraints are:

$$2x_1 + x_2 \leqslant 390$$
$$3x_1 + 3x_2 \leqslant 810$$

and the bounds on the decision variables will be:

$$x_1 \leqslant 200 \quad x_2 \leqslant 200$$

along with the sign requirements:

$$x_1 \geqslant 0 \quad x_2 \geqslant 0$$

A graph of the problem is shown in Fig. 2-10. Note that the upper bound on x_1 is not shown, as x_1

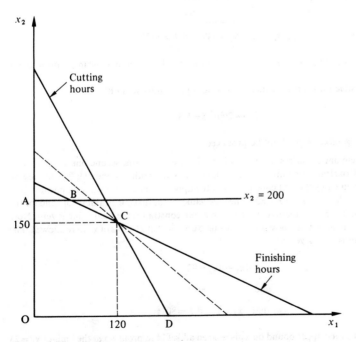

Figure 2-10

is already more tightly restricted to 195 units by the cutting hours constraint. The upper bound on x_1 is said to be a *redundant constraint* and can be omitted from the problem. The feasible region is bounded by OABCD and the optimum position is C where $x_1 = 120$ and $x_2 = 150$ with $\pi = 1320$.

The tolerance intervals for the unit profit figures are found as follows. For π_1

$$\frac{3}{3} \leqslant \frac{\pi_1}{4} \leqslant \frac{2}{1}$$

So that:

$$4 \leqslant \pi_1 \leqslant 8$$

And for π_2

$$\frac{3}{3} \leqslant \frac{6}{\pi_2} \leqslant \frac{2}{1}$$

So that:

$$3 \leqslant \pi_2 \leqslant 6$$

The dual value of cutting hours is given from:

$$6x_1 + 3x_2 = 1173$$
$$3x_1 + 3x_2 = 810$$
$$\overline{3x_1 = 363}$$

$$\therefore x_1 = 121, \ x_2 = 149 \text{ and } F = 1322$$

So the dual value of cutting hours is £2. By similar means the dual value of finishing hours is found to be £$\frac{2}{3}$.

For the possible third product there will be an opportunity loss of:

$$2(2) + 2(\tfrac{2}{3}) - 5 = 1/3$$

So that the third product should not be produced.

2-3 In this problem one of the 'resource' constraints is redundant—the second one as can be seen from Fig. 2-11. Constraint one always sets tighter limits for both x's and the feasible region OABCD is determined by the first constraint and the upper bounds. The optimum position is at point C where $x_1 = 20, x_2 = 4$ and $F = 800$. The dual value for the first constraint is 25/3 and for the second constraint (as for any redundant or non-binding constraint) the dual value is zero. Note that the upper bound on x_1 has a positive dual value. Suppose that 21 units of x_1 were allowed. The optimum position is now given by

$$4x_1 + 3x_2 = 92$$
$$\text{and} \quad x_1 = 21$$

so that $x_2 = \frac{8}{3}$ and $F = 801\frac{2}{3}$

Every unit by which the upper bound on x_1 is relaxed adds £$1\frac{2}{3}$ to profit up to the limit of $x_1 = 23$

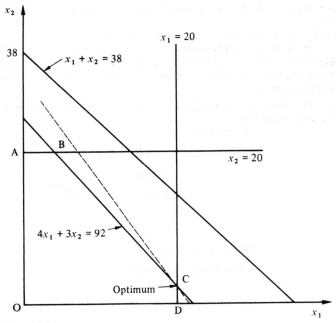

Figure 2-11

given by the first resource constraint. Thereafter, further relaxation of the upper bound is ineffective.

2-4 A graph of the problem is shown in Fig. 2-12.

(a) The feasible region is OABCDE and the optimum is at B, where 10 De Luxes and 30 Grandes are made, giving a total profit of 400. Note that the optimum is *not* point

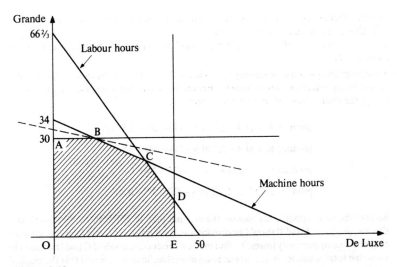

Figure 2-12

C which gives only 380 profit. In this case it is not profitable to use up all the available labour hours.

(b) It would not be worth having since the dual value is only £4.

(c) With Π_1 as the unit profit on the De Luxe model then the range emerges as: $0 \leqslant \Pi_1 \leqslant 4.8$.

(Note that it follows from this that if there is *any* profit to be had on De Luxes ($\Pi_1 > 0$) they will be produced at the optimum. If $\Pi_1 > 4.8$ then the optimum moves to point C at which more De Luxes and fewer Grandes are made.)

2-5 This problem can be divided into two sub-problems. Letting the amounts produced be x_A, x_B, x_C, and x_D the two problems are:

$$\text{Maximize } 3x_A + 9x_B$$

$$\text{subject to } 2x_A + 5x_B \leqslant 8000$$

$$4x_A + x_B \leqslant 4000$$

$$x_A \geqslant 0, \; x_B \geqslant 0$$

and

$$\text{Maximize } 5x_C + 8x_D$$

$$\text{subject to } 3x_C + 4x_D \leqslant 6000$$

$$x_C \geqslant 0, \; x_D \geqslant 0$$

The answers are:

(a) $x_A = 0$, $x_B = 1600$, $x_C = 0$, $x_D = 1500$. The profit is 26 400.

(b) This selling price is given by the unit profit such that the objective function contours have a slope of (minus) 4. This is the slope of the second constraint to which the objective function contours would then be parallel. We have

$$\frac{\Pi_A}{\Pi_B} = \frac{3}{\Pi_B} = 4 \quad \therefore \quad \Pi_B = \frac{3}{4}$$

So with other data unchanged, the selling price that would give this level of unit profit is $18\frac{3}{4}$. This is the requisite minimum price.

(c) The dual value of skilled labour if £2. Thus the maximum overtime wage rate is £3 + £2 = £5.

2-6 (a) The opportunity loss on the existing plan is found by first finding the opportunity loss per unit of each product and multiplying by the current production levels and then summing. Given the dual values the opportunity losses are:

$$\text{product A: 1 at } 4 + 1.5 \text{ at } 9 - (40 - 26) = 3.5$$

$$\text{product B: 1 at } 4 + 2.5 \text{ at } 9 - (38 - 14) = 2.5$$

$$\text{product C: 1.5 at } 4 + 1 \text{ at } 9 - (35 - 20) = 0$$

$$\text{product D: 0.5 at } 4 + 2 \text{ at } 9 - (32 - 12) = 0$$

So that the total opportunity loss on the original plan is $3.5(1000) + 2.5(900) = 5750$. Clearly, products A and B should be discontinued and products C and D produced since they show no opportunity losses. To find the new production levels of C and D we need to know the total machine hours and materials available. Since we are told that the original plan uses up all available machine hours and materials, the total amounts must be the sum of the products of the original levels and the per unit requirements of the products. Thus machine hours available are

$$1(1000) + 1(900) + 1.5(750) + 0.5(250) = 3150$$

and materials available are

$$1.5(1000) + 2.5(900) + 1(750) + 2(250) = 5000$$

We can now solve for the production levels

$$1.5x_C + 0.5x_D = 3150$$
$$x_C + 2x_D = 5000$$

Thus $x_C = 1520$ and $x_D = 1740$.

(b) At such prices that made their opportunity losses zero. The price of A must go up by 3.5 and the price of B must go up by 2.5. The resulting prices are then 43.5 for A and 40.5 for B.

2-7 (a) Assume that the company's objective is profit maximization. There are numerous other possible criteria, notably those based upon 'growth'. However, no data are provided that would allow such a formulation. Given the data, one of the few alternative objectives would have been maximization of turnover. Economic justification for such a criterion is weak, however. In general, a company's ability to do things will depend ultimately upon profitability.

In order to maximize profits, the greatest possible sum should be made available to set against overheads. Thus contribution should be maximized.

In the problem data this means that fixed overheads will not be included in the unit 'costs'. Let X_a be the number of units made of product A. Unit contribution will be $48 - (15 + 18) = 15$. Following similar notation and procedure for the other products the objective function is

$$\text{Maximize } F = 15X_a + 12X_b + 16X_c + 12X_d + 7X_e$$

$$\text{subject to} \quad X_a \qquad \leqslant 1500$$
$$X_b \qquad \leqslant 1200$$
$$X_c \qquad \leqslant 900$$
$$X_d \leqslant 600$$
$$X_e \leqslant 600$$

and for the component constraint:

$$X_a + X_b + 3X_c + 4X_d + 5X_e \leqslant 5800$$

For the labour constraint the requirements per unit of each product will be the direct labour costs divided by 1.5. Thus

$$12X_a + 10\tfrac{2}{3}X_b + 4X_c + 2\tfrac{2}{3}X_d + 2\tfrac{2}{3}X_e \leqslant 20\,000$$

and for material expenditures

$$15X_a + 14X_b + 16X_c + 15X_d + 16X_e \leqslant 30\,000$$

and the sign requirements

$$X_a \geqslant 0, \; X_b \geqslant 0, \; X_c \geqslant 0, \; X_d \geqslant 0, \; X_e \geqslant 0$$

(b) There are many 'practical' problems. There are the problems of deciding what the objective is to be, identifying the constraints, and obtaining the data. Then there may be non-linearities (usually dealt with by an approximating device), random influences, and whole-number problems. However, recall that sensitivity analysis would be of great value in assessing the consequences of possible inaccuracies and changed conditions.

2-8 As was shown in section 2-4, in general, the idea of maximum utilization of capacity will not lead to profit maximization. When it so does, however, this is merely fortuitous.

All costs except materials are fixed. The problem is then to maximize contribution:

$$\text{Maximize } F = 14X_a + 6X_b$$

(Note: the '14' and '6' here are only coincidentally equal to the standard product costs. In the objective function they represent the unit contributions.)

The capacity constraint is

$$X_a + X_b \leqslant 1200$$

and the finishing labour hours constraint is

$$3X_a + X_b \leqslant 2400$$

The graph of the problem is shown in Fig. 2-13 from which it is seen that the feasible region is

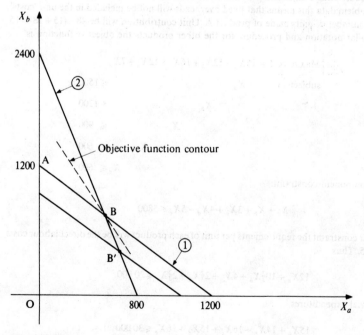

Figure 2-13

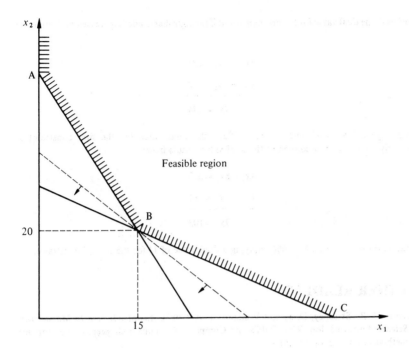

Figure 2-14

OABC and that point B is optimal $(X_a = 600, X_b = 600)$ so that it happens that both resources *are* fully used at the optimum.

      (ii) During the overhaul the optimum moves to B' at which point $X_a = 700$, $X_b = 300$.

   (b) (i) Net profit for product A is $16 - 14 = 2$ and for product B is $8 - 6 = 2$. Thus with 600 units of each product manufactured the standard net profit is $600 \times 2 + 600 \times 2 = 2400$.

      (ii) Maximum contribution at B' is 11 600. With 500 units of each product made the contribution is 10 000. Thus 1600 would be lost.

2-9 The problem is graphed in Fig. 2-14. The feasible region is the open area bounded from below by the axes and ABC. Point B is optimal, being in contact with the lowest objective function contour. At point B, $x_1 = 15$, $x_2 = 20$ and $F = 165$. The tolerance interval for the objective function coefficient of $x_1(C_1)$ is given by:

$$\frac{1}{2} \leqslant \frac{C_1}{3} \leqslant 4$$

So that the interval is:

$$1.5 \leqslant C_1 \leqslant 12$$

By similar means the confidence interval for the objective function coefficient of $x_2(C_2)$ is found to be:

$$1.75 \leqslant C_2 \leqslant 14$$

To establish the dual value for the first constraint if the right-hand side is increased to 56 units we have:

$$4x_1 + 8x_2 = 224$$
$$4x_1 + x_2 = 80$$
$$\overline{\hspace{2cm}}$$
$$7x_2 = 144$$

So that $x_2 = 20\frac{4}{7}$, $x_1 = 14\frac{6}{7}$ and $F = 165\frac{5}{7}$. Thus the dual value for the first constraint is $\frac{5}{7}$. Similarly for the second constraint the dual value results from:

$$4x_1 + 8x_2 = 220$$
$$4x_1 + x_2 = 81$$
$$\overline{\hspace{2cm}}$$
$$7x_2 = 103$$

So that $x_2 = 19\frac{6}{7}$, $x_1 = 15\frac{2}{7}$, $F = 166\frac{4}{7}$ implying a dual value of $1\frac{4}{7}$ for the second constraint.

FURTHER READING

Anderson, D. R., Sweeney, D. J., and Williams, T. A. (1985), *An Introduction to Management Science*, fourth edition, West Publishing Company. Contains a chapter on the graphical method of linear programming.

Littlechild, S. C. (1977) *Operational Research for Managers*, Philip Allan. Graphical method and applications.

Taha, H. A. (1987), *Operations Research*, fourth edition, Collier Macmillan. Contains general but more technical introduction to LP.

THREE

LINEAR PROGRAMMING—THE SIMPLEX METHOD

3-1 INTRODUCTION

The graphical method described in Chapter Two, while essential to an understanding of LP problem structure, is limited to two variable problems (with any number of constraints) as a solution procedure. A variant of the method can handle problems in two constraints and any number of variables but where there are more than two variables *and* more than two constraints (and the problem does not partition into manageable sub-problems) a tabular solution procedure is necessary.

The *simplex method* is a highly efficient iterative procedure suited to both hand and computer calculation requiring no more than a few simple rules and the four operations of common arithmetic. The method has the added advantage of producing the dual values for the constraints along with the best values of the decision variables. In the following sections, we shall develop the method in the context of the Azed problem of Chapter Two. A typical format of the solution to this problem by computer will be shown in section 3-9.

3-2 SLACK VARIABLES

Equations have more exploitable properties than inequalities and it will be helpful to transform the inequality relationships of the constraints into strict equalities. This is done by the introduction of *slack variables* one for each constraint. In constraint (1), for instance, we introduce s_1 where:

$$4x_1 + x_2 + s_1 = 800$$

i.e., s_1 is the shortfall between usage $(4x_1 + x_2)$ and availability of material (800 kg). Similarly unused labour hours are s_2 where:

$$2x_1 + 3x_2 + s_2 = 900$$

We shall also need a slack variable in the third constraint; this will be s_3 where:

$$x_1 + s_3 = 180$$

and s_3 is simply the amount by which x_1 is below its permitted maximum. For instance in the solution that we already know is optimal, $x_1 = 150$, so that in this solution $s_3 = 30$. The fourth constraint will not be represented as it is redundant. Note that unlike the x's, the slack variables appear only in one constraint each. The slacks *must be non-negative* or the original constraints would be violated. For instance if $s_1 = -10$, this would mean that $4x_1 + x_2 = 810$ which would break the original requirement. In most contexts slack variables do not appear in the objective function or rather the slacks have *zero coefficients in the objective function*. Now write everything out in full. The problem is to:

Maximize $\qquad \pi = 6x_1 + 5x_2 + 0s_1 + 0s_2 + 0s_3$

subject to $\qquad 4x_1 + 1x_2 + 1s_1 + 0s_2 + 0s_3 = 800$

$\qquad\qquad\qquad 2x_1 + 3x_2 + 0s_1 + 1s_2 + 0s_3 = 900$

$\qquad\qquad\qquad 1x_1 + 0x_2 + 0s_1 + 0s_2 + 1s_3 = 180$

and $\qquad\qquad x_1 \geqslant 0, x_2 \geqslant 0, s_1 \geqslant 0, s_2 \geqslant 0, s_3 \geqslant 0$

Notice that the slack variables have zero coefficients everywhere except in the one constraint to which they are specific. Where it is necessary to distinguish them from the slack variables the x's are referred to as *structural* variables. The next step is to rearrange the information in the form of a tableau as follows:

6	5	0	0	0
x_1	x_2	s_1	s_2	s_3
4	1	1	0	0
2	3	0	1	0
1	0	0	0	1

in which there is one row which identifies the variables, above which are the coefficients in the objective function. All of the coefficients of x_1 are in the x_1 column, all of the coefficients of x_2 are in the x_2 column—and so on. This is a helpful arrangement to which we shall shortly return. Having introduced slack variables, the logic of the simplex method can now be set out.

3-3 THE LOGIC OF THE SIMPLEX METHOD

The logic of the simplex procedure rests on the fact that *only the corner points* of the feasible region can be unique optima. No point in the feasible region can ever be better than all the corner points. Thus we need only concentrate on the corners. These are termed *extreme points* and correspond to *basic solutions* or, strictly, *basic feasible solutions* (bfs) to the problem.

A distinguishing feature of bfs is that there are no more positive variables than there are constraints. Except in degenerate solutions (which need not detain us here) there will be precisely the same number of positive variables as there are constraints. Thus each corner of the feasible region should have three variables positive. These are identified in Fig. 3-1 in which the positive variables are shown in brackets. The remaining two variables in each case are zero. Notice something else. Each bfs has two 'neighbours'. For instance B has A and C next door to it; D has O and C and so on. If you move from one bfs to a neighbour the group of positive variables changes by one element, viz., in moving from B to C, s_3 'drops out' of the group and is 'replaced' by s_2. In moving from O to D, s_3 drops out and is replaced by x_1. One last point: the feasible region is *convex*. In everyday terms this simply means that there are no

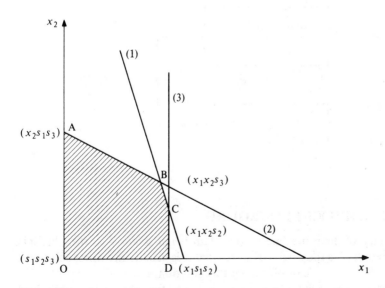

Figure 3-1

indentations. When a linear function is being maximized over a convex region, to reach the optimum it is only necessary that each 'step' taken from some starting point increases the value of π. In other words one can move from one bfs to a better neighbour and carry on in this short-sighted fashion and be sure of reaching the top. This is called an *adjacent extreme point solution procedure*. Rather like a walker trying to gain the summit of a dome-shaped hill in a fog. So long as he keeps going up there is only one place that he can finish—the top (we are ignoring the subtleties of asymptotic increases). This contrasts with the case of a twin-peaked hill, in which case there would be no guarantee of attaining the greater summit by purely myopic progress. LP is comparable to the single-peaked case.

1. Obtain any bfs to start with.
2. Check neighbouring solutions to see if they are better.
3. If there is a better neighbouring solution, move to it.
4. Repeat steps (2) and (3) until no further improvement is possible.

Figure 3-2 sets out the steps in the form of a simple flow diagram. The loop between steps (2) and (3) is the *iterative* part of the procedure. We can now set out the detailed workings in tableau form.

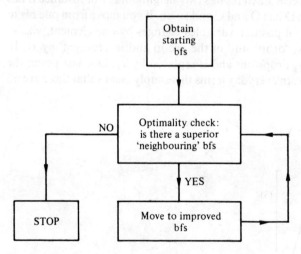

Figure 3-2

3-4 THE SIMPLEX PROCEDURE

The first step of the procedure is to find an *initial solution*–starting bfs. The easiest bfs to find is the origin. The fact that it is usually the worst solution is outweighed by the ease of obtaining this solution.

A description of the origin is now added to the tableau so far obtained.

This is done thus:

			6	5	0	0	0
			x_1	x_2	s_1	s_2	s_3
0	s_1	800	4	1	1	0	0
0	s_2	900	2	3	0	1	0
0	s_3	180	1	0	0	0	1

In the central column to the left are listed the variables in the solution (i.e., positive) at the origin, adjacent to their appropriate constraints. To the right are shown the values of these variables. Since the slacks equal the right-hand sides of the constraints, all resources would be unused. To the left of the solution variables are their objective function coefficients. All variables not listed in this left-hand (solution) part of the tableau are zero, i.e., at the origin $x_1 = 0$, $x_2 = 0$.

The next step is to determine the value of the objective function at the origin and to see if any improvement is possible. The value of the objective function will be the sum of the level of each variable multiplied by its objective function coefficient. This is a trivial exercise at the origin. We obtain $\pi = 800(0) + 900(0) + 180(0) = 0$. This value is inserted immediately below the solution column. Next we must ascertain if improvement is possible. This is done by considering the consequences of introducing each non-basic (not-in-the-solution) variable to *unit level*. Suppose we set $x_1 = 1$. Geometrically we move a little way along the x_1 axis away from the origin—towards D in fact. Clearly, if we set $x_1 = 1$ this will affect the levels of the slack variables. In fact the column of coefficients under x_1 (viz., 4, 2, 1) shows by how much each of the variables in the solution will have to be reduced to accommodate one unit of x_1. Thus s_1 must go down by 4, s_2 must go down by 2 and s_3 must go down by 1. If not obviously correct the results may be checked by reference back to the constraints themselves. Now, if at some stage we are cutting back on the levels of variables in the solution the objective function will be affected if these variables have new zero objective function coefficients (ofcs). The effect on the objective function of the adjustments necessary to accommodate one unit of x_1 is the sum of products of 'rates of exchange' in the x_1 column and the ofcs of solution variables. Thus on account of the alterations necessary, the objective function alters by

$$4(0) + 2(0) + 1(0) = 0$$

but in return we get one unit of x_1 worth (from the head of the x_1 column) 6. The *net* decrease in the objective function is then

$$4(0) + 2(0) + 1(0) - 6 = -6$$

that is, an *increase* of 6. The number -6 is now entered in a new row—the *index row* (or $z_j - c_j$ row as it is sometimes called) under x_1. A negative number in the index row thus represents *improvement* possibility. A decrease of -6 is, of course, an increase of $+6$. This rather backhanded way of going about things has a reason which we shall come to later on. An index row number is now determined for each variable. For x_2, for instance, we obtain

$$1(0) + 3(0) + 0(0) - 5 = -5$$

All basic variables (those already in the solution) have zero index row numbers as may be verified by completing the workings. *Provided* that the slack variables have zero ofcs the first index row will be the negation of the ofcs. The complete picture is:

			6	5	0	0	0	
			x_1	x_2	s_1	s_2	s_3	
0	s_1	800	4	1	1	0	0	
0	s_2	900	2	3	0	1	0	
0	s_3	180	1	0	0	0	1	
Value of $\pi \rightarrow$		0	-6	-5	0	0	0	$\leftarrow$index row

We now select the variable with 'most negative' index row number to come into the solution. This is called the *entering variable* and the variable showing the greatest *per unit* improvement in π. We now introduce this variable, x_1, to the maximum extent. This will correspond to movement to point D. Notice from Fig. 3-1 that in moving from O to D, x_1 enters the group of positive variables and s_3 drops out. From the simplex tableau the variable to drop out is identified by forming the ratios of solution values to rates of exchange of incoming variable. Thus we have

$$\text{for } s_1: \text{ratio} = 800/4 = 200$$
$$\text{for } s_2: \text{ratio} = 900/2 = 450$$
$$\text{for } s_3: \text{ratio} = 180/1 = 180$$

The smallest ratio identifies the *leaving variable*—variable to leave the basis. The ratios are the maximum extent to which x_1 can be introduced without making the respective basic variable negative. This procedure of selecting the leaving variable guarantees that no solution variables will ever be negative, i.e., we are confined to basic *feasible* solutions. The row of numbers corresponding to the variable going out is called the *pivotal row*. The column of numbers corresponding to the entering variable is termed the *pivotal column*. The number at the junction is called the *pivotal element*. It is convenient to 'block in' the pivotal row and column as shown below. The description of the new solution (corresponding to point D) can now begin. We shall produce a new tableau beneath the (now) old one. Start by writing down the variables in this new solution and to the left the three-element column of objective function coefficients. Thus we obtain:

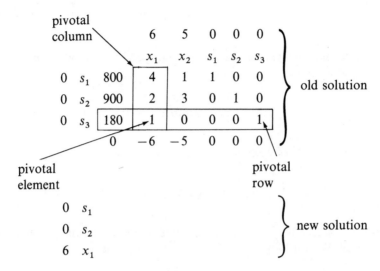

The next step is to provide a full numerical description of this solution—with solution values for s_1, s_2, and x_1 and the rates of exchange. In other words we must now fill in the blanks in the new solution tableau.

There are two rote pieces of arithmetic involved in forming the new tableau. We first form the *main row*. The main row is the row in the new tableau in the *same position* as the pivotal row in the old tableau. All main row numbers are pivotal row numbers divided by the pivotal element. Since the pivotal element is unity (in this case) the main row is the same as the old pivotal row. Thus we write in

$$
\begin{array}{llllllll}
0 & s_1 & & & & & & \\
0 & s_2 & & & & & & \\
6 & x_1 & 180 & 1 & 0 & 0 & 0 & 1
\end{array}
$$

Now we must find the remaining numbers, which are all found by the same means. Suppose we start with the new level of s_2. Call this the 'new number'. Call the number in the same position in the old solution (the old level of s_2) the 'old number'. Now use the formula:

new number = old number − corresponding main row number

× corresponding pivotal column number

The 'corresponding main row number' is the number in the main row in the same column as the new number. The 'corresponding pivotal column number' is the number in the pivotal column in the same row as the old number. Thus, using the formula

$$\text{new value of } s_2 = 900 - 180 \times 2 = 540$$

Now find the rate of exchange between s_2 and x_2. This was 3 in the old tableau. Now we have

$$\text{new number} = 3 - 0 \times 2 = 3$$

The new rate of exchange between s_2 and x_1 is

$$\text{new number} = 2 - 1 \times 2 = 0$$

In this case the 'corresponding pivotal column number' is the old number itself. We can now fill in the entire s_2 row. It is

$$0 \quad s_2 \quad 540 \quad 0 \quad 3 \quad 0 \quad 1 \quad -2$$

Note that the rate of exchange between s_2 and s_3 is negative. For each unit of s_3 brought into the solution s_2 would *increase* by two units. For all the numbers in the s_1 row the corresponding pivotal column number is 4. The new level of s_1 itself is given by

$$\text{new level of } s_1 = 800 - 180 \times 4 = 80$$

The rate of exchange between s_1 and x_2 is

$$\text{new number} = 1 - 0 \times 4 = 1$$

The remaining numbers in the new s_1 row are found in similar fashion and the complete s_1 row in the new solution is

$$0 \quad s_1 \quad 80 \quad 0 \quad 1 \quad 1 \quad 0 \quad -4$$

To complete the first iteration we have now only to compute the index row for the new solution. The value of the solution is now 1080 while the full tableau is shown below:

			6	5	0	0	0
			x_1	x_2	s_1	s_2	s_3
0	s_1	800	4	1	1	0	0
0	s_2	900	2	3	0	1	0
0	s_3	180	1	0	0	0	1
		0	−6	−5	0	0	0
0	s_1	80	0	1	1	0	−4
0	s_2	540	0	3	0	1	−2
6	x_1	180	1	0	0	0	1
		1080	0	−5	0	0	+6	←new index row

The index row elements are formed just as before. To recap on the number for s_3 this will be:

$$0(-4)+0(-2)+6(1)-0= +6$$

The new tableau describes the situation at point D. A profit of 1080 is made but the presence of a negative number in the index row (under x_2) means that the solution is not optimal. Specifically the variable x_2 must be brought into the solution. This will correspond to a move from D to C. The new pivotal column (determined by the −5) and the new pivotal row (determined by the smallest of the ratios 800/1, 540/3, 180/0) are indicated above. All that now needs to be done is to repeat the procedure until a solution is found with no negative numbers in the index row.

The next solution (point C) is:

			6	5	0	0	0
			x_1	x_2	s_1	s_2	s_3
5	x_2	80	0	1	1	0	−4
0	s_2	300	0	0	−3	1	10
6	x_1	180	1	0	0	0	1
		1480	0	0	+5	0	−14	← index row

Again this solution is not optimal as evidenced by the presence of a negative number in the index row. This time s_2 must be introduced. For once the pivotal element is not unity so that the main row will be

$$s_2 \quad 30 \quad 0 \quad 0 \quad -0.3 \quad 0.1 \quad 1$$

and the full solution is:

			6	5	0	0	0	
			x_1	x_2	s_1	s_2	s_3	
5	x_2	200	0	1	−0.2	0.4	0	
0	s_3	30	0	0	−0.3	0.1	1	
6	x_1	150	1	0	0.3	−0.1	0	
		1900	0	0	0.8	1.4	0	← index row

This solution is optimal, since there are no negative numbers in the index row. This is the *stopping rule* (no negative index row numbers) and is the point at which the iterative loop in Fig. 3-2 is exited.

Note that in obtaining the entries in the new x_2 row, the corresponding pivotal column element is −4 so that, unless the corresponding main row number is also negative, there will be increases in solution values and rates of exchange.

The optimal solution calls for 200 units of the Omega model ($x_2 = 200$), 150 units of the Alpha model ($x_1 = 150$) and $s_3 = 30$. The value of s_3 is simply the extent to which x_1 is below its maximum permitted level. Any variable that does not appear in the solution part of the tableau at zero level. Thus since s_1 and s_2 do not appear, $s_1 = 0$ and $s_2 = 0$ at the optimum.

If at any stage in the simplex workings, a zero appears in the solution column (following a tie between two rows for pivotal row) the solution contains one fewer positive variable than there are constraints and is said to be *degenerate*. Although there is a theoretical possibility of a problem 'cycling' between solutions, degeneracy does not usually cause difficulties in hand calculation and will disappear when a solution column zero has a negative rate of exchange in the pivotal column.

The construction of any simplex tableau is equivalent to the solution of a set of simultaneous equations. The iterative procedure of moving from one tableau to another is, in effect, a highly efficient way of moving from the solution of one set of simultaneous equations to another.

One important and useful feature of the simplex method is that the dual values (marginal values or shadow prices) are automatically obtained in the solution to the problem. The dual value of a resource (or of any binding constraint) appears in the final index row under the slack variable corresponding to that resource. Thus in the index row under s_1 we see that the dual value of resource one is 0.8 and under s_2 we have the shadow price of resource two, 1.4. It is seen that the dual value under s_3 is zero. Although s_3 does not correspond to a physical resource, if the upper bound on x_3 had been binding there would have been a positive shadow price.

One interesting feature of the dual values should be noted. If each dual value is multiplied by the total amount of the resource (or upper bound) to which it corresponds, then the number thus achieved is the optimal value of the objective function, viz., $800(0.8) + 900(1.4) + 180(0) = 1900$. This is always the case. The dual values, in a sense, give an *average* valuation of resources as well as a marginal one. We say 'in a sense' because it does *not* follow that a resource with zero dual value is worthless on average and thus can be dispensed with. It is a useful partial check on the workings to multiply the dual values by the right-hand sides of the constraints to confirm that the current value of the objective function is obtained.

3-5 SENSITIVITY ANALYSIS

Sensitivity analysis on the objective function coefficients—obtaining tolerance intervals for π_1 and π_2—is conveniently carried out by use of the simplex tableau. The basic principle rests on the fact that index row numbers must remain non-negative if the solution is to remain optimal. If the ofc of x_1 is being considered then π_1 is substituted for the specific value 6 in the optimal simplex tableau and index row numbers calculated in terms of π_1 with the requirement that they be non-negative. These expressions for the index row numbers will imply bounds on π_1—all of which must be satisfied.

Carrying out a sensitivity analysis on π_1 leaves the final simplex tableau as follows:

			π_1	5	0	0	0
			x_1	x_2	s_1	s_2	s_3
5	x_2	200	0	1	-0.2	0.4	0
0	s_3	30	0	0	-0.3	0.1	1
π_1	x_1	150	1	0	0.3	-0.1	0
		1900	0	0	*	+	0

The only index row numbers affected will be those under s_1 and s_2 indicated as * and + both of which must remain non-negative for the solution to remain optimal. Comparing the numbers in the usual fashion we obtain the conditions:

$$* = -0.2(5) - 0.3(0) + 0.3(\pi_1) - 0 \geqslant 0$$

$$+ = 0.4(5) + 0.1(0) - 0.1(\pi_1) - 0 \geqslant 0$$

From the first requirement it emerges that:

$$-1+0.3\pi_1 \geqslant 0 \quad \therefore \pi_1 \geqslant \frac{10}{3}$$

and from the second:

$$2-0.1\pi_1 \geqslant 0 \quad \therefore \quad \pi_1 \leqslant 20$$

So that the tolerance interval emerges as:

$$\frac{10}{3} \leqslant \pi_1 \leqslant 20$$

A similar analysis on the objective function coefficient of x_2, π_2 gives:

$$* = -0.2\pi_2 - 0.3(0) + 0.3(6) - 0 \geqslant 0$$
$$+ = \quad 0.4\pi_2 - 0.3(0) - 0.1(6) - 0 \geqslant 0$$

which respectively yield $\pi_2 \leqslant 9$ and $\pi_2 \geqslant 1.5$.

A joint analysis on the two objective function coefficients produces:

$$* = -0.2\pi_2 + 0.3\pi_1 \geqslant 0 \quad \therefore \quad \pi_2 \leqslant 1.5\pi_1$$

and

$$+ = \quad 0.4\pi_2 - 0.1\pi_1 \geqslant 0 \quad \therefore \quad \pi_2 \geqslant 0.25\pi_1$$

So, in addition to providing dual values without further calculation being required, the simplex tableau provides a convenient format for sensitivity analysis on objective function coefficients. In fact, tableau-based sensitivity work can be extended to determining the maximum permissible variations in resource levels, the right-hand side (RHS) of the constraints as a whole and other more advanced work. Wilkes (1983) gives further details.

3-6 MINIMIZATION PROBLEMS

The simplex method is a procedure geared to maximization problems but adaptation of minimization problems to suitable form is not difficult. To see an illustration of the method, consider the minimization problem shown in Chapter Two. This was:

$$\text{Minimize } F = 3x_1 + 5x_2$$

$$\text{subject to} \quad x_1 + 4x_2 \geqslant 60$$

$$2x_1 + x_2 \geqslant 50$$

$$x_1 \geqslant 0 x_2 \geqslant 0$$

Adjustments of two kinds are needed in respect of the objective function and the constraints. First, consider the constraints. Slack variables can be subtracted to produce:

$$x_1 + 4x_2 - s_1 = 60$$

$$2x_1 + x_2 - s_2 = 50$$

where $s_1 \geqslant 0$ and $s_2 \geqslant 0$. However, a problem arises in that the origin cannot be used as the starting solution since it is not in the feasible region. Setting x_1 and x_2 to zero would give $s_1 = -60$ and $s_2 = -50$ in the solution column of the simplex tableau—which is not permissible. To avoid this problem, an *artificial variable* is added to each equation to produce:

$$x_1 + 4x_2 - s_1 + u_1 = 60$$

$$2x_1 + x_2 - s_2 + u_2 = 50$$

where $u_1 \geqslant 0$ and $u_2 \geqslant 0$ are the artificial variables. We can now set both the x's *and* the slack variables equal to zero and set $u_1 = 60$ and $u_2 = 50$ in the initial simplex tableau. However, we must eliminate u_1 and u_2 from the tableau in order to produce a real solution of the problem. This is done by attaching arbitrarily large penalties to u_1 and u_2 in the objective function. An unspecified coefficient, M, is attached to each artificial variable so that the full objective function becomes:

$$\text{Minimize } F = 3x_1 + 5x_2 + 0s_1 + 0s_2 + Mu_1 + Mu_2$$

where M is large enough to dominate any other number in the problem. So no solution can be minimal if either u_1 or u_2 appears in it. This guarantees the exclusion of the artificial variables from the optimal solution. They are merely computational devices for getting the problem started. Once this is done they have served their purpose and are eliminated. The objective function must now be converted to maximization form. This is easily done simply by multiplying by -1 throughout. Thus in full the problem is to:

$$\text{Maximize} \quad -3x_1 - 5x_2 - 0s_1 - 0s_2 - Mu_1 - Mu_2$$

$$\text{subject to} \quad x_1 + 4x_2 - s_1 - 0s_2 + u_1 + 0u_2 = 60$$

$$2x_1 + x_2 - 0s_1 - s_2 + 0u_1 + u_2 = 50$$

$$x_1, x_2, s_1, s_2, u_1, u_2, \geqslant 0$$

The simplex workings are as follows:

		-3	-5	0	0	$-M$	$-M$
		x_1	x_2	s_1	s_2	u_1	u_2
$-Mu_1$	60	1	4	-1	0	1	0
$-Mu_2$	50	2	1	0	-1	0	1
	$-110M$	$-3M+3$	$-5M+5$	$+M$	$+M$	0	0
$-5x_2$	15	$\frac{1}{4}$	1	$-\frac{1}{4}$	0	$\frac{1}{4}$	0
$-Mu_2$	35	$\frac{7}{4}$	0	$\frac{1}{4}$	-1	$-\frac{1}{4}$	1
	$-35M-75$	$\frac{7}{4}-\frac{7}{4}M$	0	$\frac{3}{4}-\frac{1}{4}M$	M	$-\frac{3}{4}+\frac{5}{4}M$	0
$-5x_2$	10	0	1	$-\frac{2}{7}$	$\frac{1}{7}$	$\frac{2}{7}$	$-\frac{1}{7}$
$-3x_1$	20	1	0	$-\frac{1}{7}$	$-\frac{4}{7}$	$-\frac{1}{7}$	$\frac{4}{7}$
	-110	0	0	1	1	$-1+M$	$-1+M$

In the initial tableau, the fact that M is arbitrarily large means that $-3M+3$ and $-5M+5$ are negative numbers. The variable x_2 is introduced and replaces u_1. In the second tableau, the 'most negative' index row number is $\frac{7}{4}-\frac{7M}{4}$ under x_1 So the entering variable here is x_1 and the pivotal row is the u_2 row. The next iteration produces the optimal solution with all index row numbers positive. Note that the true value of the objective function is 110 (the negation was a computational device). The dual values associated with the constraints are found in the final index row under the slack variables. Further technical detail relating to the use of the simplex method can be found in Wilkes (1983).

3-7 DUALITY

With every LP problem there is associated, in a symmetrical relationship, a *dual* problem. Consider the problem:

$$\text{Maximize } F = 10x_1 + 12x_2$$
$$\text{subject to} \quad 4x_1 + 2x_2 \leqslant 76$$
$$3x_1 + 5x_2 \leqslant 85$$
$$x_1, x_2 \geqslant 0$$

The dual to this problem is:

$$\text{Minimize } G = 76y_1 + 85y_2$$
$$\text{subject to} \quad 4y_1 + 3y_2 \geqslant 10$$
$$2y_1 + 5y_2 \geqslant 12$$
$$y_1, y_2 \geqslant 0$$

The maximization problem is usually referred to as the *primal* problem and the minimization problem as the dual, although they are duals of each other. The dual problem employs all the data of the primal problem but in a different arrangement. The coefficients of the objective function of the primal are the constraint levels of the dual; the constraint levels of the primal are the objective function coefficients of the dual; *columns* of constraint coefficients in the primal become *rows* of constraint coefficients in the dual. If 'primal' and 'dual' are interchanged in the previous sentence the statements are still valid; that is, there is *no asymmetry* between the problems. The primal and dual problems are graphed in Fig. 3.3(a) and (b). The feasible area for the primal problem is OABC and the optimum is at joint B with the objective function shown as a dashed line. The feasible area for the dual is the open area with lower bound given by E'B'D'. The optimal solution is at point B' which minimizes the dual objective function G. Each basic feasible solution (bfs) of the primal problem has a corresponding basic (not necessarily feasible) solution in the dual. Indeed it turns out that there is only one bfs in the primal problem that corresponds to

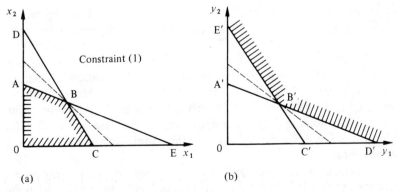

(a) (b)

Figure 3-3

a bfs in the dual. These corresponding bfs are also optimal! This point is true in general.

Apart from the symmetrical relationship between primal and dual, why should the dual be of interest? Firstly, the dual structural variables, y, turn out to be the *dual values* (*shadow prices* or *marginal values*) of the primal problem, i.e. the index row numbers under the slack variables. Thus the dual has great importance for economic interpretation and sensitivity analysis. Secondly, just as the optimal values of the dual variables can be found from the solution to the primal problem (being index row numbers) so also can the optimal values of primal variables be found from the solution to the dual problem. This is an important property since sometimes it is easier to solve the dual of a problem than the original problem. The solutions in tableau form, to primal and dual, are given in Figs. 3-4 and 3-5 respectively.

		10	12	0	0
		x_1	x_2	s_1	s_2
0	s_1	76	4	2	1	0
0	s_2	85	3	5	0	1
		0	-10	-12	0	0
0	s_1	42	14/5	0	1	$-2/5$
12	x_2	17	3/5	1	0	1/5
		204	$-14/5$	0	0	12/5
10	x_1	15	1	0	5/14	$-2/14$
12	x_2	8	0	1	$-3/14$	4/14
		246	0	0	1	2

Figure 3-4

The maximum value of the primal objective function is achieved by setting $x_1 = 15$, $x_2 = 8$, $s_1 = 0$, $s_2 = 0$ for a value of F of 246. The shadow prices of the resources are 1 for resource one and 2 for resource two. The optimal solution to the dual problem is to set $y_1 = 1$, $y_2 = 2$, $t_1 = 0$, $t_2 = 0$ for a value of G of 246.

The equality of the optimal values of primal and dual objective functions is the case in general. All feasible solutions to the dual have values of G greater than or equal to all values of F for feasible solutions to the primal problem, with the equality holding only at the optimum. The dual marginal values (in the index row of Fig. 3-5 under t_1 and t_2) are the optimal values of the x's in the primal problem.

The full extent of the primal-dual symmetry is now apparent. In the primal problem the optimal values of the structure variables, y, may be found in the

		-76	-85	0	0	$-M$	$-M$
		y_1	y_2	t_1	t_2	u_1	u_2
$-Mu_1$	10	4	3	-1	0	1	0
$-Mu_2$	12	2	5	0	-1	0	1
	$-22M$	$-6M+76$	$-8M+85$	$+M$	$+M$	0	0
$-Mu_1$	$14/5$	$14/5$	0	-1	$3/5$	1	$-3/5$
$-85y_2$	$12/5$	$2/5$	1	0	$-1/5$	0	$1/5$
	$-14/5M-204$	$-14/5M+42$	0	$+M$	$-3/5M+17$	0	$8/5M-17$
$-76y_1$	1	1	0	$-5/14$	$3/14$	$5/14$	$-3/14$
$-85y_2$	2	0	1	$2/14$	$-4/14$	$-2/14$	$4/14$
	-246	0	0	15	8	$-15+M$	$-8+M$

Figure 3-5

final index row under the primal *slack* variables, hence $y_1 = 1$ and $y_2 = 2$. The optimal values of the dual slack variables, t, may be found in the final index row of the primal problem under the primal *structural* variables, hence $t_1 = 0$ and $t_2 = 0$. The same statements apply in respect of the solution to the dual problem. The optimal values of the primal structural variables may be found from the final index row of the dual problem under the dual slack variables, hence $x_1 = 15$ and $x_2 = 8$. The optimal values of the primal slack variables are found in the final index row of the dual problem under the structural variables. Note that finding an optimal solution to the primal problem (finding a solution with a non-negative index row) is finding a feasible solution to the dual problem. If the dual was being solved the process would be equivalent to finding a feasible solution to the primal problem.

The optimal solutions illustrate a further aspect of the symmetrical relationship between primal and dual. This is the *complementary slackness* condition:

(a) $s_1 y_1 = 0$ and   (c) $x_1 t_1 = 0$

(b) $s_2 y_2 = 0$ (d) $x_2 t_2 = 0$

The products of corresponding pairs of primal structural variables and dual slack variables dual structural and primal slack variables must be zero at an optimum. Expression (a) states that if $s_1 > 0$, $y_1 = 0$, i.e. in a production context if any of the first resources is left over the shadow price (marginal value) of that resource is zero. Also if $y_1 > 0$ then $s_1 = 0$, that is, any resource with positive value at the margin must be fully used. The condition (c) states that if $x_1 > 0$

then $t_1 = 0$, i.e. if the first primal structural variable is positive then the first dual slack variable is zero.

The dual slack variable are, in fact, the *opportunity losses* on production of the respective x's. This concept was introduced in section 2-6. Consider the first dual constraint.

$$4y_1 + 3y_2 \geqslant 10 \tag{3-1}$$

The slack variable t_1 is the excess of the left-hand side (LHS) of (3-1) over the right-hand side (RHS) value of 10. The coefficients 4 and 3 are the amounts of resources one and two tied up in the acquisition of one unit of x_1 whilst the magnitudes of y_1 and y_2 are the values per unit of each resource *if resources are used optimally*. In other words, each unit of resource one can make a profit of y_1 and each unit of resource two can be used to make a profit of y_2. Consequently the LHS of (3-1) is the *opportunity cost* of producing one unit of x_1—it is therefore the profit forgone in using resources to produce x_1. Obviously, if the strict inequality holds in (3-1) this means that the profit forgone in producing x_1 is greater than the profit obtained on x_1. That is, if $t_1 > 0$ there is a positive opportunity loss involved in production of x_1, the optimal value of which must then be zero. So, only when equality obtains in (3-1) will x_1 be positive. Note that in the nature of things there can never be an *opportunity* profit. y_1 and y_2 are determined by the *best* use of resources—these values allocate *all* profit to resources (the value of the dual objective function equals the value of the primal). In mathematical terms at best an equality can obtain in (3-1) in which case x_1 can be positive. All this is not to say that an *accounting profit* cannot be made but simply that there is no *better* use of resources than the best! When $t_1 > 0$ therefore, the optimal value of $x_1 = 0$, although we should recall that x_1 may still make an accounting profit. This concludes our brief look at duality in linear programming problems. Further material can be found in Taha (1987) or Wilkes (1983).

3-8 OTHER PROGRAMMING PROBLEMS

When some of the key provisions underlying linear programming (see section 2-9) are not met, and when it is impossible to retain the LP framework, a programming problem of more advanced form results.

A *quadratic programming* (QP) problem is one in which the constraints and sign requirements are as in LP but where the objective function contains quadratic elements. For example, the problem:

$$\text{Maximize } F = 264x_1 - x_1^2 + 396x_2 - 2x_2^2$$

$$\text{Subject to} \quad 5x_1 + 4x_2 \leqslant 792$$

$$10x_1 + x_2 \leqslant 1073$$

$$x_1 \geqslant 0, x_2 \geqslant 0$$

is a QP problem. A method developed from the simplex method can be used to solve QP problems. Further details are contained in Wilkes (1983). The solution to the above problem is, incidentally, $x_1 = 92$, $x_2 = 83$ and $F = 34\,914$.

Integer Linear programming problems are LP problems where some or all of the variables must take whole number values. Integer LP problems fall into three categories:

1. all integer problems
2. mixed integer-continuous variable problems
3. zero-one problems

The first category (also known as pure integer problems) consists of those problems in which all of the variables, including the slack variables, are required to take whole number values.

The second category consists of problems in which some, but not all of the variables must take only integral values. Frequently, the slack variables may be divisible while the x's are not.

In zero-one problems the structural variables may assume only the values zero or one. These variables are said to be *two-state* and correspond to *reject* (zero) or *accept* (one).

Among the solution procedures for categories (1) and (2) are those which use a modified form of the simplex method. Category (C) requires other methods of solution.

In *stochastic programming* problems, some of the coefficients of an otherwise LP problem may be random variables. Under certain conditions, procedures based on the simplex method can be used. Further details are contained in Wilkes (1983).

Goal programming is a method which adapts linear programming to accommodate problems in which there are several objectives rather than just one. Some of the goals may not even be consistent with each other but they must be put into order of priority by the decision maker. The method—an extension of the simplex method—fulfils as many high-ranking goals as possible, therefore minimizing an appropriately weighted average of the amount by which targets are missed.

It will be evident from the above that simplex-related methods are very important in mathematical programming. One further type of problem, dynamic programming, is covered in Chapter Sixteen.

3-9 COMPUTERS AND LP

Next to computer simulation, linear programming is the most widely-used operational research technique. This is largely due to improvements in the speed and capacity of computers and matching reductions in costs. Modern mainframe computers can handle large-scale practical linear programming problems involving thousands of variables *and* thousands of constraints. The majority of linear programming problems in industry will occupy only a few minutes of mainframe computer time with the not-so-large problems being solved in seconds rather than minutes. It should be borne in mind that this time will only be a tiny fraction of the total time involved in inputting the data, acquiring the data and setting up the mathematical model. The major computing companies have LP packages available for commercial use but these days it is not necessary to have access to a mainframe computer to solve quite sizeable linear programming problems with over a hundred variables.

There is a considerable choice of user-friendly software available suitable for use on personal computers. The particular features of each package, the manner of data input and the arrangement of output will vary somewhat, but this is not usually a source of difficulty. There is one minor irritant in comparison with hand-solved problems in respect of rounding. A rational coefficient such as $\frac{5}{3}$ would have to be entered as 1.666 67 with the possible result that what would otherwise have been an integral solution value of, for example, $x_1 = 100$ may be printed out as 99.9985.

Typically, the computer output will list the optimal values of the structural (x) variables and may present the optimal values of the slack variables separately. Sensitivity analysis on objective function coefficients and constraint levels (right-hand side values) is usually available on request—at least in single parameter form. Limited consideration of simultaneous changes may also be possible.

The output may be printed out in a form similar to the following. For the problem illustrated in section 3-4, the results could appear as:

AZED LINEAR PROGRAMME

OBJECTIVE FUNCTION VALUE

1	1900.00000

VARIABLE	VALUE	DUAL
x_1	150.000 00	0.000 00
x_2	200.000 00	0.000 00

LINE	SLACK	DUAL
2	0.000 00	0.800 00
3	0.000 00	1.400 00
4	30.000 00	0.000 00

SENSITIVITY ANALYSIS

	OBJECTIVE FUNCTION COEFFICIENTS		
VARIABLE	COEFFICIENT	DECREASE	INCREASE
x_1	6	2.666 67	14.000 00
x_2	5	3.500 00	4.000 0

RIGHT-HAND SIDE

LINE	RHS	DECREASE	INCREASE
2	800.000 00	500.000 00	100.000 00
3	900.000 00	300.000 00	1500.000 00
4	180.000 00	30.000 00	UNLIMITED

From a print-out of this form, the solution values of the x's are easily located. The 'dual' column next to the solution values gives the index row numbers. The values of the slack variables are listed next. The slack variable (S_1) of the first constraint appears on line 2 (typically line 1 is reserved for the objective function). Corresponding dual values are shown in the adjacent column. The sensitivity analysis is printed out in two parts. The first section deals with the objective function coefficients. Following a listing of the current values of the coefficients, the maximum decrease and increase possible so that the original solution remains optimal are shown. Thus, for x_1 from the current coefficient of 6 a decrease of $2\frac{2}{3}$ and an increase of 14 correspond to the tolerance interval (calculated by hand in section 3-5) of $\frac{10}{3} \leqslant \pi \leqslant 20$.

Next follows the sensitivity analysis on the right-hand side. The decreases and increases shown here give the maximum range of variation of the resource level or upper bound for which the original basis remains feasible (i.e., for which all current solution variables remain non-negative) and for which the dual values apply. For example, in the case of the labour hours constraint, so long as the number of labour hours available is in the range (900–300) to (900 + 1500) the dual value of 1.4 applies. These ranges give a useful indication of the magnitude of resource variation possible for which the current optimal production plan (product mix) remains feasible. These ranges can, incidentally, also be obtained by hand calculation from the simplex tableau.

In this way, computers prove to be of great value at all levels in the application of linear programming. Algorithms based on the simplex method are highly efficient. Unfortunately, this efficiency cannot be anywhere near matched when integer or quadratic programmes are involved and it is best to retain the LP framework wherever possible.

EXERCISES

3-1 Revision exercise
  (i) Why is the simplex method needed to solve most LP problems?
  (ii) What advantages does the simplex method have over the graphical method, when either could be used?
  (iii) What principal gain results from the introduction of slack variables?
  (iv) Set out the broad logic of the simplex method.
  (v) How does the simplex method guarantee that the sign requirements in LP problems are met?
  (vi) What is the significance of an all non-negative index row?
  (vii) What is the basic principle involved in sensitivity analysis on objective function coefficients from the simplex tableau?

(viii) What steps are necessary to make minimization problems suitable for solution by the simplex method?

(ix) Explain the symmetrical relationship that exists between primal and dual problems in linear programming.

(x) Explain the usefulness of computers in the solution of linear programming problems.

(xi) Cite examples of more advanced programming problems. Should these methods always be used if all of the assumptions underlying LP do not strictly hold?

3-2 Solve the Latin Manufacturing Co.'s problem (Exercise 2-2) using the simplex method.

3-3 Use the simplex method to solve the problem:

$$\text{Maximize} \quad x_1 + x_2$$

$$x_1 + 2x_2 \leqslant 100$$

$$2x_1 + x_2 \leqslant 110$$

$$x_1 \geqslant 0, \, x_2 \geqslant 0$$

State the values of the dual variables and carry out a joint sensitivity analysis on the objective function coefficients.

3-4 Use the simplex method to solve the dual problem to the Azed Enterprises' problem (see section 3-7). Inspect the final tableau to confirm that the index row contains the solution to the original (primal) Azed problem.

3-5 A small independent engineering company has bought a job lot of 350 positronic circuits for £1500 and wishes to put these circuits to the most profitable use and so is exploring all possible applications. The first use would be for a small car vacuum cleaner (one circuit per cleaner). From experience it is known that at least 350 cleaners could be sold at a price of £45 each. The other necessary components are available at £15 a set for each cleaner. The time to assemble each vacuum cleaner is one hour. Alternatively, the circuits could be used in making de luxe house vacuum cleaners (one circuit per cleaner) which will sell at £120 each, other necessary components costing £80 per set (one set per cleaner). The time to assemble each cleaner is two hours. However, the maximum estimate of sales is only 10 such cleaners. Recently, several people have enquired about a slightly cheaper house vacuum cleaner. On investigation the firm finds that it can produce a standard cleaner still using one circuit for each cleaner, to sell at £110, extra components costing £60 per cleaner. Assembly time, however, is higher at three hours per cleaner and sales would be, at maximum, not more than 20. Assembly workers are paid £1 per hour and a fixed amount of 380 hours of assembly time will be available during the period.

Required:

(a) Formulate a linear programming model to help the firm decide on the best mix of products.

(b) The following is a computer printout of the final tableau

	X_1	X_2	X_3	S_1	S_2	S_3	S_4	
X_1	1	0	$\frac{1}{2}$	$1\frac{1}{2}$	$-\frac{1}{2}$	0	0	335
X_2	0	1	$\frac{1}{2}$	$-\frac{1}{2}$	$\frac{1}{2}$	0	0	15
S_3	0	0	$-\frac{1}{2}$	$\frac{1}{2}$	$-\frac{1}{2}$	1	0	5
S_4	0	0	1	0	0	0	1	10
	0	0	0	-20	-10	0	0	10 800

where X_1 = number of car vacuum cleaners,

$\quad X_2$ = number of standard vacuum cleaners,

$\quad X_3$ = number of de luxe vacuum cleaners,

$\quad S_1$ = number of electronic circuits not used,

$\quad S_2$ = number of assembly hours not used,

$\quad S_3$ = demand not met for standard vacuum cleaners,

$\quad S_4$ = demand not met for de luxe vacuum cleaners.

Using the tableau, explain the production plan, and the implications of adopting it.

(c) If assembly labour were willing to work overtime at a cost of £3 per hour, would it be worth employing it and what would be the maximum additional profit attainable?

(d) If it were possible to sell all or some of the positronic circuits at £28 each instead of using them to make vacuum cleaners, how should the linear programming model be adapted?

(Chartered Association of Certified Accountants)

3-6 (a) The following details are taken from the forecasts of XYZ Limited:

Sales demand:		Thousands of units per annum, maximum
Super de luxe model	(x_1)	500
De luxe model	(x_1)	750
Export model	(x_3)	400

Production: two production facilities are required, machining and assembly, and these are common to each model. Capacity in each facility is limited by the number of direct labour hours available.

	Direct labour total hours available in millions	Direct labour hours per unit for each model		
		x_1	x_2	x_3
Machining (x_4)	1.4	0.5	0.5	1.0
Assembly (x_5)	1.2	0.5	0.5	2.0

Contribution, estimated to be

Model	Amount per thousand units in £
x_1	1500
x_2	1300
x_3	2500

You are required, using the above information, to set up the first tableau of a linear programme to determine the product mix which will maximize total contribution and then to complete the first iteration only.

(b) Interpret the following tableau, given that it is the final solution to the above problem. The S variables $(S_1, S_2, S_3, S_4, S_5)$ relate to the constraints in the same sequence as presented in (a) above.

x_1	x_2	x_3	S_1	S_2	S_3	S_4	S_5	b_{ij}
1	0	0	1	0	0	0	0	500
0	0	0	0.25	0.25	1	0	−0.5	112.5
0	0	1	−0.25	−0.25	0	0	0.5	287.5
0	0	0	−0.25	−0.25	0	1	−0.5	487.5
0	1	0	0	1	0	0	0	750
0	0	0	−875	−675	0	0	−1250	−2443 750

(The Chartered Institute of Management Accountants)

Solution guides

3-2 Noting first that unit profit on the Prima product is 6 and on the Seconda product it is 4, and letting x_1 be the number of Primas made and x_2 be the number of Secondas made the simplex workings are:

			6	4	0	0	0
			x_1	x_2	S_1	S_2	S_3
0	S_1	390	2	1	1	0	0
0	S_2	810	3	3	0	1	0
0	S_3	200	0	1	0	0	1
		0	−6	−4	0	0	0
6	x_1	195	1	$\frac{1}{2}$	$\frac{1}{2}$	0	0
0	S_2	225	0	$\frac{3}{2}$	$-\frac{3}{2}$	1	0
0	S_3	200	0	1	0	0	1
		1170	0	−1	3	0	0
6	x_1	120	1	0	1	$-\frac{1}{3}$	0
4	x_2	150	0	1	−1	$\frac{2}{3}$	0
0	S_3	50	0	0	1	$-\frac{2}{3}$	1
		1320	0	0	2	$\frac{2}{3}$	0

So that the answers are:

(a) 120 Primas, 150 Seconds (giving total profits 1320).

(b) The dual values are: cutting hours; 2, finishing hours; 2/3.

(c) Opportunity loss on third product:

$$2 \text{ at } 2+2 \text{ at } \tfrac{2}{3}-5=\tfrac{1}{3}$$

So do not produce the third product.

(d) Letting the Prima unit profit be Π_1 the range is

$$4 \leqslant \Pi_1 \leqslant 8$$

3-3 Having introduced slack variables s_1 and s_2, the full solution in tableau form is

			1	1	0	0	
			x_1	x_2	s_1	s_2	
0	s_1	100	1	2	1	0	
0	s_2	110	2	1	0	1	←pivotal row (no. 1)
		0	−1	−1	0	0	
0	s_1	45	0	3/2	1	−1/2	←pivotal row (no. 2)
1	x_1	55	1	1/2	0	1/2	←main row (no. 1)
		55	0	−1/2	0	1/2	
1	x_2	30	0	1	2/3	−1/3	←main row (no. 2)
1	x_1	40	1	0	−1/3	2/3	
		70	0	0	1/3	1/3	←index row

Thus, at the optimum $x_1 = 40$, $x_2 = 30$, $s_1 = 0$, $s_2 = 0$ and the dual values are $1/3$ for each constraint. A general point is that only when a constraint is satisfied as a strict equality (there are no unused units of the resource) will the corresponding dual value be positive.

Using π_1 and π_2 to represent the objective function coefficients of x_1 and x_2 in the tableau, the non-zero index row numbers under s_1 and s_2 become:

$$\frac{2}{3}\pi_2 - \frac{1}{3}\pi_1 \geqslant 0 \text{ and } -\frac{1}{3}\pi_2 + \frac{2}{3}\pi_1 \geqslant 0$$

which implies that:

$$0.5\pi_1 \leqslant \pi_2 \leqslant 2\pi_1$$

3-4 With slack variables (sometimes called *surplus variables* in this context), subtracted and artificial variables added, the problem in full is:

$$\text{Minimize } 800y_1 + 900y_2 + 180y_3 + 0s_1 + 0s_2 + Mu_1 + Mu_2$$

$$\text{subject to } 4y_1 + 2y_2 + y_3 - s_1 + u_1 = 6$$

$$y_1 + 3y_2 - s_2 + u_2 = 5$$

$$y_1, y_2, s_1, s_2, u_1, u_2 \geqslant 0.$$

The simplex tableau is:

		-800	-900	-180	0	0	$-M$	$-M$
		y_1	y_2	y_3	s_1	s_2	u_1	u_2
$-Mu_1$	6	4	2	1	-1	0	1	0
$-Mu_2$	5	1	3	0	0	-1	0	1
	$-11M$	$800-5M$	$900-5M$	$180-M$	M	M	0	0
$-800\,y_1$	$\frac{6}{4}$	1	$\frac{2}{4}$	$\frac{1}{4}$	$-\frac{1}{4}$	0	$\frac{1}{4}$	0
$-Mu_2$	$\frac{14}{4}$	0	$\frac{10}{4}$	$-\frac{1}{4}$	$\frac{1}{4}$	-1	$-\frac{1}{4}$	1
		$500-2.5M$						
$-800\,y_1$	0.8	1	0	0.3	-0.3	0.2	0.3	-0.2
$-900\,y_2$	1.4	0	1	-0.1	0.1	-0.4	-0.1	0.4
	-1900	0	0	30	150	200		

So that the optimal values of y_1 and y_2 are 0.8 and 1.4 respectively (these are the dual values in the original, primal problem). In the final index row under the dual slack variables are the optimal values of primal variables x_1 and x_2 (150 and 200 respectively). Under y_3 in the final index row is the optimal value of primal slack variable 3 at 30.

3-5 (a) The question assumes that assembly time labour is paid the rate of £1 per hour *whether used or not* so in this case, assembly time labour is a fixed cost. The objective is stated to be profit maximization. With the assumption given about costs, the unit profit figures are:

$$\text{for } x_1, \text{ unit profit } = 45 - 15 = 30$$

$$\text{for } x_2, \text{ unit profit } = 110 - 60 = 50$$

$$\text{for } x_3, \text{ unit profit } = 120 - 80 = 40$$

Thus the objective function is:

$$\text{Maximize } F = 30x_1 + 50x_2 + 40x_3$$

There are four constraints in this problem. The first relates to the circuits. Since each product requires one circuit per unit:

$$x_1 + x_2 + x_3 \leqslant 350$$

Incidentally, we are here consistent with the question in designating this constraint as the 'first', since slack variable no. 1, S_1, relates to unused circuits. The second constraint is for assembly time.

$$x_1 + 3x_2 + 2x_3 \leqslant 380$$

Finally there are the two upper bounds on sales:

$$x_2 \leqslant 20 \quad \text{and} \quad x_3 \leqslant 10$$

The full problem, with sign requirements and slacks included is therefore to:

$$\text{Maximize } F = 30x_1 + 50x_2 + 40x_3$$

$$\text{subject to } x_1 + \quad x_2 + \quad x_3 + S_1 = 350$$

$$x_1 + \quad 3x_2 + \quad 2x_3 + S_2 = 380$$

$$x_2 \qquad\qquad + S_3 = \quad 20$$

$$x_3 + S_4 = \quad 10$$

$$x_1 \geqslant 0, x_2 \geqslant 0, x_3 \geqslant 0,$$

$$S_1 \geqslant 0, S_2 \geqslant 0, S_3 \geqslant 0, S_4 \geqslant 0$$

(b) It is apparent from the tableau that there is no unique best mix of products. The solution shown gives $x_1 = 335$ and $x_2 = 15$ with $x_3 = 0$. However, the index row number under x_3 is zero. Since x_3 is not 'in the solution' this means that there is another solution, in which x_3 is included, which is just as good. In the solution given, the usual convention of showing optimal index row numbers as non-negative has *not* been followed. In the notation of this text and most others, the index row numbers under S_1 and S_2 would be shown as $+20$ and $+10$ respectively. This change will be made in the workings shown below. One further iteration produces the alternative best plan involving x_3. With x_3 as the pivotal column and S_4 as the pivotal row the solution is:

			30	50	40	0	0	0	0
			x_1	x_2	x_3	S_1	S_2	S_3	S_4
30	x_1	330	1	0	0	$1\frac{1}{2}$	$-\frac{1}{2}$	0	$-\frac{1}{2}$
50	x_2	10	0	1	0	$-\frac{1}{2}$	$\frac{1}{2}$	0	$-\frac{1}{2}$
0	S_3	10	0	0	0	$\frac{1}{2}$	$-\frac{1}{2}$	1	$\frac{1}{2}$
40	x_3	10	0	0	1	0	0	0	1
		10 800	0	0	0	20	10	0	0

Thus 330 car vacuums, 10 standard vacuums, and 10 de luxe vacuums could equally well have been produced. In fact, of course, any non-basic solution *between* the two basic optima would also have served as well. The reader should verify that 334 car vacuums, 14 standard vacuums, and 2 de luxe vacuums would be just as profitable.

(c) The dual value for assembly time labour is found in the index row under slack variable S_2. This is $+10$. Since we are assuming that assembly time labour represents a fixed charge [for LP purposes the variable costs of standard rate assembly time labour are zero] the $+10$ represents the *total* amount that could be paid, in the extreme, for one hour's overtime. The overtime wage rate is much less than this (at £3) so it is certainly well worth having. But how much overtime should the company use? This is an important question to answer.

One way to proceed is as follows. Using more assembly labour is mathematically equivalent to leaving the total available at 380 but allowing slack variable S_2 to be *negative*. Thus if $S_2 = -1$ then this is equivalent to having 381 hours of labour. When a variable is brought in to negative level, positive index row numbers (in our notation) mean improvement. If overtime labour was *free*, if S_2 was set at -1 the objective function would go up by 10. If S_2 was set at -2 it would increase contribution by 20, and so on. So we shall bring in S_2 to negative level. But which one of the *non-unique* bases shall we start from? It turns out to be more convenient to start from the basis involving x_3 (given above). It is possible to start from the basis involving S_4 but one extra iteration is required in this event. Now overtime labour is *not* free, it costs £3 per hour. To accommodate this give S_2 an objective function coefficient of 3. This will do the trick but care must then be exercised in interpreting the resulting dual values (for further discussion see Wilkes (1983)). The dual lacks one positive variable and is *degenerate*. Non-uniqueness in one problem is the same thing as degeneracy in its dual. The workings below show the outcome in the present case:

			30	50	40	0	(3)	0	0
			x_1	x_2	x_3	S_1	S_2	S_3	S_4
30	x_1	320	1	0	0	1	0	−1	−1
50	x_2	20	0	1	0	0	0	1	0
(3)	S_2	−20	0	0	0	−1	1	−2	−1
40	x_3	10	0	0	1	0	0	0	1
		10 940	0	0	0	27	0	14	7

So far as the S_2 row is concerned, with the heretical −20, all that needs to be said is that the −20 means that 20 hours overtime would be optimal. Otherwise this row can be ignored. The new production levels are 320 car vacuums, 20 standard vacuums, and 10 de luxe vacuums. Total contribution is 10 940. (Note: scrutiny of the original tableau might suggest that only 10 hours overtime was desirable. This is incorrect. The figure of 10 is only the upper bound for feasibility of the original solution involving S_4.)

(d) There are two ways in which this new provision can be met. A new variable, x_4, could be introduced into the problem: x_4 would represent the sale of the circuits and would have an objective function coefficient of 28. If this was done there would be no need to start the problem all over again (see Wilkes, 1983). A simpler method is to alter the S_1 objective function coefficient to 28 (again care would be required in interpreting index row numbers). The reader may verify that the resulting optimal solution is as shown below. The fact that $S_1 = 20$ at the new optimum simply means that 20 of the circuits would be re-sold. Total profit would be £10 960.

			30	50	40	28	0	0	0
			x_1	x_2	x_3	S_1	S_2	S_3	S_4
30	x_1	300	1	0	0	0	1	−3	−2
50	x_2	20	0	1	0	0	0	1	0
28	S_1	20	0	0	0	1	−1	2	1
40	x_3	10	0	0	1	0	0	0	1
		10 960	0	0	0	0	2	16	8

3-6 (a) The model will be (slack variables included):

$$\text{Maximize } F = 1500x_1 + 1300x_2 + 2500x_3$$

$$\text{subject to} \qquad x_1 + S_1 = 500$$

$$x_2 + S_2 = 750$$

$$x_3 + S_3 = 400$$

$$0.5x_1 + 0.5x_2 + x_3 + S_4 = 1400$$

$$0.5x_1 + 0.5x_2 + 2x_3 + S_5 = 1200$$

and sign requirements on all variables.

In the style of layout adopted in part (b) of the question, the first two tableaux would be:

1500	1300	2500	0	0	0	0	0		
x_1	x_2	x_3	S_1	S_2	S_3	S_4	S_5		
1	0	0	1	0	0	0	0	500	S_1
0	1	0	0	1	0	0	0	750	S_2
0	0	1	0	0	1	0	0	400	S_3
0.5	0.5	1	0	0	0	1	0	1400	S_4
0.5	0.5	2	0	0	0	0	1	1200	S_5
1500	1300	2500	0	0	0	0	0	0	

1	0	0	1	0	0	0	0	500	S_1	
0	1	0	0	1	0	0	0	750	S_2	
0	0	1	0	0	1	0	0	400	x_3	2500
0.5	0.5	0	0	0	-1	1	0	1000	S_4	
0.5	0.5	0	0	0	-2	0	1	400	S_5	
1500	1300	0	0	0	-2500	0	0	1 000 000		

A column identifying the variables in the solution has been added and to the right of this column the objective function coefficient (when not zero) has been placed. Note that since optimal index row numbers are shown as *negative* in part (b), for consistency there will be positive numbers entered in the index row to start with (they will be just *minus* the usual index row numbers).

(b) In tableau layouts that do not have a column labelling the solution variables, the variable concerned can be found by reading across the row of rates of exchange until a unit entry is found in a column which otherwise contains zeros. Thus the first entry in the column headed by b_{ij} refers to x_1, the second entry refers to S_3 and so on. The full solution is (in units of 1000)

$$x_1 = 500, x_2 = 750, x_3 = 287.5, S_1 = 0, S_2 = 0,$$
$$S_3 = 112.5, S_4 = 487.5, S_5 = 0.$$

The total contribution made (in £'s) is 2 443 750. The fact that S_3 is in the solution simply means that the upper bound on x_3 is not reached. The fact that S_4 is in the solution means that there are unused machine hours.

The dual values are interpreted as follows. If the upper bound on x_1 could be relaxed by 1000 units an extra £875 contribution would be made. Similarly, if the bound on x_2 could be relaxed by 1000 units an extra £675 contribution could be made. Finally, if an additional 1000 hours of assembly time were available *at the existing price* then £1250 would be added to contribution.

REFERENCES

Taha, H. A. (1987), *Operations Research*, fourth edition, Collier Macmillan.

Wilkes, F. M. (1983), *Capital Budgeting Techniques*, second edition, Wiley.

FURTHER READING

Anderson, D. R., Sweeney, D. J., and Williams, T. A. (1985), *An Introduction to Management Science*, fifth edition, West Publishing Company. Contains a chapter on sensitivity analysis, duality and computer solution.

Cohen, S. S. (1985), *Operational Research*, Edward Arnold. Contains simple computer program for L.P.

Cook, T. M., and Russell, R. A. (1981), *Introduction to Management Science*, second edition Prentice-Hall. Contains chapters on the simplex method and sensitivity analysis with reference to applications.

FOUR

TRANSPORTATION PROBLEMS

4-1 INTRODUCTION

Production, storage and consumption points rarely coincide—factories, warehouses and retail outlets are usually geographically separate. Where there are several sources of supply—such as in a multi-plant enterprise—and a number of demand points, the question arises as to which customers are best supplied from which sources. Finding the least cost pattern of shipments defines a transportation problem.

Transportation problems turn out to be linear programming problems—but with a very special structure. So much so that it is worth devising a special solution procedure or *algorithm*. And as even the very smallest problem has at least four variables a graphical approach is not possible.

The method also turns out to apply to several problems in other areas of management that have the same underlying structure but which do not involve the physical movement of goods. One example is *purchasing* (sourcing) problems. Another is short-term financial management—particularly cash which has to be 'transported' from one period of usage to another. In stock control too it is possible to view January's production being 'transported' to July via inventory and the method can also be applied to some problems in personnel selection.

The standard form of the transportation problem was set out by Hitchcock in 1941 and the method of solution employed (the 'stepping-stone method') was developed by Charnes and Cooper in 1954.

4-2 THE LOGIC OF THE METHOD

The logic of the solution procedure parallels the simplex method. In fact, although it is not obvious (due to a very different tableau arrangement), the iterative phase is a simplified version of the iterative phase of the simplex method, with advantage taken of the simpler problem structure. Figure 4-1 sets out the broad flow diagram of the procedure. In transportation problems, it is possible to find very good initial (starting) solutions. We shall look at just two methods of finding a good starting solution, although there are many more. The only solutions we need examine either as starting solutions or in the iterative phase (going round the 'loop' in Fig. 4-1) are those which have the 'correct' number of routes used. These are called *basic* feasible solutions. Basic feasible solutions correspond to corner points (if there were enough dimensions to graph the problems). We saw in Chapter Two that only corner points need be considered in LP problems of which transportation problems are but a special case. Let us now consider how a good starting solution can be found.

4-3 FINDING A STARTING SOLUTION

Consider the following transportation problem: A wholesaling company has three warehouses from which supplies are drawn for four retail customers. The

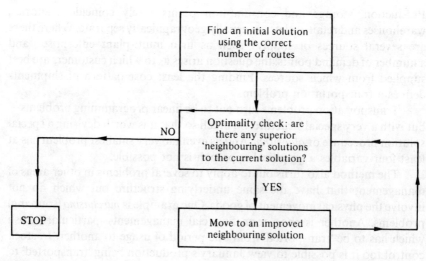

Figure 4-1

company deals in a single product, the supplies of which at each warehouse are:

Warehouse no.	Supply (units)
1	20
2	28
3	17
	65 = total supply

The customer demands are:

Customer no.	Demand (units)
1	15
2	19
3	13
4	18
	65 = total demand

Conveniently, total supply at the warehouses is equal to total demand from the customers. The table gives the transportation costs *per unit* shipped from each warehouse to each customer. Thus it costs £3 for each unit shipped from warehouse no. 1 to customer no. 1. It costs £5 for each unit shipped from warehouse no. 2 to customer no. 4. The operative word here is *each*. This implies linearity and the absence of any economies or diseconomies of scale.

All of the data are shown in the form of a *cost and requirements table* of Fig. 4-2. The supplies available at each warehouse are shown at the end of each row

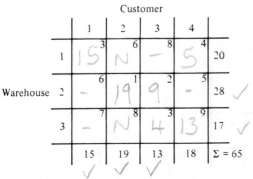

Figure 4-2

and the demands from each customer are shown at the foot of each column. Collectively these perimeter data are shown as the *rim conditions* of the problem. When total supply equals total demand the rim conditions are said to be *balanced*.

All parts of the method require balanced rim conditions but, as we shall see later, a simple adjustment is possible in problems where total supply does not initially equate with total demand.

The first starting solution we shall examine is the commonsense *least cost first* (LCF) approach. The LCF procedure is simple—starting with the overall cheapest route assign as much as possible to that route and successively make similar *maximal assignments* to the cheapest available remaining route. Thus, initially, 19 units are assigned from Warehouse 1 to Customer 2—identified as a circled nineteen ⑲ in the square representing that route. As this completely fills Customer 2's requirement, no further supplies may be shipped there, thus no further entries may be made in column 2. The next cheapest route not in column 2 is from Warehouse 2 to Customer 3. The maximal assignment that can be made to this route is the smaller of the remaining supply at Warehouse 2 (9 units) and total demand by Customer 3 (13 units). Hence an entry of ⑨ is made in square 2,3. No further entries may then be made in the second row. Of the remaining available squares, square 1,1 and 3,3 tie for cheapest cost of £3. Arbitrarily resolve this tie in favour of route 1,1 at which a maximal assignment of ⑮ is possible. The next cheapest route of the four remaining available is from Warehouse 3 to Customer 3 who has four units of demand unsatisfied. There then remains no option but to place a ⑤ in square 1,4 and a ⑬ in square 3,4. The result is the least cost first initial solution shown in Fig. 4-3. The total cost of the LCF solution is found by multiplying the amounts shipped along each route by the cost per unit shipped. This totals £231. Notice that six routes are actually used out of the twelve routes available. Six is the 'correct' number of used routes or 'assignments'—a point we shall return to later on.

LCF is an easily obtainable and generally quite good starting solution—these are its main advantages. The main disadvantage of the LCF approach is

	1	2	3	4	
1	⑮ (3)	(6)	(8)	⑤ (4)	20
Warehouse 2	(6)	⑲ (1)	⑨ (2)	(5)	28
3	(7)	(8)	④ (3)	⑬ (9)	17
	15	19	13	18	

Figure 4-3

that, in determining the routes to be used, only one cost figure is considered at a time. How the cost figures stand in relation to each other is important too. This is evidenced by the fact that of the LCF solution's total cost of £231, more than half (£117) resulted from the enforced use of the very expensive route from Warehouse 3 to Customer 4.

Vogel's approximation method—VAM—takes into account relative costs, provides (on average) a starting solution sufficiently superior to LCF to warrant the somewhat longer time required to obtain the VAM solution. Indeed, with problems of the size we shall be working with here, the VAM initial solution itself turns out to be optimal in about half the cases.

The VAM starting solution requires the determination of a *VAM number* for each row and column. This number is simply the *difference* in cost between the two most economical routes in that row or column. The first set of VAM numbers are shown in Fig. 4-4. So for row (1), the two best routes from

		Customer					Row VAM nos
		1	2	3	4		
Warehouse	1	3	6	8	4	20	1
	2	6	1	2	5	28	1
	3	7	8	3	9	17	4
		15	19	13	18		

Column VAM nos: 3   5   1   1

Figure 4-4

Warehouse 1 are to Customer 1 (cost £3) and to Customer 4 (cost £4) thus the VAM difference = £4 − £3 = £1. For column (2), the two best routes to Customer 2 are from warehouse no. 2 (cost £1) and from Warehouse no. 1 (cost £6). Thus the VAM number for this column is 6 − 1 = 5. And so on for all the remaining rows and columns. Now select the row or column with the *largest* VAM number and dispatch as much as possible along the cheapest route in the row or column selected. Thus we select column (2) and send 19 units from Warehouse 2. This is shown as 19 in square 2,2. The maximum dispatch or assignment will be given by the smaller of the supply and demand figures corresponding to the cheapest square in the row or column selected. Thus, Customer 2 is completely supplied and no further entries (for the moment at least) may be made in column (2). This fact is indicated with crosses in that column. The column is said to be *deleted*. The second set of VAM numbers are now calculated ignoring the deleted column (or row). These are shown in Fig. 4-5. Row (3) now has the largest VAM difference so that 13 (the smaller of 13

	1	2	3	4		VAM nos	
1	3	× 6	8	4	20	X	1
2	6	⑲ 1	2	5	28	X	3
3	7	× 8	3	9	17	X	4
	15	19	13	18			
VAM nos:	3	5	X	X			
	3		1	1			

Figure 4-5

and 17) is assigned to the best undeleted square in the row. This is the square 3,3. Once again this deletes a column (it will not always be a column that is deleted) and VAM numbers are recomputed. The results are shown in Fig. 4-6. In Fig. 4-6, column (1) is now indicated with a VAM difference of 3; 15 units may be inserted in square 1,1 which deletes column (1). After making this entry, the remaining entries are forced. There *must* be 5 units sent from 1 to 4; there *must* be 4 units dispatched from 3 to 4; and there *must* be 9 units sent from 2 to 4. Only in this way can supplies be exhausted at the warehouses and demand met for Customer 4. We have now arrived at the *VAM initial solution*. This is shown in Fig. 4-7. The cost of the VAM solution (15@3 + 5@4, etc.) totals £204 a significant 11.7 per cent improvement on the LCF solution. VAM gives good results since in contrast to the LCF method which simply makes the next assignment to the best square remaining, VAM looks ahead. The VAM number is an *opportunity cost* figure. It is the *least* penalty (at some stage in the problem) per unit that will be incurred if an assignment is *not* placed in the best available square in the row or column concerned. In other words VAM considers some of the *consequences* of choices, whereas LCF does not. Clearly,

	1	2	3	4		VAM nos		
1	3	× 6	× 8	4	20	X	X	1
2	6	⑲ 1	× 2	5	28	X	3	1
3	7	× 8	⑬ 3	9	17	X	X	2
	15	19	13	18				
VAM nos:	3	5	X	X				
	3		X	X				
	3			1				

Figure 4-6

	1	2	3	4	
1	(15) 3	× 6	× 8	(5) 4	20
2	× 6	(19) 1	× 2	(9) 5	28
3	× 7	× 8	(13) 3	(4) 9	17
	15	19	13	18	

Figure 4-7

the LCF solution cannot be optimal here but is VAM? Inspection of Fig. 4-7 reveals that this is not a trivial question.

4-4 THE ITERATIVE PROCEDURE

We shall use the VAM solution as the starting-point for the iterative phase of the procedure but note that LCF or some other feasible solution with six routes used could serve as a starting solution. Can the VAM solution be improved upon? Consider first the route Warehouse 2 to Customer 3 which is presently unused but costs only £2 per unit shipped. Would it be worth using this route? In the context of the simplex method, would it be worth bringing a new variable x_{23} into the solution at unit level? What adjustments would be needed to other shipments to make room for this and what would the cost consequences be? Necessary changes are shown in Fig. 4-8. If $+1$ is sent from 2 to 3, then one less must be sent from 2 to somewhere else. Less can only be sent to Customers 2 or 4. If less were sent to Customer 2 then more would have to be sent to Customer 2 from somewhere else. This could only be done by introducing another new assignment and it is a central part of the method that only *one* new route is investigated at a time. Solutions which differ in this minimal way correspond to neighbouring corner points and if none of the neighbouring corner points is superior to the current solution then

	1	2	3	4	
1	(15) 3	6	8	4 (5)	20
2	6	(19) 1	2 start +1	5 (9) −1	28
3	7 (4)	8	(13) 3 −1	9 (4) +1	17
	15	19	13	18	

Figure 4-8

the current solution is optimal. So, one less must be sent to customer 4—hence the −1 in this square. The remaining changes—one *more* unit to Customer 4 from Warehouse 3 and one less from Warehouse 3 to customer 3—follow from similar arguments. The pattern of changes shown is the *only* pattern of alterations that involves no new assignments other than square 2, 3. The +1 and −1 entries in each row and column must cancel and the changes can be linked by arrows (here shown going clockwise) forming a *closed path* or *closed loop* starting and finishing at 2, 3.

Once a closed path has been formed, the cost effect of the changes can be determined. Adding up the costs at squares where one less is being sent (3+5=8) and at places where more will be sent (2+9=11) gives a net *worsening* of £3 in cost. This is represented by 8−11=−3 which is the *evaluation* of the square 2, 3 in the current solution. The sign convention in transportation problems is that positive numbers represent improvement.

The rules for establishing the closed path for a square are simple. The only turns allowed are 90°, turns can *only* be made at 'assignment' squares although some may be passed over, the path must finish at the 'vacant' square it started at (i.e., it must be 'closed'). The pattern of adjustments is easily found by putting alternate plus and minus signs *at turning points* in the path, starting with a plus sign at the vacant square being evaluated. The evaluation is then found by adding up costs at 'negative' (reducing) places in the closed path and subtracting the sum of costs at 'positive' places in the path. *Positive* evaluations will represent improvement possibility. Thus square 2, 3 although it is the cheapest unused route will not at present show improvement.

All the closed paths for the vacant squares in this case are simple rectangular paths. Those for squares 1, 2 and 1, 3 are shown in Fig. 4-9. The reader should identify the closed paths for the remaining vacant squares and confirm the following table of evaluations:

Square	Evaluation
1, 2	−6
1, 3	−10
2, 1	−2
2, 3	−3
3, 1	+1
3, 2	−3

Evidently, the only square showing improvement potential is 3, 1 even though it is itself one of the more expensive unused routes. The reason is that using this square enables less to be sent along the even more expensive route 3, 4 which is at a negative place in the closed path.

Thus we decide to 'introduce' square 3, 1. Since the problem is an LP problem *every* unit shipped via 3, 1 will save £1. The most that can be sent is determined by the *smallest assignment at a negative place in the closed path*. The

	1	2	3	4	
1	⑮ ³	6	8	⑤ ⁴	20
2	6	⑲ ¹	2	⑨ ⁵	28
3	7	8	⑬ ³	④ ⁹	17
	15	19	13	18	

	1	2	3	4	
1	⑮ ³	6	8	⑤ ⁴	20
2	6	⑲ ¹	2	⑨ ⁵	28
3	7	8	⑬ ³	④ ⁹	17
	15	19	13	18	

Figure 4-9

closed path consists of the four corner squares. Assignment levels will increase at 3, 1 and 1, 4 and decrease at 1, 1 and 3, 4. So by the time *four* units have been 'shipped round the path' the assignment in 3, 4 has gone down to zero. This leaves the number of used routes at six and represents a move to an improved corner (basic) solution as shown in Fig. 4-10. What has been done so far constitutes a complete solution procedure that need only be repeated to produce the optimum. Closed paths could be established for each vacant square and an evaluation conducted. The closed path for square 2, 3 is shown. This is a non-rectangular path, but as always it is unique. The reader may verify that the path for square 3, 2 is also non-rectangular. Incidentally, closed paths do not *have* to turn when an assignment square is reached (they may have to pass over) and the path may cross itself. There is no significance in either of these events.

Although we shall still need closed paths, there is a quicker way of carrying out the vacant-square evaluations.

Numbers (call them u_i) are assigned to each row and numbers (call them v_j) are attached to each column in such a way that *if* square i, j is an assignment square $u_i + v_j = cost$ *for that square.*

	$v_1 = 3$	$v_2 = 0$	$v_3 = -1$	$v_4 = 4$	
$u_1 = 0$	⑪ ³	6	8	⑨ ⁴	20
$u_2 = 1$	6	⑲ ¹	2	⑨ ⁵	28
$u_3 = 4$	④	7	8	⓭ ³	9	17
	15	19	13	18	

Figure 4-10

It is necessary to determine one of these values arbitrarily and the convention is to set $u_1 = 0$ (see if it makes any difference to the subsequent evaluations if v_2 is first set $= 7$ or $u_3 = -22$). Now, if $u_1 = 0$ and, by the rule $u_1 + v_1 = $ cost in square 1, 1 (since there is an assignment here) then $u_1 + v_1 = 1$ so that $v_1 = 1$. Next, since there is also an assignment in square 1, 4 then $u_1 + v_4 = $ cost in square 1, 4 $= 4$ so that $v_4 = 4$. Note that there is no necessity for $u_1 + v_2 = 6$ since there is no assignment in square 1, 2. Continuing, if $v_4 = 4$ then $v_4 + u_2 = 5$, so $u_2 = 1$. If $u_2 = 1$ and $u_2 + v_2 = 1$, $v_2 = 0$. Now, we found earlier that $v_1 = 3$. If $v_1 = 3$ and $u_3 + v_1 = 7$, then $u_3 = 4$. If $u_3 = 4$ and $u_3 + v_3 = 3$, then $v_3 = -1$. This completes the row and column numbering as shown in Fig. 4-10. Negative numbers, as we have seen, are allowed although most will be positive. There is no connection between u and v numbers (*fictitious costs*) and VAM numbers. Vacant squares are now quickly evaluated. The evaluation of any square i, j shown as e_{ij} is:

$$e_{ij} = u_i + v_j - c_{ij}$$

so that the following results are produced:

Square	u_i	v_j	c_{ij}	Evaluation
1, 2	0	0	6	-6
1, 3	0	-1	8	-9
2, 1	1	3	6	-2
2, 3	1	-1	2	-2
3, 2	4	0	8	-4
3, 4	4	4	9	-1

These evaluations may be checked by the closed-path method. All evaluations are negative; which fact indicates that the solution is optimal with a total cost of £200. Had it *not* been optimal, we should have picked the square with the largest positive evaluation, established the closed path for the square, shipped as much round the path as possible, recalculated new u_i and v_j (they change when the solution does), and re-evaluated vacant squares. The procedure stops when there are no positive evaluations. If a vacant square as a *zero* evaluation this means that there is another solution with the same cost; the solution would be *non-unique*. As an exercise, the reader should use the u_i and v_j method to check the evaluations obtained for the VAM initial solution.

The use of the u_i and v_j row and column numbers and closed paths has been variously called the *modified distribution method* (MODI) the *row-column sum method* or the *stepping-stone method* or the *transportation simplex method* and is a highly efficient solution procedure based upon, though not superficially resembling, the simplex method for LP. Indeed it is sometimes also referred to as the *transportation simplex method*.

This brings us to the point of explaining why six assignments is the 'correct' number for the current problem. Since transportation problems are LP problems of special form, only basic feasible (corner point) solutions need be considered. In a transportation problem with m rows and n columns, all basic feasible solutions should have $m + n - 1$ routes used—hence six in the current problem. It is no accident that the LCF solution and the VAM solution gave the correct number of assignments. This is because at each stage a row or column fulfilling assignment (the maximum possible) was made. There would therefore be $m + n$ assignments or routes used were it not for the fact that the last assignment made will simultaneously fulfil a row *and* a column because total supply equals total demand. The modified distribution/stepping-stone method then preserves this number of assignments by introducing only one new route at a time and that to the maximum possible extent resulting in the elimination of one of the existing routes.

4-5 SENSITIVITY ANALYSIS

(i) Objective function coefficients

Consider first the objective function coefficients. As with LP as a whole, any *proportionate* increase or decrease in all objective function coefficients will leave the optimum solution unchanged. Route usages should be the same and total cost will go up or down in the given proportion. So, for example, uniform inflation of costs will not change the optimal pattern of distribution. In transportation problems it is also the case that an equal *absolute* amount added to all objective function coefficients in any row or column or throughout the entire problem will leave the optimum arrangement unchanged. Suppose now that a change occurs to an individual cost. If this cost is that of an unused route, any increase in cost cannot bring the route into consideration—the evaluation e_{ij} will worsen. If, however, the cost reduces so that e_{ij} for an unused route becomes positive then the original solution is no longer optimal and the route in question should be introduced. The limit for the original solution to remain optimal is, for an unused route, a reduction in cost of $-e_{ij}$. Thus for square 2, 1 with an original cost figure of 6, the original solution will remain optimal so long as the cost in that square C_{21} is such that:

$$4 \leqslant C_{21} \leqslant +\infty$$

This is the tolerance interval for C_{21}.

If the cost of a used route changes, this will affect some of the u_i and v_j values. The original solution will remain optimal so long as none of the evaluations e_{ij} that depend on the changed u_i and v_j have become positive. Consider an example. Let the cost in square 3, 1 be C_{31} instead of 7. The u_i and

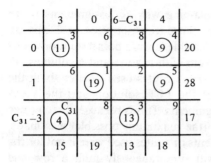

Figure 4-11

v_j values are then as shown in Fig. 4-11. Thus the only evaluations that change are for routes in column 3 and row 3: e_{13}, e_{23}, e_{32} and e_{34}. These are recalculated in terms of C_{31} which must not be such as the cause the e_{ij} to become positive. The results are:

$$e_{13} = 0 + 6 - C_{31} - 8 \leqslant 0 \ \therefore C_{31} \geqslant -2$$
$$e_{23} = 1 + 6 - C_{31} - 2 \leqslant 0 \ \therefore C_{31} \geqslant \ \ 5$$
$$e_{32} = C_{31} - 3 + 0 - 8 \leqslant 0 \ \therefore C_{31} \leqslant \ 11$$
$$e_{34} = C_{31} - 3 + 4 - 9 \leqslant 0 \ \therefore C_{31} \leqslant \ \ 8$$

All of the above bounds must be observed or at least one of the e_{ij} will become positive. The tolerance interval for C_{31} is therefore between the greatest of the lower bounds (GLB) and the least of the upper bounds (LUB) thus:

$$5 \leqslant C_{31} \leqslant 8$$

Similar analysis can be carried out on each objective function coefficient individually. Individual cost data may change when, for example, a new road is built or a weight restriction introduced on part of a route.

4-6 SENSITIVITY ANALYSIS

(ii) Rim conditions

Now consider changes in the supply and demand figures. We can determine the effects of changed rim conditions by use of the u_i and v_j which are in fact *dual values* but in the transportation problem only the relative sizes of the u_i and v_j are meaningful. To illustrate the use of the u_i and v_j consider the following situation. Management wishes to run down Warehouse 3 while making a compensating increase in capacity at Warehouse 1. How much would this save? By reference to Fig. 4-9 it is easy to see that this would save £4 for every unit of capacity so transferred. This would be effected by one unit less from Warehouse 3 to Customer 1 (saving £7) and one unit more from Warehouse 1 to Customer 1 (costing an extra £3). The same saving of £4 is arrived at by multiplying the u values by the respective changes in supply. The change in cost, ΔC is given by:

$$\Delta C = u_3(-1) + u_1(+1) = -4$$

This figure would hold up to a limit of four units of capacity transferred by which time usage of route 3, 1 would have been reduced to zero. In a similar way, the result of a unit of capacity transferred from Warehouse 3 to Warehouse 2 can be determined. The result is:

$$\Delta C = u_3(-1) + u_2(+1)$$
$$= 4(-1) + 1(+1) = -3$$

In a similar way, balanced changes of demand figures can be checked for their effect on costs. One unit less demand from Customer 1 combined with one unit more from Customer 3 would save £4:

$$\Delta C = v_1(-1) + v_3(+1)$$
$$= 3(-1) + -1(+1) = -4$$

Simultaneous and balanced changes in supply and demand figures can also be evaluated. If there were 2 units more demanded from Customer 1 with the extra 2 units of supply available at Warehouse 2 the effect on cost would be an increase of £8 in overall cost:

$$C = v_1(+2) + u_2(+2)$$
$$= 3(+2) + 1(+2) = 8$$

The cost consequences of a varied pattern of changes in supplies and demands can be worked out by multiplying each change by the u_i or v_j figure in its row or column and summing up. This will give the effect on costs subject to two conditions:

(1) That overall supply remains equal to overall demand.
(2) That the changes are such that only the original routes continue to be used.

In respect of condition (1) the method can be extended to deal with this situation. In respect of (2) the tableau must be inspected to verify this. Several adjustments may be needed to the assignment levels. A simple gross check is that if the supply and demand adjustments in total are not in excess of the smallest assignment in the tableau it *must* be possible to accommodate the changes using the same routes.

Consider now what would happen if one more unit was demanded by Customer 3 with the extra units supply at Warehouse 1. Total cost would actually go *down* by £1 as a result of the *extra* unit to be shipped. This phenomenon is called the *paradox of transportation* or the 'more for less' phenomenon. The reader may verify that the extra demand is met by shipping one more unit along each of routes 1, 1 and 3, 3 and one less along route 3, 1. Cost can go down overall because the changed pattern of supply and demand allows more intensive use of highly efficient routes (1, 1 and 3, 3) with less need to use a very expensive one (3, 1).

Finally in respect of the u_i and v_j note that if the u and v values are multiplied by their corresponding supply and demand figures and summed the result is:

$$0(20) + 1(28) + 4(17) + 3(15) + 0(19) - 1(13) + 4(18) = 200$$

which is the minimum total cost figure. The u_i and v_j are dual values and 200 is the value of the objective function of the dual problem (see section 3-7) at the optimum. This equality provides a useful gross check on the workings.

4-7 UNEQUAL SUPPLY AND DEMAND

The stepping-stone method works for problems with balanced rim conditions. Where this is not so at the outset, a simple device can be used to restore a mathematical balance. In Fig. 4-12, the supply at the warehouses is 104 while

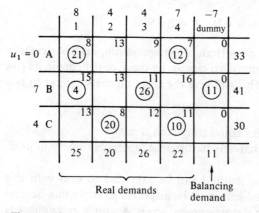

Figure 4-12

demand totals only 93. To make up the difference, an additional column, referred to as a *dummy*, is inserted with the 'missing' or balancing demand. All dummy costs are zero. Any warehouse that ships to a dummy has that many units left in stock. In this case (only the optimum is shown here) it should be warehouse B. If demand had exceeded supply we should have inserted a balancing, *dummy row*. Whichever customers received 'supplies' from the imaginary source would be short on their orders. In obtaining the VAM initial solution and in all subsequent workings, the dummy column/row and its 'costs' are treated identically to all other rows and columns.

4-8 PROHIBITED ROUTES

Not all sources of supply may have routes available to all customers and sometimes it may be necessary to ensure that entries are not made in certain cells in dummy rows and columns. These are examples of prohibited routes. For such routes, a cost figure of M is attached to the route. The unspecified amount M is large enough to dominate any other number with which it is compared—as, for example, in vacant square evaluations (the implicit comparison is with zero). Thus, for example $-0.1M + 3000$ is a negative number and $-5000 + 0.01M$ is a positive number. With M cost entries made where necessary the workings—both VAM and the iterative phase—proceed as before.

Consider, for example, the problem of Fig. 4-12. Suppose that it was essential that supply at Depot B is exhausted. This requirement means that Depot B to the dummy customer is a prohibited route and a cost of M instead of zero should be entered in this square. The new optimal solution is now shown in Fig. 4-13. The cost for the solution is £903. This figure can be compared with the £868 cost of the solution of Fig. 4-12. The difference in cost, £35, is the price that must be paid to fulfil the provision that Warehouse B supply be used up. This is valuable management information. A price can always be put on a particular provision by solving the problem with and without that provision and taking the difference.

	8	6	4	7	−2	
$u_1 = 0$	8 (11)	13	9	7 (22)	0	33
7	5 (14)	13 (1)	11 (26)	16	M	41
2	13	8 (19)	12	11	0 (11)	30
	25	20	26	22	11	

Figure 4-13

4-9 DEGENERACY

A difficulty that sometimes occurs in transportation problems is *degeneracy*. A degenerate solution is one in which there is an insufficient number of assignments to establish closed paths for all vacant squares. Equivalently not all u_i and v_j can be determined. A degenerate solution is shown in Fig. 4-14.

The only square for which a closed path can be found is B3. The degeneracy is resolved by adding in a further very small assignment ε (epsilon). The epsilon assignment, which is smaller than any other assignment, can be placed at any vacant square for which a closed path cannot be established. These are called *independent locations*. In this case only B3 is *not* independent. In Fig. 14-15(a), ε is placed in square A1. There was no particular reason for this choice rather than another independent location; u_i and v_j can now be determined and the optimum follows in one iteration. Note that the optimum shown in Figure 4-15(b) is not degenerate (ε has been set $= 0$, i.e., removed). Sometimes an unlucky choice of location results in only ε being relocated (ε is always the smallest number). One of two things must then result. *Either*

	1	2	3	
A	8	10 ⑮	7 ◯	15
B	6 ⑧	10	9	8
C	10 ②	8	4 ⑳	22
	10	15	20	

Figure 4-14

(a)

	$v_1 = 8$	$v_2 = 10$	$v_3 = 2$	
$u_1 = 0$	8 ⓔ	10 ⑮	7	$15 + \epsilon$
$u_2 = -2$	6 ⑧	10	9	8
$u_3 = 2$	10 ②	8	4 ⑳	22
	$10 + \epsilon$	15	20	

(b)

	$v_1 = 8$	$v_2 = 10$	$v_3 = 6$	
$u_1 = 0$	8 ②	10 ⑬	7	15
$u_2 = -2$	6 ⑧	10	9	8
$u_3 = -2$	10	8 ②	4 ⑳	22
	10	15	20	

Figure 4-15

a position for ε can be found such that a real amount may be shipped round a worthwhile path *or* a location for ε can be found for which there are no positive vacant square evaluations, i.e., the solution was the optimum though not recognizably so at first.

4-10 OPTIMAL SOURCING

The transportation model is useful in a number of problems that do not necessarily involve the physical movement of goods—or where this is incidental. As an example, consider the following problem in purchasing or procurement.

A department store requires the following annual quantities of five types of clothing items:

Type	A	B	C	D	E
Quantity required ('000s of units)	18	9	12	20	16

The firm received quotations from four manufacturers who have undertaken to supply not more than the quantities below (of all types combined).

Manufacturer	1	2	3	4
Total quantity ('000s of units)	20	18	25	19

The store estimates that its profits per item will vary with the type and manufacturer as shown in the following table:

		A	B	C	D	E
	1	2.0	1.9	2.3	1.5	3.2
Manufacturer	2	1.8	1.9	2.1	1.6	2.8
	3	2.5	2.4	2.2	1.7	3.6
	4	2.2	1.4	2.1	1.8	2.8

Type

Profit per unit in £s

The store manager will want to know the optimal sourcing arrangement—whose orders may be best placed for maximum profit—and whether any discretion is available in the form of equally profitable alternative arrangements.

As an additional consideration suppose that the store was already contracted to purchase 8000 units of type C from manufacturer 2 (these 8000) units being included in the demand for C and the maximum supply from 2 given above). What is the maximum amount it ought to be prepared to pay to be released from this contract?

The distinctive feature here is that the problem is one of *maximization*. In terms of VAM, the VAM numbers will now be the difference between the two *best* squares, viz., for row (1) the first VAM number will be $3.2 - 2.3 = 0.9$. The VAM initial solution is shown in Fig. 4-16. It will be seen that (a) a dummy

	$v_1 = 2.0$ A	$v_2 = 2.0$ B	$v_3 = 2.3$ C	$v_4 = 1.6$ D	$v_5 = 3.2$ E	$v_6 = 0$ dummy	
$u_1 = 0$ 1	⑧ 2.0	1.9	⑫ 2.3	1.5	ⓔ 3.2	0	20
$u_2 = 0.0$ 2	1.8	1.9	2.1	⑪ 1.6	2.8	⑦ 0	18
$u_3 = 0.4$ 3	2.5	⑨ 2.4	2.2	1.7	⑯ 3.6	0	25
$u_4 = 0.2$ 4	⑩ 2.2	1.4	2.1	⑨ 1.8	2.8	0	19
	18	9	12	20	16	7	

Figure 4-16

column was needed, and (b) the solution is degenerate. The degeneracy has been resolved by location of ε in square 1, E. The solution is not optimal. Even though the problem is one of maximization the u_i and v_j numbers can be determined just as before, viz., $u_i + v_j =$ profit in square i, j. The difference is that, as regards the evaluations, it is *negative* evaluations that now represent improvement. Thus for square 1, B the evaluation is $u_i + v_2 -$ profit $1, 2 = 0 + 2 - 1.9 = +0.1$ which means that less profit will be made (check this by establishing the closed path, and bear in mind that the method does not 'know' what the financial entries in the cells represent).

Square 3, A has a negative evaluation of $0.4 + 2.0 - 2.5 = -0.1$ and eight (thousand) units can be shipped round the corresponding path. This, coincidentally, removes the degeneracy and the solution produced is optimal. It is shown in Fig. 4-17. The total profit made is £179 400. The solution, however, is *non-unique*. Square 2, B has a zero evaluation and the solution resulting from shipment around the corresponding closed path will produce an equally good arrangement so that discretion is available to this extent. As regards any existing contract to purchase 8000 of type C from manufacturer 2, this would reduce profit by £800 $= 8 \times 1000(-0.1 + 2.3 - 2.1)$. The result of

	$v_1 = 2.1$ A	$v_2 = 2.0$ B	$v_3 = 2.3$ C	$v_4 = 1.7$ D	$v_5 = 3.2$ E	$v_6 = 0.1$ dummy	
$u_1 = 0$ 1	2.0	1.9	⑫ 2.3	1.5	⑧ 3.2	0	20
$u_2 = -0.1$ 2	1.8	1.9	2.1	⑪ 1.6	2.8	⑦ 0	18
$u_3 = 0.4$ 3	⑧ 2.5	⑨ 2.4	2.2	1.7	⑧ 3.6	0	25
$u_4 = 0.1$ 4	⑩ 2.2	1.4	2.1	⑨ 1.8	2.8	0	19
	18	9	12	20	16	7	

Figure 4-17

keeping to the contract would be to make an assignment of 8 in square 2, C, so that if the release costs less than £800 it would be worth while.

4-11 ADVANCED TOPICS

There are numerous changes that can be made using the basic transportation model. *In transhipment* problems there are intermediate locations through which goods may pass (see Wilkes, 1983). In *capacitated* problems there are limits on the amounts that may be sent along some or all routes. There may also be minimal usage necessary along some routes (or minimal purchases from some sources).

Dis-economies of scale can be allowed for (a discrete increase in unit cost along a route if used above a certain level). Unfortunately, *economies* of scale, which are perhaps more frequent, are much more troublesome computationally. Some models allow for 'losses in transit'—for instance, electrical power losses in transmission or deterioration in storage—not to mention pilfering. The US Navy used this kind of model to minimize transportation and overhaul costs at naval shipyards.

In some logistical problems all that matters is that total distribution is completed in the shortest possible time. This defines a *least time* transportation problem.

Transportation problems can be solved by computers using linear programming packages and where there are many additional complications such as capacitated routes this may be the best way to proceed. There are programmes which use the transportation geared procedure to take full advantage of the particular structure of these problems. Some special provisions such as prohibited routes can also be included.

Advanced areas of application of the transportation model include short-term investment and the management of cash (see Wilkes, 1983). Other starting solutions of comparable efficiency to VAM include *Russell's approximation method* and *Houthakker's method* of mutually preferred flows. And so the list could go on. It should by this stage be evident both that the range of uses of the method is considerable and that the basic framework is very adaptable.

EXERCISES

4-1 Revision exercise
- (i) In what areas of business activity has the transportation model found application?
- (ii) Set out the broad logic of the solution procedure for transportation problems.
- (iii) Compare VAM and LCF as methods for obtaining starting solutions. What do they have in common and where do they diverge?
- (iv) Explain the role of row and column numbers (u_i and v_j) in evaluating unused routes and in sensitivity analysis.
- (v) What is the paradox of transportation—is it really a paradox?
- (vi) Show how the problems of unequal supply and demand and degeneracy can be dealt with.
- (vii) Show how the method can be adapted to deal with maximization problems.

4-2 Obtain the VAM starting solution for the following tansportation problem and compare the cost of the *VAM* arragement with that produced by *LCF*.

Customer

		1	2	3	4	
	1	18	16	8	13	100
	2	14	14	6	10	125
Depot	3	20	15	17	15	70
	4	8	12	19	11	80
		55	130	95	95	

4-3 The following is a transportation problem from three warehouses (A, B, and C) to four customers (1, 2, 3, and 4). The capacities at the warehouses and the demands from the customers are shown around the perimeter. Per unit transport costs are shown in the cells. Cost minimization is the objective.

	1	2	3	4	
A	7	8	11	10	30
B	10	12	5	4	45
C	6	10	11	9	35
	20	28	17	33	

(i) Find the cost of the VAM initial solution.

(ii) Find the optimal solution and total cost.

(iii) By how much would the BI cost need to be reduced in order to make shipments along this route worth while?

(iv) Now suppose that demand from customer one and capacity at warehouse B both increase by five units. What is the extra cost of satisfying this increased demand? What is special about the solution so produced? What problems does this type of solution pose?

4-4 Using Vogel's approximation method for the initial solution, solve the following problem and show how the degeneracy is resolved.

	1	2	3	
A	10	16	12	25
B	7	11	11	20
C	7	9	8	15
	20	27	13	

4-5 A transportation problem has the cost and requirements table given below.

Customer

		1	2	2	
	1	9	4	7	35
Depot	2	8	12	11	42
	3	3	6	13	48
		50	38	37	

(i) Find the least cost distribution.

(ii) Conduct a sensitivity analysis on (a) the cost in square 1,1 and (b) the cost in square 3,1.

(iii) If demand from Customer 1 increased by two units and demand from Customer 3 increased by one unit, with one further unit of supply available at Depot 1 and two more units available at Depot 2, how much extra would this cost?

(iv) With the original supply levels, find the cost of not using route 3,2 at all.

4-6 A discount store requires the following monthly quantities of five different sizes of refrigerator:

Size	A	B	C	D	E
Number required	16	24	20	22	15

The store has received quotations from four manufacturers who are able to supply not more than the quantities below (of all sizes combined):

Manufacturer	1	2	3	4
Maximum supply	24	30	23	25

The store estimates that its profits per refrigerator will vary with the size and manufacturer as shown in the following table:

Manufacturer	Size				
	A	B	C	D	E
1	20	15	23	25	13
2	19	12	25	27	21
3	17	13	22	21	18
4	22	12	27	23	18

(i) How should the orders be optimally placed and what is the maximum monthly profit for the store?

(ii) Suppose that the store was already contracted to manufacturer 1 to buy seven units monthly of size E. What is the maximum sum the store would be willing to pay (per month) to be released from this obligation?

(iii) Total supplies from manufacturers 2 and 3 are fixed but the amounts obtained from 1 and 4 can be varied (for the same overall total). How would this flexibility be best employed?

(iv) Suppose that demand for size B increases to 30 units monthly and only maufacturer 2 can increase supply (to 36 units maximum). By how much could maximum profit increase?

4-7 Newton Company Ltd specializes in the manufacture of certain electronic components for local industry. The three main demand areas for these components are Sidmouth, Liverbourne, and Centapool and the company has a warehouse in each of these towns. The company's three factories are separate from its warehouses and are at East-Sidmouth, West-Liverbourne, and Martrent. Due to the present economic climate the company is suffering from an extreme shortage of business, as indicated in the following table:

Factory	Maximum output of factory per annum (units)	Warehouse	Expected demand in area served by warehouse for coming year (units)
East-Sidmouth	210 000	Sidmouth	80 000
West-Liverbourne	140 000	Liverbourne	200 000
Martrent	290 000	Centapool	200 000

The nearest warehouses to the East-Sidmouth and West-Liverbourne factories are Sidmouth and Liverbourne respectively. The Centapool warehouse is roughly equidistant from all three factories. The variable cost of distribution (£ per unit) from the factories to the warehouses are as follows:

	Sidmouth	Liverbourne	Centapool
East-Sidmouth	2	4	4
West-Liverbourne	4	3	4
Martrent	3	6	4

The variable costs of production at each factory are:

	£ per unit
East-Sidmouth	11
West-Liverbourne	14
Martrent	12

The present distribution policy of the company is as follows:

All Sidmouth warehouse requirements are supplied from East-Sidmouth. All West-Liverbourne production is transported to the Liverbourne warehouse, the remaining demand at Liverbourne being supplied from the East-Sidmouth factory. All Centapool requirements are supplied from Martrent.

Required:

(a) Evaluate the cost of applying the present distribution policy in the coming year. Why do you think the company adopted this particular policy?

(b) Determine the policy which is expected to achieve the minimum total cost of production and distribution for the coming year. What cost saving does this involve? Is this solution unique? If not give any alternative solution you find.

(c) Assume now that the company is considering the closure of the West-Liverbourne factory. What increase in the total variable cost of production and distribution will this cause assuming that the company operates in a minimum cost manner?

(Chartered Association of Certified Accountants)

4-8 The Management Services section of Mech International Ltd is planning to expand. Two of the eleven posts currently being advertised within the section require special knowledge of accounting practice and carry a basic annual salary of £5000, a further three need basic training in data processing and are worth at least £4700, while the remainder can be filled by anyone with general experience of management services and pay £4400 at minimum. It has been agreed, however, that any appointee should be paid a salary equal to the greater of his current salary and the company's minimum for the job he is to do.

Of the 14 short listed applicants, all possess adequate general experience. Two are amply qualified in both accounting and data processing, 4 in accounting only and 5 in data processing only. The present salaries of the last 3 groups of applicants are respectively £4800, £4600, and £4500, whereas those with no knowledge of either specialism are currently earning £4200 or less. Required:

The Head of Management Services has been asked to produce an estimate of total additional expenditure incurred in his section, for the coming year, on employee salaries.

   (i) By defining 'sources' and 'destinations', use the transportation technique to determine the current figure he may reasonably submit. (If your allocation in not unique, detail *all* other possible solutions.)
   (ii) Show by means of a simple algebraic example that transportation is a special case of linear programming.

(Chartered Association of Certified Accountants)

4-9 The following problem should be solved by the transportation method. XW Limited has four production plants and four wholesale warehouse outlets. The warehouses are situated away from the production plants. The production and transportation costs, the selling prices, production capacities, and sales quantities are given below:

							Per unit	
Production plants	Warehouses				Production capacity in units	Materials	Labour and overhead £
	1	2	3	4			
A	10	14	7	10	140	4	6
B	8	12	5	10	100	5	8
C	3	7	11	8	150	4	9
D	9	12	6	13	160	3	8
Warehouse requirements in units	80	120	130	110			
Selling price (ex warehouse) per unit	£ 26	£ 32	£ 30	£ 25			

The cost of transporting a unit from a given plant to a warehouse is shown in the body of the matrix in £'s per unit.
You are required to:

   (a) compute a plan for production and distribution which will achieve maximum profit for the company;
   (b) state the profit achieved by the plan you have given in answer to (a) above. Your workings should be shown and the steps in the calculations clearly described: answers not supported in this way will be regarded as inadequate.

(Chartered Institute of Management Accountants)

Solution guides

4-2 The VAM solution is:

	1	2	3	4	
1	18	(5) 16	(95) 8	13	100
2	14	(30) 14	6	(95) 10	125
3	20	(70) 15	17	15	70
4	(55) 8	(25) 12	19	11	80
	55	130	95	95	

The cost of the VAM solution is £4000. The least-cost-first solution is:

		(60)		(40)	
			(95)	(30)	
		(70)			
	(55)			(25)	

The cost of the LCF solution is £4115. The reader may confirm that the VAM solution is in this case optimal although non-unique (square 2, 3 showing zero evaluation).

4-3 (i) The VAM solution costs £606.

(ii) The unique optimum, following one iteration from the VAM solution, is shown below. The cost of this solution is £586. Note that a dummy customer is required with demand of 12.

	$v_1=6$	$v_2=8$	$v_3=10$	$v_4=9$	$v_5=0$	
$u_1=0$	7	(28) 8	11	10	(2) 0	30
$u_2=-5$	10	12	(17) 5	(28) 4	0	45
$u_3=0$	(20) 6	10	11	(5) 9	(10) 0	35
	20	28	17	33	12	

(iii) The evaluation of square B1 at the optimum is $-5+6-10=-9$. To make the square just worth while the evaluation would have to be zero. To achieve this the transportation cost would have to be reduced by 9 to only 1 per unit.

(iv) £5. The u_i+v_j value is $-5+6=1$ and to find the total increase in cost this per unit increase of 1 must be multiplied by the number of units involved (5). The new optimum would be *degenerate*.

4-4 The VAM solution is degenerate. Place the epsilon assignment in the first independent location found. This is square 1, 1.

	$v_1=10$	$v_2=16$	$v_3=12$	
$u_1=0$	ⓔ ⁱ⁰	⑫ ¹⁶	⑬ ¹²	25
$u_2=-3$	㉒ ⁷	¹¹	¹¹	20
$u_3=-7$	⁷	⑮ ⁹	⁸	15
	20	27	13	

VAM solution
with degeneracy
resolved

Square 2, 2 now shows real improvement and 12 units can be shipped round the closed path. The resulting solution is optimal (and, incidentally, no longer degenerate).

⑫ ¹⁰	¹⁶	⑬ ¹²	25
⑧ ⁷	⑫ ¹¹	¹¹	20
⁷	⑮ ⁹	⁸	15
20	27	13	

4-5 (i) The least cost distribution is shown below.

	$C_{31}-2$	4	$1+C_{31}$	
$u_1=0$	⁹	㉟ ⁴	⁷	35
$10-C_{31}$	⑤ ⁸	¹²	㊲ ¹¹	42
2	㊺ C_{31}	③ ⁶	¹³	48
	50	38	37	

u_i and v_j values are expressed in terms of C_{31} for the purposes of subsequent sensitivity analysis. Thus with $C_{31}=3$ as originally, the value of $v_1=C_{31}-2=1$.

(ii) Square 1, 1 represents an unused route with evaluation of -8. So long as cost on this route does not fall by more than 8 the original solution will remain optimal. Thus $C_{11} \geqslant 1$ is the tolerance interval. For C_{31} the situation is more complicated in that it represents a used route and u_2, v_1 and v_3 all depend on C_{31} as shown. In fact *all* vacant square evaluations in this solution are functions of C_{31} and each will set a bound on C_{31}. Vacant square evaluations must all remain non-positive. Specifically:

$$e_{11} = 0 + C_{31} - 2 - 9 \leqslant 0 \therefore C_{31} \leqslant 11$$
$$e_{13} = 0 + 1 + C_{31} - 7 \leqslant = 0 \therefore C_{31} \leqslant 6$$
$$e_{22} = 10 - C_{31} + 4 - 12 \leqslant 0 \therefore C_{31} \geqslant 2$$
$$e_{32} = 2 + 1 + C_{31} - 13 \leqslant 0 \therefore C_{31} \leqslant 10$$

The tolerance interval for C_{31} is between the greatest of the lower bounds and the least of the upper bounds, i.e.

$$2 \leqslant C_{31} \leqslant 6$$

(iii) The change in cost is $u_1 + 2u_2 + 2v_2 + v_3 = 0 + 14 + 8 + 4 = 26$

(iv) The optimal arrangement with route 3, 2 prohibited (and therefore shown with a cost of M) is

	0	4	3	
$u_1 = 0$	9	4 (35)	7	35
8	8 (2)	12 (3)	11 (37)	42
3	3 (48)	M	13	48
	50	38	37	

The cost of this arrangement is £3 more than the original optimum. Note that the evaluation of square 3, 2 is $3 + 4 - M$ which by definition must be a negative number.

4-6 (i) The unique optimum is shown below:

	$v_1=20$ A	$v_2=15$ B	$v_3=25$ C	$v_4=26$ D	$v_5=20$ E	$v_6=2$ F	
$u_1=0$; 1	(11) 20	(13) 15	23	25	13	0	24
$u_2=1$; 2	19	12	25	(22) 27	(8) 21	0	30
$u_3=-2$; 3	17	(11) 13	22	21	(7) 18	(5) 0	23
$u_4=+2$; 4	(5) 22	12	(20) 27	23	18	0	25
	16	24	20	22	15	5	

The total profit made is £2096. Note that manufacturer three is only called on to supply 18 units.

(ii) The contract would mean having to place an assignment of 7 in square 1, E. The evaluation of this square shows that profit would be reduced by 7 (this is a maximization problem) for every unit located here. Thus the total drop in profit would be £49 (the closed path for this square could just accommodate an assignment of 7 in 1, E). Thus £49 is the maximum sum that the firm would be prepared to pay.

(iii) Take more from manufacturer four and less from manufacturer one (remember that this is a maximization problem).

(iv) £96.

4-7 (a) The original policy followed by the Rental Company is shown below:

	$v_1=13$ Sidmouth	$v_2=15$ Liverb'ne	$v_3=16$ Centapool	$v_4=0$ Dummy	
East Sidmouth $u_1=0$	13 (80)	15 (60)	15	0 (70)	210
West Liverbourne $u_2=2$	18	17 (140)	18	0	140
Martrent $u_3=0$	15	18	16 (200)	0 (90)	290
	80	200	200	160	

The costs in each square represent the variable distribution costs per unit *plus* the production costs per unit. It follows at once from the stated arrangements that East Sidmouth and Martrent have unused capacities of 70 and 90 respectively. The cost of this original solution is 7520 (£000's).

(b) The original solution is not optimal as both square 1, 3 and 2, 4 show improvement. Routing 70 round the 2, 4 closed path gives the solution below which is optimal. The cost of the solution is 7380 so that a saving of 140 could be effected.

	$v_1=13$	$v_2=15$	$v_3=14$	$v_4=-2$	
$u_1=0$	(80) 13	(130) 15	15	0	210
$u_2=2$	18	(70) 17	18	(70) 0	140
$u_3=2$	15	18	(200) 16	(90) 0	290
	80	200	200	160	

The solution is not unique as square 3, 1 has zero evaluation. 70 units can be shipped round this closed path to give the alternative solution:

⑩	㉒⓪⓪			
			⑭⓪	
⑦⓪		㉒⓪⓪	⑳	

(c) The alternative optimum of (b) does not involve usage of the West-Liverbourne factory, so that there would be *no* increases in variable production and distribution costs on account of the closure. Of course, in reality, closure can be very expensive on other grounds.

4-8 (i) The sources are the categories into which the applicants fall. In the optimal tableau below B represents those qualified in both specialist areas, A in accounting only, D in data processing only, and G with general experience only.

	$v_1=50$ A	$v_2=48$ D	$v_3=46$ G	$v_4=0$ dummy	
$u_1=0$; B	50 *	48 *	48 ②	0	2
$u_2=0$; A	50 ②	M	46 ①	0 ①	4
$u_3=-1$; D	M	47 ③	45 ②	0	5
$u_4=-2$; G	M	M	44 ③	0	3
	2	3	6	3	

It will be seen that a dummy column is needed to balance the rim conditions. The 'transportation costs' represent the higher of the two relevant salary figures in each case. The figure M is an unspecified *arbitrarily large* number inserted as the cost to prevent assignments in squares where the applicants are unqualified. M is so large that any square with an M cost *always has a negative evaluation*. Some safely large (say 1000) number can be used in place of M if desired.

The cost of the optimal solution is seen to be 509 (£00). This is the least figure that can be submitted. Of course the solution does not tell us which *person* gets which job, only that, for instance, of the four people qualified in accounting only, any two should be assigned to the accounting jobs.

The solution is not unique. Those squares with zero evaluations are starred. There are three other basic solutions with the same cost corresponding to the placing of assignments in squares 1, 1 and 1, 2. The assignments are:

2 0 0 0	0 1 0 1	1 1 0 0
0 0 1 3	2 0 0 2	1 0 0 3
0 3 2 0	0 2 3 0	0 2 3 0
0 0 3 0	0 0 3 0	0 0 3 0

There is also one non-basic solution involving assignment of one at square 1, 1. The pattern in this case is:

$$
\begin{matrix}
1 & 0 & 0 & 1 \\
1 & 0 & 1 & 2 \\
0 & 3 & 2 & 0 \\
0 & 0 & 3 & 0
\end{matrix}
$$

(ii) Consider a 'two-by-two' problem in which the shipments are represented by x's. The amount to be shipped from source i to destination j is represented by x_{ij}. The cost per unit is shown by c_{ij}. Thus in tableau form:

Destination

		1	2	
		c_{11}	c_{12}	
Source	1	x_{11}	x_{12}	S_1
		c_{21}	c_{22}	
	2	x_{21}	x_{22}	S_2
		D_1	D_2	

The objective is to minimize costs overall. Thus

$$\text{Minimize } F = c_{11}x_{11} + c_{12}x_{12} + c_{21}x_{21} + c_{22}x_{22}$$

Since rim conditions are balanced $(S_1 + S_2 = D_1 + D_2)$ to satisfy the demands *all* available supplies must be used (there can be nothing remaining at either sources). Thus

$$x_{11} + x_{12} = S_1 \quad \text{and} \quad x_{21} + x_{22} = S_2$$

The demands also will be precisely met:

$$x_{11} + x_{21} = D_1 \quad \text{and} \quad x_{12} + x_{22} = D_2$$

and negative shipments are disallowed:

$$x_{11} \geqslant 0, x_{12} \geqslant 0, x_{21} \geqslant 0, x_{22} \geqslant 0$$

Thus the problem is clearly one of linear programming with the special features that all constraint coefficients of the x_{ij} are zero or one and that since rim conditions are balanced if any *three* of the constraints are satisfied then the fourth is automatically satisfied. In general with m origins and n destinations there will be $m + n$ such equations of which any one can be dropped. This is why basic solutions to transportation problems contain only $m + n - 1$ assignments. It is important to realize that transportation problems are linear programming problems; thus anything that is true for LP in general is true for transportation. Also, it follows that *some* LPs are transportation problems. If this special feature can be spotted, then the highly efficient transportation solution procedures can be adopted.

4-9 Space permits only the optimal solution to be presented here! However, it should be pointed out that in obtaining a VAM solution there are several 'ties' and some VAM solutions require several iterations. The problem is one of maximizaton. The entries in the top right of the squares are unit profits (selling price minus transportation, material, and labour costs).

	$v_1=7$ \ 1	$v_2=9$ \ 2	$v_3=13$ \ 3	$v_4=5$ \ 4	$v_6=0$ \ Dummy	
$u_1=0$; A	6	8	(30) 13	(110) 5	0	140
$u_2=0$; B	5	7	12	2	(100) 0	100
$u_3=3$; C	(80) 10	(70) 12	6	4	0	150
$u_4=0$; D	6	(50) 9	(100) 13	1	(10) 0	160
	80	120	130	110	110	

The total profit made is £4330. Note that the evaluation of square 1, 5 is zero, so that the solution is not unique.

REFERENCES

Wilkes, F. M. (1983), *Capital Budgeting Techniques*, second edition, Wiley.
Taha, H. A. (1987), *Operations Research*, fourth edition, Collier Macmillan.

FURTHER READING

Hillier, F. S., and Lieberman, G. N. (1974), *Operations Research*, second edition, Holden Day. Includes case study examples, shows transportation problems as linear programming problems; includes trans-shipment problems and Russell's approximation method.

Cook, T. M., and Russell, R. A. (1981), *Introduction to Management Science*, second edition, Prentice-Hall. Gives full description of method, applications and use of the method in an inventory problem.

Monks, J. G. (1982), *Operations Management*, second edition, McGraw-Hill. Shows the transportation problem in the context of optimal facility location and layout.

FIVE

ASSIGNMENT PROBLEMS

5-1 INTRODUCTION

Numerous business problems involve one-to-one allocation of resources to uses. Examples are:

1. Assigning operatives to machines
2. Assigning offices to staff
3. Assigning sales people to areas
4. Assigning vehicles to routes
5. Assigning products to factories
6. Assigning contracts to bidders.

For each possible allocation of resource-to-use, a measure of *effectiveness* is required; this may be expressed in terms of cost, time, revenue or profit, depending on circumstances. The objective then is to make a one-to-one allocation of resources-to-uses to maximize effectiveness. This defines an *assignment problem.*

Assignment problems are a special category of transportation problems in which all the supplies and demands are at unit level. Consequently, the number of sources must be the same as the number of destinations. Despite the resulting degeneracy, the stepping-stone method *could* be used to solve assignment problems but there is a much more efficient procedure which makes full use of the problem's special structure.

5-2 THE LOGIC OF THE SOLUTION METHOD

Consider a problem in which four people are to be allocated to four jobs on the

People

		1	2	3	4
	1	17	9	15	9
	2	19	4	11	9
Jobs	3	15	17	8	11
	4	15	13	11	6

Figure 5-1

basis of time study data. Figure 5-1 shows the time taken (in minutes) for each person to perform each task. Figure 5-1 represents an *effectiveness matrix* or *direct cost matrix*. Each person must be assigned to precisely one job and each job must be performed by one person only, to minimize the total time taken. The problem has 24 feasible solutions so one approach would be to determine the effectiveness of every possible arrangement. This is called *complete enumeration*. An assignment problem with n rows and n columns has $n!$ solutions, hence our four row/column problem has $4! = 4 \times 3 \times 2 \times 1 = 24$ solutions. But a 12 row/column problem has 12! solutions—about 479 *million* possible arrangements: therefore, something more efficient than complete enumeration is needed.

In fact LCF or VAM can be used to obtain 'good' solutions to assignment problems but there is no guarantee that the best arrangement is reached. In the present problem, LCF happens to produce the optimal solution while VAM does not, as the reader may confirm.

A commonsense approach would be to attempt to allocate each job to the person who is quickest at it. One way to show the most effective workers at each task is to subtract the minimum time in each row from all entries in that row. Zeros will therefore indicate the speediest workers at each task and

8	0	6	0
15	0	7	5
7	9	0	3
9	7	5	0

Figure 5-2

non-zero entries will show excesses over these minimal times. The results of subtracting row minima from all entries in each row are shown in Fig. 5-2. If jobs could now be assigned to people so that in all cases this coincided with a zero in the new matrix, the resulting arrangement must be optimal. However, this is not possible at this stage as there is not a zero in the first column—there are not enough zeros in the appropriate places. Can a means be found of 'generating' more zeros without distorting the problem?

Recall that assignment problems are special cases of transportation problems and that the addition or subtraction of a constant to the objective function coefficients throughout an entire row or column will not alter the optimal arrangement. Thus a zero can be generated in the first column of Fig. 5-2 by subtracting the minimum element, 7, throughout. This produces the result shown in Fig. 5-3. The question is now asked again, can a *complete assignment* (each job allocated to one person and each person allocated one job) be made to correspond only to zeros in the matrix?

1	0	6	0
8	0	7	5
0	9	0	3
2	7	5	0

Figure 5-3

Inspection of Fig. 5-3 will show that this is not the case (but note that in a larger problem this question is by no means trivial and will require a systematic procedure of its own). The principles we have employed so far in working towards a solution procedure are these:

(A) In a problem in which all data at any stage are non-negative, a complete assignment corresponding only to zero locations must be optimal.
(B) If a constant is subtracted (or added) throughout an entire row or column, all solutions are affected equally (the *relative* effectiveness of complete solutions does not change and the problem is not distorted).

In applying principle (B) to this point, we have:

1. Subtracted the minimum element in each row of the effectiveness matrix from all elements in that row and then:
2. Subtracted the minimum element in each column (of the matrix resulting from 1) from all entries in that column.

Steps 1 and 2 must produce a zero in every row and in every column. But this may not be sufficient. A complete assignment involving zeros only requires that there be a zero in every row *each in a different column*. As this is not the case in Fig. 5-3, a complete assignment in zeros is not yet possible. But could more zeros be generated (without making any elements negative) by additions and subtractions throughout complete rows and columns? This can be done, and generating zeros in this way is called *matrix reduction*.

As an example of generating further zeros, consider the first column of Fig. 5-3. Suppose that one was subtracted throughout. This would produce an extra zero at square 1,1 but would result in a −1 entry at 3,1. To eliminate the −1 add back one unit throughout row 3. This done, column 3 has a smallest value of 1 which can be subtracted throughout without further consequences. The result is shown in Fig. 5-4. Inspection of Fig. 5-4 reveals that a complete assignment in zeros now exists as indicated by the zeros surrounded by a square ⊡. It has turned out that the optimal arrangement is to allocate Job 1 to Person 1, Job 2 to Person 2, Job 3 to Person 3 and Job 4 to Person 4 as shown. This optimal arrangement produces a minimum overall time of 35 minutes, seen by reference to the original effectiveness entries.

People

Jobs		1	2	3	4
	1	⊡	0	5	0
	2	7	⊡	6	5
	3	0	10	⊡	4
	4	1	7	4	⊡

Figure 5-4

The 'reduced' data of Fig. 5-4 can be used to show the extra time that would be taken by other complete assignments. This is done by simply adding up the entries in Fig. 5-4 for each assignment. For example, the top right to bottom left diagonal solution will cost an *extra* $0 + 6 + 10 + 1 = 17$, a total of 52. The numbers can be used in this way because by restricting ourselves to operations on entire rows and columns we have at no point altered the *relative* costs of *complete* solutions. Figure 5-4 represents an *opportunity cost matrix* which can be used to cost out all other *complete* solutions. However, *individual* entries in Fig. 5-4 do *not* represent the opportunity costs of re-locating an assignment to that particular square. For example it *cannot* be said that the penalty for assigning Job 3 to Person 2 is 10 minutes extra overall. This is because our operations to generate zeros did not affect all rows and columns

0	3	3	1
4	0	2	3
1	14	0	6
0	9	2	0

Figure 5-5

identically but since each *complete* solution must have precisely one assignment in each row and column they must all be equally affected as a whole. Also, changes of assignment cannot be made in isolation—other adjustments will follow as a consequence. Only the overall total of these knock-on effects is meaningful.

The zeros in the optimal positions could have been generated in a number of ways. Figure 5-5 shows an equally valid opportunity cost matrix which, as the reader may verify, gives the extra cost of each of the 23 alternative complete assignments to the same value as Fig 5-4. This despite the fact that apart from the optimal zeros, no other entries are the same in the two figures. The broad logic of the solution procedure is shown in Fig. 5-6 and the detailed steps can now be set out.

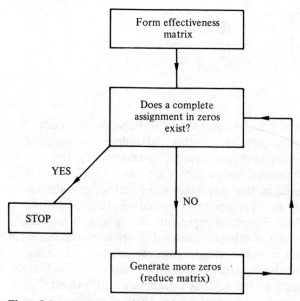

Figure 5-6

5-3 THE SOLUTION PROCEDURE

The fourteen step procedure set out below (after Sasieni *et al.*, 1959) is known as the *Hungarian method* or the *reduced matrix method*. Steps 4–6 are a systematic way of determining whether a complete solution in zeros exists. Though they may not appear so, Steps 7–12 are always equivalent to adding or subtracting constants from entire rows and columns and are sometimes referred to as the *line covering procedure*. They are based upon a 1916 theorem by the Hungarian mathematician König (from which the method takes its name) and are a very efficient way of generating zeros in useful locations. The line covering procedure gives the *minimum* number of lines needed to cover all zeros. This will equal the number of assignments that can be made at any stage using only zeros. Inspection may reveal that there are sometimes alternative ways of covering the zeros with a minimal number of lines. The optimal solution will follow from such alternative coverings but a different, although equally valid, version of the opportunity cost matrix may result. In Step 6 a systematic subroutine exists to deal with the case where there are remaining unmarked zeros (which must be at least two in every row and column in which they occur). However, for problems of modest proportions, inspection is preferable.

1. Form the effectiveness matrix.
2. Subtract the minimum element in each row from each element in the row.
3. For the matrix formed by (2) subtract the minimum element in each column from each element in the column.
4. Examine *rows* successively until a *row* with only one (unmarked) zero is found. Make that square the assignment square (mark with a □) and delete all other zeros in that *column*. Proceed until all rows have been examined and the appropriate assignments and deletions made.
5. Now examine *columns* for single unmarked zeros, mark these zeros □ and delete any other zeros in the same *row*.
6. Repeat (4) and (5) until there are no *single* unmarked zeros in any row or column. Mark □ as an assignment square or delete any remaining zeros by inspection as necessary.

If a complete solution in zeros does not exist after completion of step 6 then:

7. Identify all rows for which assignments have *not* been made. Mark such rows (—).
8. Mark columns not already marked which have *zeros* in marked rows.
9. Mark rows not already marked which have assignments in marked columns.
10. Repeat (8) and (9) until the chain of row and column marking ends.
11. Draw lines through all *unmarked* rows and through all *marked* columns.
12. Select the smallest of the elements that do *not* have a line through them

and subtract it from *all* elements that do not have a line through them. *Add* this smallest element to every element that lies at the *intersection of two lines*. Leave remaining elements unchanged.
13. Repeat steps (4)–(6) for the matrix given by (12).
14. If a complete solution in zeros is not given by (13), re-apply (7)–(13) until the optimum is obtained.

Let us now apply this procedure systematically to the following problem. A firm has five contracts to be distributed among five possible firms. Each firm will be given one contract and the cost estimates (in £1000 units) for each firm on the contracts that it could handle are given below.

		Contract				
		1	2	3	4	5
	A	35	15	—	30	30
	B	25	20	15	25	40
Firm	C	20	—	30	20	50
	D	15	40	35	15	40
	E	10	50	40	30	35

Firm A cannot take contract (3) and Firm C cannot take contract (2). How should the contracts be assigned to the firms so as to minimize total cost?

The first step is to complete the effectiveness matrix by putting a 'large' figure in the A3 and C2 position.

A cost figure of M is inserted where M, unspecified, is large enough to dominate any other number in the problem. The result of the first two stages are shown in Fig. 5-7(a). Column minima are then subtracted giving the

20	0	$M - 15$	15	15
10	5	0	10	25
0	$M - 20$	10	0	30
0	25	20	0	25
0	40	30	20	25

◄———— Result of row subtractions

(a)

20	[0]	$M - 15$	15	15
10	5	[0]	10	10
0	$M - 20$	10	[0]	15
0	25	20	0	10
[0]	40	30	20	10

(b)

Figure 5-7

numbers in Fig. 5-7(b). This completes (1) to (3). In applying (4) the middle element in row (2) is first made an assignment square ($\square$). We then come to the first element in row (5). This is 'assigned' and the two zeros above it crossed out (X). That completes the first run through the rows. Step (5) picks out the zero at the top of column (2) and the zero at the end of the first row is crossed out. Now back to Step (4). Row (3) now has an unmarked (i.e., neither $\square$ or X) zero. This is duly assigned and the zero below it crossed out. Going into step (7) we first mark (—) row (4). Step (8) then marks columns (1) and (4). Step (9) then marks Rows (3) and (5). An attempt at step (10) produces no further changes. Then comes the line-drawing stage of Step (11). Step (12) then produces the numbers of Fig. 5-8 and Step (13) produces a complete, optimal assignment. In this case

$$
\left|
\begin{array}{ccccc}
30 & \boxed{0} & M-15 & 25 & \cancel{0} \\
20 & 5 & \boxed{0} & 20 & 10 \\
\boxed{0} & M-30 & \cancel{0} & 0 & 5 \\
0 & 15 & 10 & \boxed{0} & 0 \\
0 & 30 & 20 & 20 & \boxed{0}
\end{array}
\right|
$$

Figure 5-8

it was not necessary to re-apply (7)–(13) though this may have to be done in general. In obtaining the solution Step (6) produces only the assignments in the first two rows. There then remain at least two zeros in the rows and columns without assignments. The last three assignments were determined by inspection. The reader may produce other arrangements. All that this means is that there is a *non-unique* optimum—there is more than one least-cost distribution of contracts and the firm therefore has an element of cost-free discretion. To illustrate the variety of contexts in which the assignment methodology can be applied, consider the case of a car-hire company having a single vehicle available at each time of five locations.

A customer in each of five other locations requires a vehicle. The mileages between the car locations and the customers are:

		Vehicle locations				
		1	2	3	4	5
	1	16	10	14	24	14
	2	21	26	15	20	19
Customer locations	3	20	18	20	21	19
	4	25	15	18	24	19
	5	25	12	20	27	14

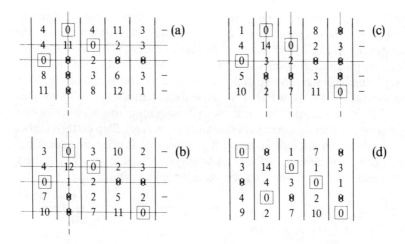

Figure 5-9

How should cars be assigned to customers so as to minimize overall mileage?

The answer is obtained in Fig. 5-9. The first matrix shown (A) is the result of the row and column subtractions; (B) and (C) are intermediate stages, and (D) is the optimum.

Notice that the (B) and (C) stages both have four assignments. This simply means that the zeros generated have not been in positions which allow an increased number of assignments to be made. Note also that an 'assignment' made at one stage may be removed at another—witness Vehicle 1 to Customer 3. As an exercise, the reader may determine that, while the optimum solution results in a mileage of 81, the best arrangement that can be made (given that Vehicle 1 is assigned to Customer 3) is a mileage total of 82.

5-4 MAXIMIZATION PROBLEMS

In some cases, the elements of the effectiveness matrix may represent revenues or profits so that the objective will be to maximize. The method presented is a minimization-geared algorithm but only a minor adjustment is necessary to use it on maximization problems. All that is strictly necessary is to multiply all entries by -1 and proceed to minimize. However, for the convenience of working with positive numbers, we may simply add to all elements (after negation!) the same positive number. The smallest such number that will eliminate all negative entries is the largest element in the original matrix. So, negate all numbers and then add back the largest one to all entries. Obviously the effect of this is to replace an original entry with the entry subtracted from the largest number. Here is an example.

Beta Corporation has four plants each of which can manufacture any one of four products. Production costs differ from one plant to another as do sales revenues (slightly different output levels and product quality). Given the revenue and cost data below, ascertain which product each plant should produce to maximize profit.

Plant	Sales revenues (£'000s) Product				Plant	Production costs (£'00s) Product			
	1	2	3	4		1	2	3	4
A	50	68	49	62	A	49	60	45	61
B	60	70	51	74	B	55	63	45	69
C	55	67	53	70	C	52	62	49	68
D	58	65	54	69	D	55	64	48	66

The first step is to produce the effective matrix by deducting the production cost matrix from the sales revenue matrix. This will give a suitable measure of profit in each case and the result is the first array in Fig. 5-10. The resulting maximization problem is then solved.

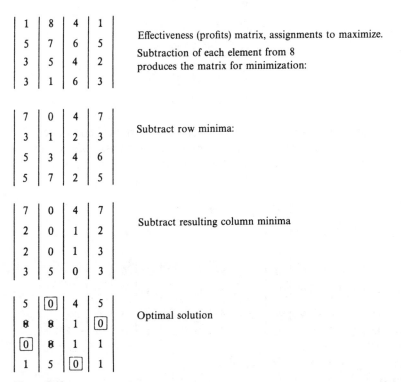

Effectiveness (profits) matrix, assignments to maximize.
Subtraction of each element from 8 produces the matrix for minimization:

Subtract row minima:

Subtract resulting column minima

Optimal solution

Figure 5-10

Thus the optimal arrangement is for Plant A to Produce product (2); plant B produces Product (4); Plant C produces Product (1) and Plant D produces Product (3). The overall profit resulting is found (by reference back to the profits matrix) to be £22 000.

The minimization procedure can be applied to the original profits matrix as it stands to find the *worst* possible arrangement. Alternatively, the opportunity cost matrix given in the optimal solution can be inspected to show that the worst arrangement would produce a profit of £10 000.

5-5 UNEQUAL DIMENSIONS AND SPECIAL PROVISIONS

Consider the following situation. A company has six people available for work on four jobs. The costs resulting from the assignment of each person to each job are:

		Job			
		1	2	3	4
	A	13	15	11	14
	B	12	7	13	13
Person	C	14	19	17	17
	D	9	17	12	15
	E	11	14	16	12
	F	15	18	18	16

which jobs should be assigned to which people to minimize costs overall?

In order to answer the question, a square effectiveness matrix must be formed. This is done as in Fig. 5-11(a) by the addition of two dummy columns.

	1	2	3	4	D_1	D_2
A	13	15	11	14	0	0
B	12	7	13	13	0	0
C	14	19	17	17	0	0
D	9	17	12	15	0	0
E	11	14	16	12	0	0
F	15	18	18	16	0	0

4	8	[0]	2	0	0
3	[0]	2	1	0	0
5	12	6	5	[0]	0
[0]	10	1	3	0	0
2	7	5	[0]	0	0
6	11	7	4	0	[0]

(a)   (b)

Figure 5-11

Clearly row subtraction will make no difference but column subtraction produces the result shown in Fig. 5-11(b). There appears at first glance to be an alternative solution in which Person C is assigned to D_2 and Person F is assigned to D_1. But of course the 'real' assignments are unchanged. Thus there is only one solution involving the real jobs. Careful inspection of the cost data shows that C and F could have been ruled out of consideration *a priori*. Each has higher 'costs' than all of A, B, D, and E on every job and so could not be assigned to a real job in any optimal solution. Thus the C and F rows could have been ruled out to start with as *dominated* rows and the problem size thus reduced in this case.

In general, assignment problems can be made square by the addition of dummy rows or columns as necessary. Where a 'real' to 'dummy' assignment is prohibited a cost figure of M can be used instead of zero. By this means, the reader may verify that, if it was required that Person 3 be assigned a job, the minimum cost of this provision would be £5.

A number of other special provisions can be met by altering the dimensions of the effectiveness matrix. For example, suppose that there are four jobs and four people but that only three of the four jobs need carrying out. Effectiveness data would be:

		Jobs			
		1	2	3	4
	A	13	15	11	14
	B	12	7	13	13
People	C	9	17	12	15
	D	11	14	16	12

A dummy row is first added to the matrix, so that the jobs assigned to this row will not be carried out.

Similarly, and in order to 'square up' the matrix, a dummy column is added. The operative assigned to this column is not allocated a real task. Finally, it is necessary to prohibit a 'dummy-to-dummy' allocation with a penal M cost. The resulting modified matrix is:

$$
\begin{array}{ccccc}
13 & 15 & 11 & 14 & 0 \\
12 & 7 & 13 & 13 & 0 \\
9 & 17 & 12 & 15 & 0 \\
11 & 14 & 16 & 12 & 0 \\
0 & 0 & 0 & 0 & M
\end{array}
$$

The reader may confirm that the Hungarian method produces the following result:

2	4	☐0	3	0
5	☐0	6	6	4
0	8	3	6	2
0	3	5	1	☐0
0	0	0	☐0	$M+11$

The optimal value of the objective function is 27 with Person D having no task allocated and Job 4 not done. Suppose now that it is possible for one person to do *two* jobs. Strictly speaking, the problem is no longer an assignment problem, since not all of the rim conditions are unity, but the assignment format can be retained by repeating the row concerned and then re-squaring the matrix with a dummy column. Thus, with the data of the previous example, if Person C could do two jobs, the modified matrix would be:

A	13	15	11	14	0
B	12	7	13	13	0
C	9	17	12	15	0
D	11	14	16	12	0
C	9	17	12	15	0

Column subtraction produces:

4	8	☐0	2	0
3	☐0	2	1	0
0	10	1	3	0
2	7	5	☐0	0
0	10	1	3	☐0

in which it is evident that Person C is not called upon twice.

Finally consider the case of a requirement that a task is performed by a particular operative (or a contract awarded to a particular bidder). In the context of the data above, suppose that Person B must be allocated Job 3. The problem is solved by making this allocation first, removing the second row and the third column from the matrix and solving the remaining 3 row 3 column problem.

The 3×3 problem is:

	1	2	4
A	13	15	14
C	9	17	15
D	11	14	12

Row and column subtraction produces:

0	0	0
0	6	5
0	1	0

Thus A is allocated 2, C gets 1 and D gets 4. The cost of the solution is 49 overall. This contrasts with an optimal cost of 39 (as the reader may confirm) without the special provision. Thus the cost of the requirement is 10.

In this section we have seen that it is possible to meet special provisions while retaining the assignment format. Other provisions could be met too. The three main tools at our disposal—as with transportation problems generally—are the addition of dummy rows and columns, M cost prohibitions and legitimate adjustment of objective function coefficients, for instance when a maximization problem is converted to minimization. We now turn to the subject of sensitivity analysis in assignment problems.

5-6 SENSITIVITY ANALYSIS

The principal scope for sensitivity analysis in assignment problems is on the objective function coefficients—the elements of the effectiveness matrix. As regards the other parameters of the problem, minor alterations in the rim conditions—such as one person being able to do two jobs—can, as we have seen, be dealt with by repeating the row and adding in a dummy column to square up the matrix. The problem is then solved and the effect on the objective function obtained. Substantial alteration to the rim conditions would best be dealt with by re-expression of the problem as a transportation problem. There is, however, the special case where the rim conditions, although not unity, are all the same value, K. The optimal solution will be to assign K units instead of one to the locations where assignments would have been made had rim conditions been unity.

The technical coefficients (the coefficients of the x's in the constraints when formulated algebraically) are fixed at zero or one as in transportation problems. Any changes here would render the problem no longer an assignment problem.

Sensitivity analysis in the assignment framework therefore concentrates on the elements of the effectiveness matrix, which are the coefficients in the objective function. Equal proportionate changes in all entries leave the optimum unchanged—as in any LP problem. Addition of a constant throughout any row or column also makes no difference to the position of the optimal assignments, but we must be careful to note that equi-proportionate changes throughout a row or column *can* make a difference unless all rows and columns are similarly affected. This is illustrated with the example:

$$\boxed{1} \quad 0.1 \qquad \text{which becomes} \qquad 1 \quad \boxed{1}$$

$$2 \quad \boxed{1} \qquad\qquad\qquad\qquad\qquad \boxed{2} \quad 10$$

when the second column alone is proportionately increased by a factor of 10. In terms of changes to individual effectiveness entries increasing the cost of a non-assignment square or reducing the cost in an assignment square cannot alter the optimal pattern. This is a stronger result than in transportation or LP, and it can be said because in the assignment context there is no scope for altering the *level* of an assignment: it is either present or absent.

Reducing non-assignment costs or increasing costs at assignment squares *can*, of course, force the solution to change. Consider the following example. For the effectiveness matrix:

$$\begin{array}{ccc} 4 & 7 & 17 \\ 8 & 12 & 20 \\ 5 & 5 & 8 \end{array}$$

determine tolerance intervals for the costs at square 3,1 and square 1, 2.

First solve the problem with the original data. The Hungarian method produces the result shown in Fig. 5-12. The minimum cost overall is 23 and we

$$\begin{array}{ccc} 0 & \boxed{0} & 7 \\ \boxed{0} & 1 & 6 \\ 3 & 0 & \boxed{0} \end{array}$$

Figure 5-12

note that square 1, 2 is an assignment square whereas square 3, 1 is not. Consider the cost at square 3, 1. Call this C_{31}. To what level must C_{31} fall before there is an equally good solution involving this square? The simplest way to answer this question is to find the cost of the best solution that *does* involve square 3, 1. This will be C_{31} *plus* the best that can be done with the costs remaining outside of row 3 and column 1. This latter figure is 27 with assignments as shown below:

$$\boxed{7} \quad 17$$

$$12 \quad \boxed{20}$$

The cost of the best solution involving square 3,1 is then $C_{31} + 27$ and there can only be an optimal solution involving square 3,1 when:

$$C_{31} + 27 \leqslant 23$$

So that:

$$C_{31} \leqslant -4$$

So C_{31} would have to be reduced by *nine* units from its original value for the square to be involved in an equally good solution to the original optimum. This is not a conclusion that could readily have been deduced from the opportunity cost matrix of Fig. 5-12. While there is a technical means of obtaining the information from an opportunity cost matrix (which we shall not set out here) the individual opportunity cost figure in square 3,1 is no more than a lower bound on the necessary change in C_{31}.

Now consider square 1, 2. Call the cost here C_{12}. To what level must C_{12} rise before there is an equally good solution that does not involve square 1, 2? This will determine the upper limit for C_{12}. The best solution that does not involve a particular square can be found by putting an M cost figure in that position. With M replacing the original cost of 7, the Hungarian method produces the opportunity cost matrix shown in Fig. 5-13. The cost of the solution is 24, just one unit above the original optimum.

$$\boxed{0} \quad M-8 \quad 6$$

$$0 \quad \boxed{0} \quad 5$$

$$4 \quad 0 \quad \boxed{0}$$

Figure 5-13

Consequently a rise of more than one unit in C_{12} would render the original solution non-optimal. Thus the upper bound on C_{12} is 8.

In summary the tolerance intervals such that the original solution remains optimal are:

$$-4 \leqslant C_{31} \leqslant +\infty$$

$$-\infty \leqslant C_{12} \leqslant 8$$

EXERCISES

5-1 Revision exercise

(i) Explain why assignment problems are a special category of transportation problem and give examples of business problems that have an assignment structure.

(ii) Set out the broad logic of the solution procedure for assignment problems. What are the two main underlying principles?

(iii) Detail the 14 steps of the Hungarian or reduced matrix method and explain how this can be applied to maximization problems.

(iv) Explain how problems with unequal numbers of rows and columns and with prohibited assignments can be dealt with.

(v) What scope is there for sensitivity analysis in assignment problems?

5-2 Find the least cost complete assignment for the following effectiveness data:

3	5	10	15	8
4	7	15	18	8
8	12	20	20	12
5	5	8	10	6
10	10	15	25	10

5-3 A local authority has six contracts to be allocated to six firms that have submitted tenders. Each firm will be awarded exactly one contract. Details of the tenders submitted (in units of £10 000) are:

		Contract					
		1	2	3	4	5	6
	A	7	7	3	6	10	11
	B	8	9	No bid	5	8	10
Firm	C	9	10	11	13	13	8
	D	6	6	8	No bid	12	13
	E	5	5	9	10	10	12
	F	8	4	10	12	9	No bid

Which contract should go to each firm in order to minimize cost overall?

5-4 A time study is conducted on the performance of four jobs by four men. Expressed in terms of departures from a standard time allowance for each job the results were:

		Jobs			
		1	2	3	4
	1	9	4	15	2
	2	4	−1	10	−3
People	3	3	−2	9	−4
	4	7	2	13	0

Comment on the results.

5-5 A company presently operates five plants each of which makes a single product. Recently one of the products has become unprofitable and is being dropped from the range. The firm wishes to maintain its one-product-per-plant policy and has now to decide which plant is to be closed. The revenues (in £0000's) from the sale of each of the products (regardless of plant) are:

		Revenue
	1	80
Product no.	2	90
	3	100
	4	85

Production costs however, *do* vary between plants. The cost data (also in £0000's) are:

		Product			
		1	2	3	4
	1	71	78	93	76
	2	69	78	87	74
Plant	3	72	80	89	76
	4	73	80	86	78
	5	65	84	92	72

Closure costs are the same for each plant. Advise the firm on which plant to shut down.

5-6 Determine the optimal solution for the assignment problem below and carry out a sensitivity analysis on each of the elements of the effectiveness matrix.

30	25	22
24	19	27
21	28	23

Solution guides

5-2 The unique optimal assignment pattern is shown below with one version of the opportunity cost matrix. If you have the same assignment pattern but differing opportunity cost elements, cost out a few alternative complete solutions as a check.

1	0	[0]	3	2
0	[0]	3	4	0
[0]	1	4	2	0
5	2	0	[0]	2
4	1	1	9	[0]

5-3 The solution here is non-unique but all optimal cost 36. One optimal arrangement, with one version of the opportunity cost matrix, is shown below:

6	6	[0]	3	4	8
5	6	$M-5$	[0]	0	5
3	4	3	5	2	[0]
[0]	0	0	$M-8$	1	5
0	0	2	3	[0]	5
4	[0]	4	6	0	$M-6$

5-4 All 24 possible arrangements are optimal. All cost 17. The opportunity cost matrix is unique and consists entirely of zeros. In the original effectiveness matrix the rows can be made the same by addition of suitable constants throughout three of the rows (e.g, add 5 throughout the second row, 6 to the third, and 2 to the fourth). A similar result could be obtained for the columns.

5-5 A 'dummy' fifth product is needed to balance up the problem. This is added in; the profit data are shown below. Applying the maximization process it is soon evident that plant (3) should be closed (it gets assigned the dummy product in the unique optimum).

9	12	7	9	0
11	12	13	11	0
8	10	11	9	0
7	10	14	7	0
15	6	8	13	0

5-6 The optimal solution below follows immediately from row subtraction:

8	3	[0]
5	[0]	8
[0]	7	2

For the sensitivity analysis consider first the non-assignment squares. The best solution involving square 1,1 costs 10 more than the optimum (as can be seen from the opportunity cost matrix above) thus C_{11} could fall by up to 10 units and the original solution would remain optimal. Similarly for C_{12}, the best solution with an assignment in square 1,2 costs 72 which is 10 more than the optimum thus C_{12} could fall by up to 10 units.

For the assignment squares 1,3, 2,2, and 3,1 in each case we must find the best solution that does *not* include the square under consideration. For example, in the case of square 1,3, the best solutions without this square cost 10 more so that C_{13} could rise by up to 10 units without affecting optimality.

The tolerance intervals in full are:

$$C_{11} \geqslant 20, \quad C_{12} \geqslant 15, \quad C_{21} \geqslant 14, \quad C_{23} \geqslant 16, \quad C_{32} \geqslant 16,$$

$$C_{33} \geqslant 13, \quad C_{13} \leqslant 32, \quad C_{22} \leqslant 29, \quad C_{31} \leqslant 31$$

REFERENCE

Sasieni, M., Yaspan, A., and Friedman, L. (1959), *Operations Research, Methods and Problems*, Wiley.

FURTHER READING

Cook, T. M., and Russell, R. A. (1981), *Introduction to Management Science*, second edition Prentice-Hall. Contains a description of the Hungarian method in a contract-bid context.
Dantzig, G. B. (1963), *Linear Programming and Extensions*, Princeton University Press. Classic description of the assignment problem in a classic text.

SIX

INVESTMENT APPRAISAL

6-1 INTRODUCTION

Investment may take the form of plant and equipment, buildings, land, shares, deposits at banks, takeovers of other firms, extension of credit, changes in stock levels, and so on. All investments require money to be laid out at one or more points in time and generate income at other times—usually later on. Investment activity affects the *cash flow* of the firm or individual making the investment—the size and timing of cash inflows and outflows caused by the investment needs to be evaluated and the notion of *discounting*—weighting cash flow items according to timing and the rate of interest—is central to all modern methods of investment appraisal.

Many operational research problems will have an investment dimension if they require outlays to be made and significantly affect cash flows. Decisions to produce a new product, alter stock levels, reduce queueing times by re-designing the service area, expanding a distribution point, replacing obsolete equipment would all produce cash flow changes over time that would need to be taken into account.

The methods of investment appraisal described in this chapter are known as discounted cash flow (DCF) methods or present value methods. Chapter Thirteen shows how simulation methods can be applied to problems of capital investment appraisal under conditions of risk.

DCF methods as a whole are based upon the principles of *compound interest* which underlie the methods of discounting and it is with this topic that we shall begin.

6-2 COMPOUND INTEREST

The most familiar example of compound interest is that of the bank deposit account. If interest is paid annually at 10 per cent then £1 deposited at the start of the year will have produced £1.10 by the year's end. If this entire sum is left on deposit then all the £1.10 earns interest in the second year. Interest in the second year is paid not only on the *principal sum* but on the first year's interest also. Second year's interest is 10 per cent of £1.10, that is £0.11, so that the total sum in the account after two years is £1.21. The 'pound's progress' is shown in Fig. 6-1. After n years the original £1 would have become $£(1+0.1)^n$ at 10 per cent interest. Generalizing we can see that £1 invested for n years at $100r$ per cent would have become $£(1+r)^n$. Table 1 (page 485) gives these compound amounts or *terminal values* for various values of r and n. Thus £1 invested at 10 per cent for seven years would become £1.9487 while £1 invested for fifteen years at 25 per cent would grow to £28.4217.

Year 0	Year 1	Year 2	Year 3
1	$\rightarrow\quad 1+0.1\times1$		
	$=1.1$	$\rightarrow\quad 1.1+0.1\times1.1$	
		$=1.1(1+0.1)$	
		$=(1+0.1)^2$	
		$=1.21$	$\rightarrow\quad 1.21+0.1\times1.21$
			$=1.21(1+0.1)$
			$=(1+0.1)^3$
			$=1.331\qquad\rightarrow$

Figure 6-1

Study of Table 1 reveals the substantial consequences of quite small changes in interest rates when long periods of time are involved. Thus at 20 per cent, £1 would become £38.3376 after twenty years. But at 21 per cent the original £1 would have produced £45.2593 after 20 years. Thus a 5 per cent increase in the rate of interest, which has risen one *percentage point* from 20 to 21, has produced a much larger proportional increase in the end result—over 18 per cent.

If the horizon date changes when large rates of interest are applied, there will be substantial changes in the terminal sum. For example at 30 per cent one pound becomes £190 after 20 years or £705 after 25 years. This highlights future dangers in debt rescheduling under high rates of interest.

To find out to how much a principal sum other than £1 would accumulate after a given number of years at a stipulated interest rate, simply look up the number in Table 1 for appropriate values of r and n and multiply it by the sum involved. Consider two examples.

Problem 1

Find the future value of £75 invested for twelve years at 8 per cent.

Answer

For $r=0.08$ and $n=12$ the compound interest factor given in Table 1 is 2.5182. Thus the original £75 would accumulate to £75(2.5182)=£188.87.

Questions of this kind can be posed the other way around.

Problem 2

How much would have to be invested originally in order to produce £250 after sixteen years at fourteen per cent?

Answer

For $r=0.14$ and $n=16$ the compound interest factor is 8.1372, so if the initial sum invested is £S then £S(8.1372)=£250.

$$S=\frac{250}{8.1372}=30.72$$

6-3 DISCOUNTING AND PRESENT VALUES

In compound interest calculations it is frequently necessary to find what amount must be set aside at present to produce £1 at a later date. This sum is called the *present value* of £1 and of course depends upon the number of years and rate of interest involved. The relationship is:

$$PV=\frac{1}{(1+r)^n}$$

For if this sum, PV, is invested now its future value after n years compound interest at $100r$ per cent will be $PV(1+r)^n=1$. Table 2 (page 486) gives these present value of *discount factors* for various values of r and n. Thus, for instance, £1 due after sixteen years at 14 per cent has a present value of £0.1229 and £250 due at this time has a present value of $250 \times 0.1229 = £30.72$. Of course 0.1229 is the reciprocal of 8.1372. All the entries in this table are the reciprocals of the corresponding entries in Table 1.

The present value of a stream of receipts (or payments) can be found by summing the present values of the individual components. Thus if receipts of £100, £150 and £200 are to occur at the end of each of three consecutive years then the present value of this income stream at 10 per cent interest will be

$$PV = \frac{100}{(1+0.1)} + \frac{150}{(1+0.1)^2} + \frac{200}{(1+0.1)^3}$$

Or, more conveniently using the discount factor table:

$$PV = 100 \times 0.9091 + 150 \times 0.8264 + 200 \times 0.7513$$

$$= 364.93$$

Now consider two further examples:

Problem 1

Find the present value of £450 to be received four years from now at an interest rate of 8 per cent.

Answer

The discount factor given by Table 2 for $r=0.08$ and $n=4$ is 0.7350. Thus the present value is given by

$$£450(0.7350) = £330.75$$

Problem 2

Using a discount rate of 15 per cent find the present value of the cash flow

$t=0$	$t=1$	$t=2$	$t=3$
-600	750	-150	1050

Answer

A convenient layout for the workings is:

Year	Sum	Discount factor	PV
0	-600	1	-600
1	750	0.8696	652.20
2	-150	0.7561	-113.42
3	1050	0.6575	690.38

Total PV $= 629.16$

Note that in the stream of returns the 'return' of -600 which would be the *initial outlay* of 600 on the project has an associated discount factor of unity. Being assigned Year zero it is assumed payable at once and so is its own present value. The loss of 150 in the second year might be caused by a cyclical recession in the market, the entry of a competitor or overhaul of equipment. The figure 629.16 is the *net present value*.

6-4 NET PRESENT VALUE DECISION RULE

Investment projects typically generate a series of returns, and in general the returns to a hypothetical project might be labelled S_t where the t subscript gives the timing of the return. So, if there are n returns in all, they could be written out in full as $S_1, S_2, S_3, S_4, \ldots$, where S_1 is the return after one year, S_2 the return after two years and so on.

We shall think of the returns as accruing at equally spaced intervals of time and being the change in the cash flows in various years that are attributed to a particular investment. Thus the present value of the entire n year stream is:

$$\text{Present value} = \frac{S_1}{(1+r)} + \frac{S_2}{(1+r)^2} + \frac{S_3}{(1+r)^3} +$$

$$+ \frac{S_4}{(1+r)^4} + \cdots + \frac{S_n}{(1+r)^n}$$

This can be written more concisely in summation or 'sigma' notation as:

$$\text{Present value} = \sum_{t=1}^{n} S_t(1+r)^{-t} \tag{6-1}$$

The symbol Σ is read as 'sigma' and tells us to sum all terms which follow it (the general form of this terms being $S_t(1+r)^{-t}$) over the range of values t from $t=1$ up to and including $t=n$.

The terms S_t might not all be positive. In order to secure the returns it will usually have been necessary to invest money in one or more years. If an investment of £K now is required to secure the returns S_t then 6-1 is said to be the *gross present value* (GPV) of the investment, and the GPV minus K (the initial outlay) gives the *net present value* (NPV), that is:

$$\text{NPV} = \sum_{t=1}^{n} S_t(1+r)^{-t} - K \tag{6-2}$$

In relation to an individual investment opportunity the single project *NPV decision rule* is as follows:

Invest in the project if the NPV is positive.

Do not invest if the NPV is negative.

In tabular form the NPV decision rule is:

Outcome	Decision
NPV > 0	Accept
NPV < 0	Reject
NPV = 0	Indeterminate

If NPV = 0 it makes no difference to the investor, so far as present value is concerned, whether the project is accepted or rejected. The rationale is that if for a particular investment NPV is positive this must mean that GPV > K. GPV is the present value of the returns—it is a sum of money which if received now is equivalent to all the returns in the sense that if it was invested at $100r$ per cent it would just generate the said stream, i.e. an amount S_t could be withdrawn from the investment of GPV in the tth year. £K is that sum of money which has to be parted with now in order to secure the returns. Thus if GPV > K and therefore NPV > 0 this means that the present value of the stream of returns exceeds the present value of the money required to secure them. If on the other hand GPV < K then the outlay required at the present moment exceeds the present value of the returns that it is expected to generate. Consequently the proposed investment should be rejected. The objective of the exercise is to *compare like with like* and this is achieved with present values. GPV is a single figure equivalent of the stream of returns.

To illustrate the use of the NPV decision rule, consider the following problem.

Problem

A company has the opportunity to purchase a machine at the price of £2200. It will have a productive lifetime of three years and the net additions to cash flows (after tax and including scrap value at the end of the third year) at the end of each of three years are respectively £770, £968 and £1331. The company has sufficient funds to buy the machine without recourse to borrowing, and the best alternative is investment elsewhere at an annually compounded interest rate of 10 per cent. Should the machine be bought?

Answer

The NPV of the investment is:

$$\frac{770}{1.1} + \frac{968}{(1.1)^2} + \frac{1331}{(1.1)^3} - 2200 = 300$$

So by the NPV rule the investment should be accepted.

The tabular layout for the workings can frequently prove to be most convenient:

Year	Sum	Discount factor	PV
0	-2200	1	-2200
1	770	0.9091	700
2	968	0.8264	800
3	1331	0.7513	1000
			NPV $= +300$

The discount rate is important to the NPV decision rule. For example, if the discount rate employed to evaluate the investment in the machine in Problem 5 had been 20 per cent ($r = 0.2$) instead of 10 per cent ($r = 0.1$), then the NPV of the project would have been negative. The workings would be:

Year	Sum	Discount factor	PV
0	-2200	1	-2200
1	770	0.8333	641.64
2	968	0.6944	672.18
3	1331	0.5787	770.25
			NPV $= -115.93$

In this case the project should be rejected. Note that, although the investment in the machine is profitable in an accounting sense, the undiscounted sum of the returns that it would generate exceeds the cost of the machine—*it is not profitable enough* when interest is taken into consideration. In some circumstances *net terminal value* (NTV), or as it is sometimes called net future value, is a more convenient yardstick for projects than NPV. Both measures give the same accept or reject decision for a project if the same interest rate is used for both calculations. NTV is that sum of money that the investor will have at the conclusion of the investment over and above the amount that would have been obtained had the project not been undertaken. NTV is thus the *end-of-project excess* created by the investment. Where a single rate of interest prevails throughout $NTV = NPV(1 + r)^n$.

6-5 YIELD

The yield of a project, known also as the internal rate of return (IRR), or DCF (discounted cash flow) rate of return, or simply rate of return, is defined as that discount rate for which the NPV of a project would be zero. Yield is $100i$ per cent where i is given by:

$$\sum_{t=1}^{n} S_t(1+i)^{-t} - K = 0$$

The yield is the maximum interest rate that the investor could afford to pay calculated in the declining balance manner (as in overdrafts). The returns to the investment, paid in as they occur, would just suffice to eliminate all liability. The overdraft interest rate, in such a case, would represent the *cost of capital* to the investor. In general, ascertaining the appropriate cost of capital figure can be a complex task.

If a yield-based approach to project evaluation is adopted, the yield, when calculated, is compared with a predetermined comparison, a threshold or 'hurdle' rate which will usually be the cost of capital. The *single project yield decision rule* is:

> If the yield of the project exceeds the comparison rate (cost of capital) then undertake the investment. If the yield is less than the comparison rate reject the investment.

In tabular form the yield rule can be expressed as follows (with comparison rate 100 per cent):

Outcome	Decision
$i > r$	Accept
$i < r$	Reject
$i = r$	Indeterminate

The yield of a project is found by the following numerical method.

Consider the project $(-2200, 770, 968, 1331)$ and graph the NPV of this investment against the rate used to discount the returns. As this rate rises the NPV of a project with all positive returns will fall. This relationship is shown in Fig. 6-2.

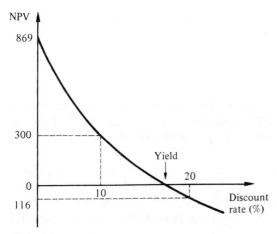

Figure 6-2

The point where the NPV graph crosses the horizontal axis is the yield figure. At a discount rate of 0 per cent the NPV is the difference between the sum of the undiscounted returns and the outlay: 869. At 10 per cent we saw that the NPV was +300 and at 20 per cent it was −116. Zero NPV is thus at a rate of discount between 10 per cent and 20 per cent, but we can be more accurate than this if by a process of trial and error we first determine the whole number rates of discount either side of the yield and then *interpolate* between these values. The workings are:

Sum	15% Discount factor	PV	16% Discount factor	PV	17% Discount factor	PV
−2200	1	−2200	1	−2200	1	−2200
770	0.8696	669.59	0.8621	663.82	0.8475	652.58
968	0.7561	731.90	0.7432	719.42	0.7305	711.48
1331	0.6575	875.13	0.6407	852.77	0.6244	831.08
		NPV = +76.62		NPV = +36.01		NPV = −4.86

A rate of 15 per cent might be tried to start with, producing an NPV of +76.62. So, since the NPV graph still lies above the horizontal axis, 15 per cent is too low. 16 per cent is then tried which gives NPV = +26.01, still too low. 17 per cent gives NPV = −4.86 from which it is clear that yield is between 16 per cent and 17 per cent but considerably nearer to the higher figure. NPV has fallen by 40.87 over a 1 per cent interval. The fall required to give zero was 36.01. Linear interpolation thus estimates the yield as:

$$\left(16 + \frac{36.01}{40.87}\right)\% = 16.9\%$$

The results of linear interpolation are normally accurate to the first decimal place—more than sufficient precision for practical purposes.

6-6 PROJECT RANKING

The yield and NPV rules always give the same decision for a single project, where a choice is to be made between alternative projects, the investments should be ranked by size of NPV, provided that there is no financial constraint.

The problem of choice may be that of (a) selecting all worthwhile projects or (b) choosing from amongst mutually exclusive ones. Using an NPV rule in the former case, all projects with positive NPV are selected and in the latter case the projects with the greater NPVs are preferred. These rules can be stated formally as:

accept all projects with positive NPV. Reject those with negative NPV.

and:

If *m* projects are to be selected from a group of *n*, select those *m* projects which have the greatest NPVs.

Using a yield approach to problem (a) all projects with yields greater than the cost of capital would be worthwhile. But it is *not* correct to select from a group of projects those with the greatest yields: decisions taken in this fashion could conflict wih NPV decisions which can be shown to be formally correct. If management requires presentation of results in terms of yield the NPV rule should be used to determine the choices and the yields of the selected projects can then be stated.

Consider the four projects shown below:

Project	Cash flow			NPV (10%)	NPV (25%)	NPV (30%)	NPV (35%)
A	−100	80	60	22.3	2.4	−3	−7.8
B	−120	40	100	−1.0	−24.0	−30.1	−35.5
C	−60	40	50	17.7	4.0	0.4	−2.9
D	−30	30	20	13.8	6.8	4.9	3.2

With a discount rate of 10 per cent, A, C, and D would be accepted and B rejected. If two projects only were to be chosen, these would be A and C. At 25 per cent, the same projects are worthwhile but only if two projects were required, these would not be C and D.

The fact that the decision is different at 25 per cent from that at 10 per cent does not discredit the NPV approach since conditions have changed. The changed cost of capital affects different projects to different degrees. In general, projects with their greater returns in the more distant future will be affected more by a rise in the cost of capital than projects with the larger returns near to the starts of the projects.

Let us now narrow the choice problem down to a straight fight between Projects A and C (this is the case where $n=2$ and $m=1$).

A and C are now *mutually exclusive*. By this it is meant that one or other project may be undertaken but not both—for example, A might be 'build the warehouse for the Midlands Area in Nottingham' and C 'build the warehouse for the Midlands Area in Leicester', only one warehouse being required. Consequently, if one project is to be chosen from the group comprising A and C then the NPV rule would select A if the discount rate was 10 per cent but would prefer C at 25 per cent. The outcome does depend on the rate of discount that applies. The situation is graphed in Fig. 6-3 where it is seen that A will be preferred to C at any discount rate below 20.7 per cent.

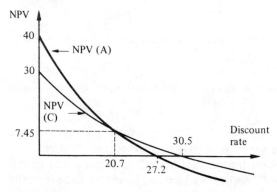

Figure 6-3

6-7 ANNUITIES

An income stream in which the sum received is the same in each year is called an *annuity*. Examples of annuities in business are provided by hire-purchase contracts, leases, consols, endowment policies (neglecting the lump sum) and mortgages (with constant interest rate). Clearly the present value of an annuity could be found as for an irregular income stream, but there is a short cut. Consider an annuity of £100 for four years at 10 per cent interest. Assume that the first payment will be made after one year. Using the discount factor table the present value is:

$$100 \times 0.9091 + 100 \times 0.8264 + 100 \times 0.7513 + 100 \times 0.6830$$
$$= 100(0.9091 + 0.8264 + 0.7513 + 0.6830)$$
$$= 100 \times 3.1699$$
$$= 316.99$$

The significant line of workings above is the second. All that has to be done is to multiply the amount involved, £100, by the sum of the first four discount factors: 3.1699 (the last digit of this sum is nine rather than eight due to the rounding of the discount factors). Table 3 (page 488) is the annuity table and shows the sum of the discount factors up to *n* years. The entries then are the present values of annuities of £1. An annuity where the first payment is made after one year is called an *immediate annuity* and these are the values shown in Table 3.

Where the first payment occurs at once this is called an *annuity due* and the entries of Table 3 must be increased by one to get the present value in this case. Now consider an example.

Problem 1

(i) Find the present value of an immediate annuity of £125 running for six years at 11 per cent
(ii) Use Table 3 to find the present value of 12 per cent of the stream:

Year 1	Year 2	Year 3	Year 4	Year 5	Year 6
1.400	1.400	1.400	600	600	600

Answer

(i) $125 \times 4.2305 = 528.81$
(ii) Note that the cash flow can be considered as the sum of two annuities: an annuity of 600 for six years *plus* an annuity of 800 for three years. Thus present value is:

$$800 \times 2.4018 = 1921.44$$
$$+ 600 \times 4.1114 = 2466.84$$

$$\text{Total PV} = 4388.28$$

A special case of an annuity is where a contract runs indefinitely, there being no end to the payments. This is called a *perpetuity*. Perpetuities are rare phenomena in the private sector, but certain government securities are undated—for instance, consols and war loans. The principal sum on these investments will never be repaid. There is a very simple formula for ascertaining the present value of a perpetuity. This is simply the sum involved divided by the interest rate as a decimal. If the annual sum is £S and the interest rate is $100r$ per cent then:

$$PV = \frac{S}{r}$$

Thus at a 10 per cent rate of interest a perpetuity of £50 has a present value of £500, and if the security is negotiable we might expect it to change hands at around this price. For instance, what should be the price of a unit at $3\frac{1}{2}$ per cent war loan stock if the current market rate of interest for this kind of very low risk security is 12 per cent? War loan is quoted in units of £100 nominal value and the annual interest payment is $3\frac{1}{2}$ per cent of this figure, i.e. £3.50. Assuming for simplicity a single annual payment the price should be PV given by:

$$PV = \frac{3.5}{0.12} = £29.17$$

Most bonds provide a fixed return for a set number of years plus a lump sum (the nominal issue price) in the year that the bond is redeemed. The rate of return on such a security is called the *yield to maturity* or *redemption yield*. The yield to maturity can be found by interpolation using the annuity table (Table 3) and the present value table (Table 2). For instance, consider a security currently priced at £900 (ex interest) which gives an anual interest payment of £100 with a redemption value of £1000 after five years. The cash flow on the investment is then:

$t=0$	$t=1$	$t=2$	$t=3$	$t=4$	$t=5$
-900	100	100	100	100	$100+1000$

and the workings are:

	At 12%	At 13%
Present value of interest	360.48	351.72
Present value of lump sum	567.4	542.8
	927.88	894.52

Thus the yield to maturity is estimated as:

$$\left[12 + \frac{27.88}{33.36} \right]\% = 12.84\%$$

In loan repayment situations the idea of a *sinking fund* is most useful. Table 4 (page 490), the sinking fund table, shows how much must be set aside each year in order to achieve a terminal value of £1. With a 12 per cent rate of interest, £0.0813 would need to be set aside annually in order to give a total of £1 after eight years.

Consider an example. A company has loan stock of £750 000 due to mature in seven years time. The company does not wish to make an issue of fresh stock at this time but rather to pay off the debt. At an interest rate of 10 per cent how much should be set aside annually to meet the liability when it falls due? To give a terminal value of £1 after seven years at 10 per cent £0.1054 must be put aside each year; thus to finish with £750 000 the amount required annually is £750 000 × 0.1054 = £79 050.

In the analysis of certain problems it is helpful to convert a lump sum of a series of equal payments over time (i.e. an annuity) with the same present value. Thus a lump sum of £1 is equivalent to an immediate annuity for two years at 10 per cent of £0.5762. Table 5 (page 492), the *annual equivalent annuity* table, shows the size of annuity required to give a present value of £1 for various rates of interest and numbers of years.

To illustrate the use of the table suppose that the capital cost of a machine tool is £25 000 and that the expected life of the equipment is ten years. At an interest rate of 8 per cent the lump sum is equivalent, in present value terms, to an anual charge of £25 000 × 0.1490 = £3725. The figure of £3725 could be compared with an annual charge resulting from alternative financing arrangements.

Consider an exercise in the conversion of cash flow to annuity form.

Problem 2

Using Tables 2 and 5 find the annual equivalent annuity for two years at 10% for a project which produces the cash flow:

$$
\begin{array}{ccc}
t=0 & t=1 & t=2 \\
-700 & 650 & 800
\end{array}
$$

Answer

First find the net present value for the project in the usual manner:

Year	Sum	Discount factor	PV
0	−700	1	−700
1	650	0.9091	590.92
2	800	0.8264	661.12

$$NPV = 552.04$$

Second, convert the lump sum NPV to the annual equivalent figure for two years at 10 per cent. This will be £552.04 × 0.5672 = £318.09.

6-8 EQUIPMENT REPLACEMENT

When should an asset be scrapped and with what, if anything, should it be replaced? As an asset ages the operating and maintenance costs are likely to rise and in some cases the quality of output produced may fall causing reduced revenues. However, the longer an asset is kept the more is postponed the capital outlay associated with replacement. In those cases in which a particular item of capital equipment will be replaced by 'financially identical' equipment when it is scrapped, the problem is to determine the optimal interval between the installation of new machinery—the length of replacement cycle.

The data necessary to answer the problem are:

1. A table of residual values of the asset (net of expense of changeover);
2. Capital cost of new asset;

3. Operating costs and maintenance expenses ('O and M');
4. The revenues produced in each period.

With this information to hand, the problem is best solved by use of annual equivalent annuities—the AE method. Suppose that a firm operates one machine of a certain type and that all such machines, both existing asset and replacements, have a maximum life of four years with the specific data:

Time (years) t :	0	1	2	3	4
Initial outlay (£):	10 000				
O and M (£):		3000	4000	5000	6000
Residual value (£):		6000	4500	3000	1000

The cost of capital is 10 per cent and the objective is to choose the length of replacement cycle which minimizes the present value of costs.

First compute the total present values of costs (some will be negative) associated with keeping the first machine for different lengths of time. The workings are:

$t =$	1 yr	2 yrs	3 yrs	4 yrs
0	10 000	10 000	10 000	10 000
1	−3 000	3 000	3 000	3 000
2		− 500	4 000	4 000
3			2 000	5 000
4				5 000
PV at 10%	7 272.72	12 314.05	17 535.69	23 204.70

The 1 yr column contains the cash flows associated with keeping the initial asset for just one year. Thus an outlay of £10 000 is required at $t = 0$, but at $t = 1$ the machine is scrapped for £6000 and only incurs O and M costs of £3000. Thus the net figure for costs is −£3000. Similarly in the 2 yr column at $t = 2$, O and M costs are in this case £4000, but scrapping at this point produces £4500, a net inflow of £500, i.e. a 'cost' of −£500. Other entries are similarly determined and the present values of each cash flow calculated.

Each of the numbers in the last row covers the firm for a different period. In the case where the machine is retained for just one year a new machine will be required at $t = 1$ which will again (if kept for one year) produce a stream of costs which will give a present value at $t = 1$ of 7272.72. One way of comparing these different length cycles is to find that constant annual sum (the annual equivalent annuity) which would give a present value at $t = 0$ equal to indefinitely repeated cycles of the given lengths. For instance, in the case of a cycle length of one year a payment of £8000 at $t = 1$ would give a PV of 7272.72. This is found by multiplying 7272.72 by the AE factor for one year at 10 per cent in Table 5.

In the case of the two year cycle length, the annual equivalent annuity for two years at 10 per cent that would produce a PV of 12 314.05 is 7095.24. The full results of converting the cycle present values to an equivalent basis for comparison—the AE annuities—are:

Cycle length (yrs)	PV of one cycle	AE factor	AE annuity
1	7 272.72	1.1000	8000.00
2	12 314.05	0.5762	7095.36
3	17 535.69	0.4021	7051.10
4	23 204.70	0.3155	7321.08

Thus a three year cycle length is optimal; each machine is scrapped and replaced by a financially identical machine after three years. Over an infinite horizon, the total present value of costs under this alternative will be £70 511; the lowest figure that can be achieved.

Frequently, the problem that arises in practice is when to replace existing equipment with a superior design. We need to determine the most cost effective point to break into the cycle for the existing type of equipment and introduce an optimal cycle with new machinery. Consider an example.

A firm's existing machine of an old design has O and M costs and scrap value as follows:

Time (years) $t = $:	0	1	2	3
O and M (£) :	0	3600	4800	6000
Residual value (£):	3500	2000	1000	0

The column headed 0 means that if the old machine was scrapped at once there would be no O and M costs associated with it and that a scrap value of £3500 could be realized. If scrapping occurred after one year there would be a single net outflow of £1600 at $t = 1$.

The old machine can be scrapped at any of the four values of t and replaced permanently by machines with the cost structure of the preceding example for which we have seen that a three year replacement cycle is optimal. The total present value of costs for the new machines was £70 511 *from the date of introduction of these machines.* Thus if the new cycle was brought in at $t = 2$ (i.e. scrapping the old machine at this time) the present value of costs on the new machines at $t = 0$ would be £70 511 × 0.8264 = £58 270. The whole picture is presented in Fig. 6-4. Thus the optimal policy is to keep the old machine for two years and then replace with the three year cycle on the new machines. The figure 64 683 is obtained thus: 3600 × 0.9091 + (3800 + 70 511) × 0.8264, the other figures in the present value column being obtained in similar fashion. It is

Replace at:	Cashflow $t=$				Total present value
	0	1	2	3	
$t=0$	−3,500 70,511				67.011
$t=1$	0	1.600 70.511			65.556
$t=2$	0	3.600	3.800 70.511		64.683
$t=3$	0	3.600	4.800	6.000 70.511	64.722

Figure 6-4

evident that there is little practical difference between the two year and three year options—just £39 in present value terms.

The AE approach can be extended to deal with anticipated inflation at a uniform rate (see Wilkes 1983).

When machines are not financially identical and where the costs over time do not vary in a systematic fashion then the *finite horizon method* can be used. In this approach a long 'horizon' date is set (20–50 years) and any possible cash flows outside this time are ignored. The best available forecasts of the cash flows are made, and the NPVs are calculated for each possible case. The alternative giving the smallest NPV of costs is then selected.

6-9 CAPITAL RATIONING

Capital rationing arises when there are insufficient funds to finance all projects with positive NPVs. Other resources may be in limited supply too and the problem defined can by solved be linear programming. The use of LP methods to solve such multi-constraint rationing problems is developed in Wilkes (1983). Here we shall consider a method suitable for one constraint problems which frequently arise when budgets are known only for one year. The method will be explained in the context of a numerical example in which the sole constraint relates to initial capital expenditure. The method could equally well be applied to other problems in which the single scarce resource was not finance but floor-space, materials or some other factor of production.

A company's cost of capital is 10 per cent. It has £215 000 for outlay on six investments. The objective is to select that group of investments which maximizes net present value overall. There are no other investment opportunities available. The cash flows from the investments, the net present values at 10 per cent and the yields on the investments are shown in Fig. 6-5.

Year				Investment			
		1	2	3	4	5	6
Year:	0	−25 000	−60 000	−90 000	−100 000	−120 000	−35 000
	1	7 500	17 500	25 000	0	75 000	40 000
	2	7 500	17 500	25 000	0	75 000	0
	3	7 500	17 500	25 000	50 000	0	0
	4	7 500	17 500	25 000	50 000	0	0
	5	7 500	17 500	25 000	50 000	0	0
NPV (10%)		3 431	6 339	4 770	2 759	10 163	1 364
Yield (%)		15.2	14.1	12.1	11.6	16.3	14.3

Figure 6-5

Since all projects have NPV > 0 they are all worthwhile in their own right but insufficient finance is available. Which projects would be selected?

The correct procedure is to rank projects by *ratio of NPV to outlay*. Justification for this method will be given presently. First consider the results:

Project	Ratio	NPV	Outlay	Total expended
1	0.137	3 431	25 000	25 000
2	0.106	6 339	60 000	85 000
5	0.085	10 163	120 000	205 000
1/9 of 3	0.053	530	10 000	215 000
6	0.039			
4	0.028			
		20 463		

A total NPV of £20 463 is achieved. The reader may confirm that if projects were ranked by NPV those selected would be 5, 2 and $\frac{7}{18}$ of 3 giving a total NPV of £18 357. If the projects were ranked by yield, those selected would be 5, 1, 6 and $\frac{7}{12}$ of 2 with a resultant NPV of £18 656.

The ratio method works because the project at the top of the list has the *highest achievement of objective per unit of scarce resource*. Indeed if it was possible to take more than 100 per cent of an investment *only* Project 1 would be accepted. We should then take 8.6 units of Project 1 producing an NPV of £29 507. However, with the 100 per cent limit and Project 1 removed from the scene Project 2 makes best use of the scarce resource. If it was now possible to take several units of this project, the best plan would be to set $x_1 = 1$, $x_2 = 3\frac{1}{6}$ and achieve an NPV of £23 505. The process of working down the ratio list always ensures that the best possible use is made of remaining funds.

We have used the ratio of *net* present value to outlay to rank the projects. Equally well, the ratio of *gross* present value (GPV) to outlay could have been used—the ratio will simply increase by one for each project. The ratio of GPV to outlay is called the *profitability index* (PI) and the next example is expressed in these terms.

Suppose that the group of projects contains a mutually exclusive pair. Can the ratio method still be applied? Some care is necessary here. Consider the following problem.

The following four investment possibilities face a company:

	Outlay (£)	PI
A	1 m	1.4
B	0.1 m	1.45
C	1 m	1.1
D	0.1 m	1.35

The company has 1.1 m available for investment. Projects A and B are mutually exclusive. All projects are divisible. Which group of projects maximizes NPV? What is the NPV figure thus obtained? First note that it would be quite incorrect to eliminate Project A to start with on the grounds that B has the greater PI. If this was done the projects selected would be B, D and 9/10 of C and total NPV achieved would be $100\,000 \times 0.45 + 100\,000 \times 0.35 + 0.9 \times 1\,000\,000 \times 0.1 = 170\,000$. The optimal solution is to take A and D producing an NPV figure of £435 000. When there is a mutually exclusive pair two sub-problems have to be solved—one containing A and the other B.

Sub-problem 1	Sub-problem 2
A	B
C	C
D	D

Sub-problem 1 produces the £435 000 result and sub-problem 2 gives £170 000 as the best answer. The overall solution is the best answer from either sub-problem. In problems where fractional projects are ruled out, a problem in *integer linear programming* is defined. However, it is always desirable to retain as simple a framework as possible. This can often be done by redefining variables, adjusting budget levels or otherwise re-expressing the problem.

6-10 SENSITIVITY ANALYSIS

Data for NPV calculations may be subject to variability. Project returns may have to be estimated several years ahead, rates of interest may change and obsolescence or legislation may truncate project lifetime. Sophisticated techniques exist to take advantage of high quality probabilistic information when this exists (see Wilkes, 1983). More often, the investor may have point estimates of returns, discount rate, outlay, etc., and may simply be aware that considerable uncertainty surrounds these figures. Sensitivity analysis is an approach that is particularly useful in such circumstances.

In *single parameter analysis*, the NPV is first calculated using the original data and then a particular parameter—for instance the discount rate—is singled out and the value found for this parameter that would produce zero NPV. If this latter figure is little different from the original point estimate then we should say that the viability of the project is sensitive to the value of the discount rate. This would point up the desirability of further consideration of the cost of capital problem. The analysis is repeated for some or all of the other parameters and the results are tabulated. It should then be apparent what the critical factors are and where management effort (either in estimation *ex ante* or control *ex post*) should be concentrated.

Consider an example. A manufacturing project requires an initial outlay of £40 000 and would run for six years. Returns, R, result from the sales of a product and it is estimated that sales volume, q, would be 2000 units per year in each of the first two years, 3000 units per year in each of the next two years and 1500 units per year in each of the final years. Selling price, p, is estimated at £20 per unit throughout the lifetime of the project and unit costs, c, are expected to be £15. The appropriate discount rate is estimated to be 10 per cent.

The return on the investment in any year t is given by $R_t = (p - c)q_t$ so that anticipated cash flows over the six-year life are: $-40\,000$, $+10\,000$, $+10\,000$, $+15\,000$, $+15\,000$, $+7500$, $+7500$. At the discount rate of 10 per cent it emerges that GPV = £47 761 and therefore NPV = £7761 so that the project would be worth while if the original estimates obtained. The question to be answered now is: for what range of variation in each of the estimated figures will the NPV of the project remain non-negative?

First consider the unit profit on the product. This is $p - c$ and is currently £5. Any variation in this figure would have equal proportionate effect on each return and hence on GPV as a whole, so that so long as unit profit is not less than (40 000/47 761)(£5) = £4.19 with the other data unchanged NPV will not become negative. Thus with unchanged unit costs, so long as selling price is not less than £19.19, the project will still be viable. In other words pice must not drop by more than 4.05 per cent. On the other hand, if unit costs remain below £15.81 then NPV will be positive, so that any increase must not exceed 5.40 per cent. If unit profits are unchanged but sales are 83.75 per cent = (40 000/47 761)(100) of the original estimates in each year (i.e. do not fall by more than 16.25 per cent) the project is viable.

For the remaining parameters, again considered individually, NPV will become zero for an initial outlay for £47 761, that is 19.40 per cent above the original figure. As regards the discount rate the yield of the project turns out to be 16.75 per cent so that a 65.7 per cent increase over the original value for discount rate is tolerable.

Variation in project lifetime is somewhat more difficult to allow for as some approximating assumption will be necessary if reductions in life involving a fraction of a year are involved. If the project's life was four years, that is if the last two returns of £7500 are ignored, the GPV would be £38 870, a decrease of £8891. To make GPV £40 000 the contribution to present value of returns in the fifth year needs to be £1130.

Suppose that if the project runs for some fraction, f, of the fifth year then the return that arises is 7500f to be received at $t = 4 + f$. Thus if the truncated fifth year is to produce a return giving present value 1130 then f must be such as to satisfy:

$$\frac{7500f}{(1.1)^{4+f}} = 1130$$

or:

$$750f = 113(1.1)^{4+f}$$

Numerical workings are:

f	750f	$113(1.1)^{4+f}$
0.2	150.00	168.63
0.23	172.50	169.11
0.225	168.75	169.03
0.226	169.50	169.05
0.2254	169.05	169.04
0.2253	168.98	169.03

The object is to choose a value of f so as to equate the left- and right-hand sides of the equation. This is accomplished for $f = 0.2254$. Thus the break-even lifetime is 4.2254 years, a reduction of 1.7746 years or 29.58 per cent.

The full results of the one-parameter break-even exercise are shown in Fig. 6.6. Entries in the % change column are the unfavourable change (decreases or increases as the case may be) which, if occurring individually, would reduce NPV to zero. It is evident that the present value of this particular project is much more sensitive to sales price and unit costs than any other datum. What is indicated by this is that management efforts should be concentrated in these areas either before the event in obtaining more precise estimates of the figures, or, if it is decided to go ahead with the project, in controlling any unfavourable variations that may arise.

Sensitivity analysis is a most valuable and flexible method that produces

Datum	% change
Selling price	4.05
Unit cost	5.40
Sales volume	16.25
Initial outlay	19.40
Discount rate	65.70
Project lifetime	29.58

Figure 6-6

tolerance regions for parameters such as unit cost or price—ranges of values consistent with acceptable outcomes for the project. Indeed, when the parameters under study are controllable, the *starting point* may be a target outcome. Working back from this desired result produces the appropriate range of values for the parameter. This procedure is known as *backwards iteration.*

Multiparameter sensitivity analysis considers groups of changes that are thought possible. The problem is to specify how the changes are related—to spell out the structure of the simultaneous changes. If this can be done, the analysis can be applied as before. What *cannot* be made are general statements about the consequences of group changes *regardless* of the functional relationships within the group. This is not a limitation of the method, but merely a statement that it has been provided with insufficient information.

This completes our discussion of sensitivity analysis. Where cash flow data such as returns are variable but with known probability distributions, *simulation* methods can be of value. An illustration of the use of simulation in investment appraisal is given in Chapter Thirteen.

6-11 COMPUTERS AND INVESTMENT APPRAISAL

Discounted cash flow calculations take a form which is particularly well suited to computerization. Even the smaller micro-computers are able to handle quite substantial net present value calculations. For example, a simple program (written in BBC Basic) to compute the net present value of cash flow is as follows:

```
REM BBC Basic program to compute net present value.
REM Set up data-structure with model variables represented by arrays, with 5 elements in each

DIM sales(5): DIM fixedcost(5): DIM totvarcost(5): DIMnetcashin(5)

REM Notice that totvarcost excludes depreciation in NPV formula.
REM now read in data for sales and costs

FOR i=1 to 5
   READ sales(i)
```

```
NEXT i
FOR i = 1 to 5
  READ fixedcost(i)
NEXT i
FOR i = 1 to 5
  READ totvarcost(i)
NEXT i

REM now calculate endogenous variables

FOR i = 1 to 5
  netcashin (i) = sales(i) − fixedcost(i) − totvarcost(i)
NEXT i

REM now calculate NPV
INPUT "Discount Rate"; d
npv = 0
FOR i = 1 to 5
npv = npv + netcashin(i)/(1 + d) ∧ i
NEXT i

REM now print out the result.
PRINT "Net Cashinflow."
FOR i = 1 to 5
  PRINT netcashin(i),
NEXT i
PRINT
PRINT "Net Present Value = "; npv

REM Problem Case Data

DATA 100,200,300,400,500
DATA 50,80,80,100,100
DATA 30,60,90,120,150
```

(Reproduced by permission of Mr J. Morris, University of Birmingham.)

As can be seen from the program the cash flow in each year is assumed to be made up of sales revenue less variable costs less fixed costs. Data is congregated at the end of the program (with specimen values shown). An initial outlay of other than zero can be included by modifying the appropriate line of the program and a horizon of other than five years could be built in too. The value of the discount rate, d, would be input each time the programme is run.

An alternative implementation of the NPV programme can be developed for a tabular data structure (spreadsheet) as for example in a further program by J. Morris in Wilkes and Brayshaw (1986). Computer programs have also been written for sensitivity analysis and simulation in investment appraisal. The yield of an investment can also be computed by program using Newton's method. A computer program for the calculation of payback period is also available. For further details of these and other programmes see Wilkes and Brayshaw (1986).

EXERCISES

6-1 Revision exercise
   (i) Set out the various forms that investment can take and show how operational research in other areas of a firm's activity may have an investment dimension.
   (ii) Outline the basic principles of compound interest and present value.
   (iii) Set out the NPV decision rule for
      (*a*) single projects and
      (*b*) choice between several alternative projects.
   (iv) Explain what is meant by the yield of an investment and the single project yield decision rule.
   (v) Explain the meaning of the following terms: immediate annuity; annuity due; perpetuity; sinking fund; annual equivalent annuity.
   (vi) Show how annual equivalent annuities are used in the equipment replacement decision.
   (vii) What is meant by capital rationing? What is the appropriate criterion in one constraint rationing problems?
   (viii) Show how sensitivity analysis can be used when project data are subject to uncertainty.
   (ix) In what ways can micro-computers be employed in the investment appraisal process?

6-2 Using a 12 per cent rate of discount, determine the NPV of the project:

$t=0$	$t=1$	$t=2$	$t=3$
-400	500	-100	700

6-3 Find the yield of the project:

$t=0$	$t=1$	$t=2$	$t=3$
-1400	600	700	400

6-4 With no restriction on expenditure, and with the following projects available:

	$t=0$	$t=1$	$t=2$
A:	-60	60	40
B:	-120	80	100
C:	-200	160	120

   (i) Which project would be chosen on the basis of NPV at
      (*a*) 10 per cent?
      (*b*) 25 per cent?
   (ii) Which project has the greatest yield?

6-5 Use the relevant formula to find the present value of an immediate annuity of £100 for six years at 10 per cent compound interest.

6-6 What is the present value of a perpetuity of £200 at 4 per cent?

6-7 A security is currently priced at £1200 (ex-interest) and gives an annual interest payment of £150. The security has a redemption value of £1500 five years hence. Estimate the yield to maturity.

6-8 A company has loan stock of £5 000 000 due to mature in nine years time. At an interest rate of 15 per cent how much should be set aside annually in order to meet the liability when it falls due?

6-9 Find the annual equivalent annuity (for 2 years) at 15 per cent of:

$t=0$	$t=1$	$t=2$
1200	350	500

6-10 For a machine with the financial data given below, determine the optimal length of replacement cycle when the appropriate interest rate is 12 per cent:

Time	0	1	2	3	4
Outlay	5000				
Operating costs		1400	1500	1600	1700
Maintenance			300	400	500
Value if scrapped		3400	2000	800	600

6-11 A firm currently operates a machine of dated design which has the following cost and residual value data:

t	Operating expenditure	Maintenance	Residual value
0	0	0	1500
1	2500	500	1000
2	3000	1000	600
3	3500	1500	100
4	4000	1700	0

The machine is to be replaced by one of a new type for which financial data are:

	t_0	t_1	t_2	t_3	t_4
Outlay	7000				
Operating		1800	2200	2600	2800
Maintenance		200	500	900	1200
Residual value		4000	3000	2000	1000

The appropriate interest rate is 8 per cent. At what time should the old type of machine be scrapped?

6-12 A company's cost of capital is 10 per cent. It has £4300 available for outlay on the following investments:

Investment year	1	2	3	4	5
0	−2400	−2000	−1800	−1200	−500
1	1500	0	500	350	150
2	1500	0	500	350	150
3	0	1000	500	350	150
4	0	1000	500	350	150
5	0	1000	500	350	150

No investment may be repeated but a fractional share may be taken in any one. Which group of investments maximize NPV?

6-13 A company is faced by the following five investment opportunities:

Investment no.	Profitability index	Initial outlay
1	1.3	500 000
2	1.4	100 000
3	1.1	400 000
4	1.5	200 000
5	1.6	150 000

The company has 750 000 available for investment. Projects three and four are mutually exclusive. All of the projects are divisible. Which group should be selected in order to maximize net present value? What is the NPV figure that results?

6-14 For an investment project the following tentative initial estimates have been made:

Outlay:	£100 000	*Sales volumes*	
Sales price:	£30	year one	4000 units
Unit cost:	£20	year two	6000 units
Discount rate:	10%p.a.	year three	3000 units
Life	3 years		

The £100 000 purchases equipment which will manufacture a product produced at the above unit cost and selling at the sales price in the volumes indicated.

(a) Calculate the maximum tolerable unfavourable change (as a percentage of the original estimated value) in
  (i) sales price
  (ii) unit cost,
  (iii) sales volume,
  (iv) initial outlay,
  (v) project lifetime.
Comment on the results. Could the sales volumes be treated *separately* in the analysis?

Solution guides

6-2 The net present value will be:

$$-400 + \frac{500}{(1.12)} - \frac{100}{1.12^2} + \frac{700}{(1.12)^3}$$

With an electronic calculator the result emerges at 464.96.
Using the four-figure discount factors given in the textbook the result is:

$$-400 + 500(0.8929) - 100(0.7972) + 700(0.7118) = 464.99$$

The wholly negligible difference in the two results is due to rounding in the table values.

6-3 The undiscounted returns total 1700, well above the 1400 outlay, so try a rate somewhat over 10 per cent to start with—say 12 per cent:

$$\text{NPV at } 12\% = -21.50$$

So 12 per cent is a little too high. Try 11 per cent:

$$\text{NPV at } 11\% = +1.14$$

So 11 per cent is almost correct but just a little too low. By interpolation:

$$\text{Yield} \simeq \left[11 + \frac{1.14}{1.14 + 21.50} \right]\% \quad = 11.05\%$$

For comparison suppose our two guessed interest rates were 10 per cent and 11 per cent. At 10 per cent NPV = +24.46. In this case we could (at the cost of a slightly less accurate approximation) interpolate over a 2 per cent interval. The result would be:

$$\text{Yield} \simeq 10 + 2 \left[\frac{24.46}{24.46 + 21.50} \right]\% \quad = 11.06\%$$

6-4

	NPV (10%)	NPV (25%)
Project A	27.60	13.60
Project B	35.37	8.00
Project C	44.63	4.80

So that at 10 per cent Project C should be selected, while at 25 per cent Project A should be chosen. The yield figures can be obtained by interpolation or by direct solution since only quadratics are involved. Thus, for instance, to find the yield of project A we should solve:

$$60R^2 - 60R - 40 = 0$$

Where the yield figure is $(R - 1)$ 100%.

The resulting yield figures are 45.74 per cent for A, 30.52 per cent for B and 27.18 per cent for C.

6-5 The relevant expression is:

$$\frac{1 - (1 + r)^{-n}}{r}$$

Substituting for $r = 0.1$ and $n = 6$ gives:

$$\frac{1 - (1.1)^{-6}}{0.1} = 4.355\ 26$$

which gives the present value of an annuity of 1 correct to five decimal places. So the required answer is:

$$4.355\ 26(100) = £435.526$$

(The value given by Table 4 is £435.53 which is correct to four decimal places.)

6-6 The present value of a perpetuity of £1 at $100r$ per cent discount is given by:

$$\frac{1}{r}$$

So the required result will be:

$$\frac{200}{0.04} = £5000$$

6-7 Purchase of the security would represent a cash flow as follows:

$t = 0$	$t = 1$	$t = 2$	$t = 3$	$t = 4$	$t = 5$
-1200	150	150	150	150	$(150 + 1500)$

Guessing 15 per cent to start with gives the following present values:

Interest:	150(3.3522) =	502.830
Lump sum:	1500(0.4972) =	745.800
		1248.630

So the yield is greater than 15 per cent. Trying 16 per cent next:

Interest:	150(3.2743) =	491.145
Lump sum:	1500(0.4761) =	714.150
		1205.295

So 16 per cent is a little too low, though it clearly is the 'whole number' part of the result. Trying 17 per cent:

Interest:	150(3.1993) =	479.895
Lump sum:	1500(0.4561) =	684.150
		1164.045

So that by *interpolation*, the yield to maturity will be:

$$\left[16 + \frac{(1205.295 - 1200)}{(1205.295 - 1164.045)} \right]\% = 16.13\%$$

6-8 The relevant formula is that for a *sinking fund*, namely:

$$\frac{r}{(1+r)^n - 1}$$

values for which are given in Table 4. The required answer is:

$$5\,000\,000(0.0596) = 298\,000$$

6-9 Present value at 15 per cent = 1882.41. So annual equivalent annuity is given by 1882.41 (0.6151) = 1157.87.

6-10

Alternative cycle lengths:		1 yr	2 yr	3 yr	4 yr
	$t=0$	5 000	5 000	5 000	5 000
	$t=1$	−2 000	1 400	1 400	1 400
Net	$t=2$		−200	1 800	1 800
cash	$t=3$			1 200	2 000
flow	$t=4$				1 600
NPV(12%)		3 214.29	6 090.56	8 539.09	10 125.34
AE factor		1.12	0.5917	0.4163	0.3929
AE annuity		3 600	3 604	3 555	3 333

Thus a four-year cycle length is indicated since it produces the lowest annual equivalent annuity figure.

6-11 First find the optimal cycle length and total present value of costs for the new type of machine.

Alternative cycle lengths:		1 yr	2 yr	3 yr	4 yr
	$t=0$	7 000	7 000	7 000	7 000
	$t=1$	−2 000	2 000	2 000	2 000
Net	$t=2$		− 300	2 700	2 700
cash	$t=3$			1 500	3 500
flow	$t=4$				3 000
NPV(8%)		5 148.15	8 594.65	12 100.21	16 150.17
AE factor		1.08	0.5608	0.3880	0.3019
AE annuity		5 560	4 820	4 695	4 876

This indicates that a three-year cycle length should be adopted for the new machinery. The 'present' value of all future costs for the new machine *dating from the time of installation* would be the value of a perpetuity of £4695 at 8 per cent. This is £58 688. The costs associated with different possible scrapping dates for the old machine and the 'present' value of costs from the new one are as given below.

Alternative scrapping dates:		$t=0$	$t=1$	$t=2$
	$t=0$	−1 500 + 58 688	0	0
Net	$t=1$		2 000 + 58 688	3 000
costs	$t=2$			3 400 + 58 688

Alternative scrapping dates:		$t=3$	$t=4$
	$t=0$	0	0
Net	$t=1$	3 000	3 000
costs	$t=2$	4 000	4 000
	$t=3$	4 900 + 58 688	5 000
	$t=4$		5 700 + 58 688

Again, using the 8 per cent discount rate, the total present values (at $t=0$) of these costs are:

Scrapping date	NPV costs
$t=0$	57 188
$t=1$	56 193
$t=2$	56 008
$t=3$	56 685
$t=4$	57 503

The optimum date at which to retire the machinery is therefore $t=2$.

6-12 First determine the NPV of each investment. Then obtain the NPV/outlay ratio. The values are:

Investment	1	2	3	4	5
NPV	2603	2092	1895	1327	569
NPV/outlay	1.085	1.046	1.053	1.106	1.138

Now rank the projects by size of NPV/outlay ratio, and work down the list until the budget is exhausted. We have:

	Investment	Ratio	Σoutlay	ΣNPV
	5	1.138	500	569
	4	1.106	1700	1896
	1	1.085	4100	4499
($\frac{1}{9}$ of)	3	1.053	4300	4710

So that the maximum NPV achievable is £4710. Note that if it had been possible to place all the funds in investment 5 (i.e. take 8.6 units instead of one) the achievable NPV would have been £4893.4.

6-13 First of all divide the investments up into two mutually exclusive sets. Set A (containing investment 3) consists of 1, 2, 3 and 5. Set B (which contains investment 4) comprises 1, 2, 4 and 5. Now find the best selection that can be made from each set. Thus for set A we obtain:

Investment	PI	Σoutlay	ΣNPV
5	1.6	150 000	90 000
2	1.4	250 000	190 000
1	1.3	750 000	415 000

where we note that the NPV of any project is found as outlay multiplied by PI minus one. Thus with Set A the best that can be done is a total NPV of 415 000. For Set B we have:

Investment	PI	Σoutlay	ΣNPV
5	1.6	150 000	90 000
4	1.5	350 000	265 000
2	1.4	450 000	445 000
1($\frac{2}{3}$)	1.3	750 000	580 000

Thus Set B provides by far the better result with the selection of 5, 4, 2 and $\frac{2}{3}$ of 1 giving a total NPV of 580 000

6-14 With sales price p, unit cost c, and sales volume v, in any year the return will be R where

$$R = v(p-c)$$

Thus in the first year of the project where $p = 30$, $c = 20$ and $v = 4000$ the return will be 40 000. On the basis of the original estimates the cash flow will be $-100\,000$; 40 000; 60 000; 30 000; so that net present value will be:

$$NPV = -100\,000 + \frac{40\,000}{(1.1)} + \frac{60\,000}{(1.21)} + \frac{30\,000}{(1.331)} = 8490$$

Thus the project is worthwhile. Now if the revenues changed in such a way that gross present value came down from 108 490 to 100 000 the project would break even with zero NPV. Now although the revenues are unequal in the three years they will all be affected in *equal proportion* by a change in v or a change in $(p-c)$. In particular if the value of $p-c$ was halved to 5 then GPV would be halved. Similarly if $p-c$ was replaced by:

$$\frac{100\,000}{108\,490}(p-c)$$

then GPV would be 100 000; giving zero NPV. If c remains constant at 20, then if p was such that the margin was:

$$\frac{100\,000 \times 10}{108\,490}$$

then NPV would be zero. Thus p must be such that the margin is 9.22. The minimum value of p, *ceteris paribus*, is 29.22. This represents a fall of 0.78 or just 2.60 per cent. On the other hand, given $p = 30$ the value of c required to give a margin of 9.22 is 20.78, which would represent a rise of 3.90 per cent.

In respect of sales volume, if each year was affected in the same *proportion* and if all volume figures stood at:

$$\left[\frac{100\,000}{108\,490}\right] 100\%$$

of the original values, then NPV would be zero. Thus the requisite percentage fall in v is:

$$\left[\frac{8490}{108\,490}\right] 100\% = 7.83\%$$

If GPV remains at 108 490 then the initial outlay must not exceed this figure. Obviously this would represent a rise of 8.49%.

In analysing the effects of variation in the project's lifetime we start by considering the present values if the project only ran for *two* years. This would be:

$$\text{NPV (2 years)} = -100\,000 + \frac{40\,000}{(1.1)} + \frac{60\,000}{(1.21)} = -14\,050$$

Thus for viability the project needs to run for such a part (f) of the third year that the present value of the part return is 14 050. So f is given by:

$$\frac{30\,000f}{(1.1)^{2+f}} = 14\,050.$$

A trial and error procedure produced the following results:

f	$\dfrac{30\,000f}{(1.1)^{2+f}}$
0.70	16 235
0.65	15 148
0.60	14 049 ⇐
0.61	14 270

Thus the appropriate value of f is 0.6. So if the project ran for 2.6 years instead of a 3 years then break-even would be achieved. This would represent a reduction in lifetime 13.33 per cent.

The results in total are presented in the following table:

Factor	% variation
Price	2.60
Unit cost	3.90
Sales volume	7.83
Outlay	8.49
Lifetime	13.33

Sales volumes in the individual years could be examined. For instance, assuming that everything is as originally estimated in years 2 and 3, and that sales volume in year 1 is v, then v_1 must be such as to produce zero NPV. Thus:

$$\frac{10v_1}{(1.1)} + \frac{60\,000}{(1.21)} + \frac{30\,000}{(1.331)} = 100\,000$$

This equation solves for $v_1 = 3066$, a reduction of 23.35 per cent. For year 2 the equation is:

$$\frac{40\,000}{(1.1)} + \frac{10v_2}{(1.21)} + \frac{30\,000}{(1.331)} = 100\,000$$

which solves for $v_2 = 4973$, a reduction of 17.12 per cent. Finally, for year 3:

$$\frac{40\,000}{(1.1)} + \frac{60\,000}{(1.21)} + \frac{10v_3}{(1.331)} = 100\,000$$

solves for $v_3 = 1870$, a reduction of 37.67 per cent. It would appear then that the project is most sensitive to sales performance in the second year, and least sensitive in the third year.

REFERENCES

Wilkes, F. M. (1983), *Capital Budgeting Techniques*, second edition, Wiley.
Wilkes, F. M., and Brayshaw, R. E. (1986), *Company Finance and its Management*, Van Nostrand Reinhold.

FURTHER READING

Lumby, S. (1984), *Investment Appraisal*, second edition, Van Nostrand Reinhold. Good basic introduction to all aspects of investment appraisal.
Samuels, J. M., and Wilkes, F. M. (1986), *Management of Company Finance*, fourth edition, Van Nostrand Reinhold. Contains chapters on capital rationing, risk and uncertainty, and portfolio theory.

SEVEN

CRITICAL PATH METHOD

7-1 INTRODUCTION

Critical path method (CPM) is one of the most widely used operational research techniques. Nowadays, this simple procedure is essential to the effective control and management of large projects. Up until the mid-1950s Gantt charts and other bar charts were the principal tools of project planning. Although still useful for 'macro' monitoring, their place in detailed project analysis and control is nowadays occupied by critical path and related methods. The concept of a key sequence of tasks which determine the minimum completion time of a project—the critical path—originated in England around 1955. The principal development of the subject thereafter occurred in the United States. Numerous techniques similar to CPM centring around the idea of a time critical sequence of jobs arose in the late 1950s. Differences between these methods mainly reflected the character of the particular problems they were developed to address. The most widely used of these has been PERT (programme evaluation and review technique) in cases where job times are uncertain.

In the earliest applications of CPM, time was frequently the over-riding consideration, lateness penalties being prohibitive. In most applications nowadays, cost is at least equally important and CPM or PERT can be used to minimize project cost subject to a time constraint.

Before considering CPM itself it will be useful to briefly examine the use of bar charts in project monitoring.

7-2 BAR CHARTS

Sometimes known as Gantt project planning charts, bar charts remain a useful tool for broad brush studies, presentation and highly aggregated 'macro' monitoring of projects. Detailed scheduling, resource utilization and cash flow projection are the domain of CPM.

Consider the example of Fig. 7-1. A project has been divided into eight phases or jobs shown on the vertical axis. On the horizontal axis 'calendar

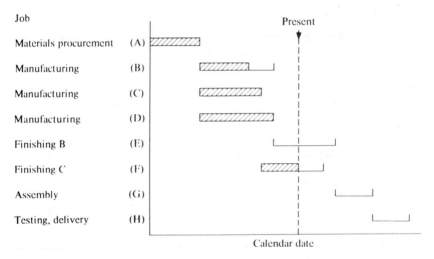

Figure 7-1

time' is used in preference to 'abstract time' ($t = 0$, 1, etc.) since breaks in work such as holidays can more easily be allowed for. The arrow indicates the present. The beginning and end of each bar mark the anticipated starting and finishing date of each task. Shading shows the progress of jobs. Thus A, C, and D have been finished as scheduled while F is on schedule. Job B, however, is running well behind schedule which has caused the start of E to be delayed. This will cause more delays further down the line unless there is some speeding up or rearrangement of schedules.

Requirements for the use of Gantt charts are:

1. Identification of distinct jobs.

2. Job orderings.
3. Job time estimates.
4. Regular reviews.

Benefits to be obtained are:

1. A systematic setting down of the stages of work.
2. Actual progress can be compared with planned progress.
3. Easily understandable.
4. Resources scheduling can be conducted.

The use of Gantt charts in resources scheduling is described in section 7-12. *Control* functions such as resources scheduling are also effectively carried out by CPM. Let us now begin consideration of the critical path method itself.

7-3 THE CRITICAL PATH

Consider the following project. It is a manufacturing and assembly operation as set out in the *dependency table* below.

Job	Job label	Immediate predecessor	Job time (days)
Procure materials	A		30
Manufacture component one	B	A	40
Manufacture component two	C	A	30
Manufacture component three	D	A	35
Finish component one	E	B	25
Finish component two	F	C, D	30
Assemble components	G	E	15
Test and deliver	H	G, F	20

The first column in the dependency table is a literal description of the tasks of which the project is comprised and these *jobs*—sometimes also called *activities*—are identified by alphabetical labels in the second column. The third column 'immediate predecessor' gives the crucial sequencing information. In practice much work will be required to obtain this information and also the initial job time estimates in the final column. Taking the dependency table as the starting point, we must now represent this information in the form of a network.

In the diagram form we shall use here jobs are represented by *arrows* marked with the job label and time. Thus Job C would appear as:

C30

————————————————————————▶

The beginning of each job, and its end is marked by a circle or *node* thus:

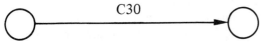

For ease of reference, these nodes will in due course be numbered as the full network is constructed. An individual node may mark the start of or the completion of several jobs but it is a rule of this type of diagrammatic form that any two nodes are joined by only one job (there are other diagrammatic forms where this rule is not applied). Construction of the network diagram can now begin. The first Job, A, marks the start of the project and its start and end are marked with a node. Examining the dependency table, we note from the immediate predecessor column that three jobs, B, C and D all follow directly from Job A. In terms of the diagram this means that their three 'arrows' will all emanate from Job A's end node. This is shown as follows:

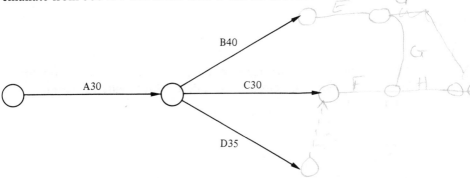

There is no significance in this diagram form in the length of the arrows or the angles at which they emerge from the node and it is not necessary that Job B be on the top, C in the middle and D on the lowest arrow. A network or somewhat different appearance would result if, say, Job C was on the top arrow and Job B on the middle arrow. This does not matter. Each arrangement would be a valid representation of the orderings in the dependency table and all the conclusions that will be deduced later on would be the same. Continue now with the network construction. Looking ahead in the predecessor column, we see that E must follow B and G must follow E. This much is fairly straightforward and at a first drawing may be shown as:

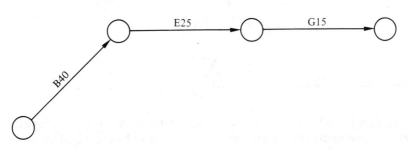

Node numberings will be selected later on. Now consider Job F. This has *both* of C and D as its immediate predecessors. How can this be accommodated given the rule that any two nodes must only be joined by one arrow? We must interpose an imaginary or *dummy* job taking no time to preserve the order relationships (the *network logic*). This could appear as:

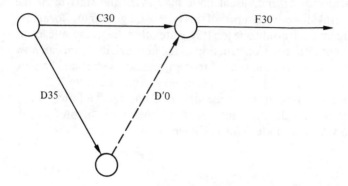

where D′ is the order preserving *zero-time dummy* (in some problems there are real time dummies which also represent delay). An equally valid arrangement would have been:

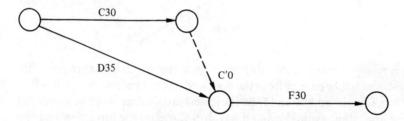

Again, the final appearance of the network would have been different but the *logic* would have been the same. Now consider Job H. This has both of F and G as its predecessors. One way to accommodate this would have been as follows:

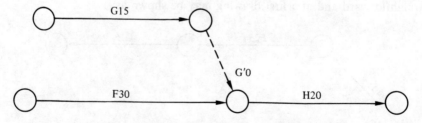

The logic is perfectly valid and no errors would result from this layout. However, the dummy after Job G can be suppressed and the same node can be used to mark the end of both G and F thus:

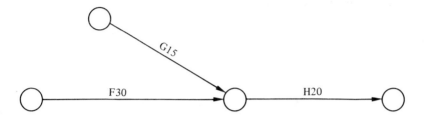

A completed network (following any necessary tidyings up) is as shown in Fig. 7-2. The network contains no more and no less information than that contained in the dependency table but has the considerable advantage that the order relationships stand out much more clearly. The project shown in the network is the one illustrated in the Gantt chart.

Not all networks are so conveniently constructed, of course. Although computer software exists to identify critical jobs it is perfectly feasible to construct networks containing hundreds of jobs entirely by hand. One other complicating factor apart from sheer size is that in practice the exercise has to be carried out without the benefit of a dependency table. The network *can* often be constructed from the mass of 'raw' verbal information about the order relationship between jobs, but it may be helpful (and it can provide a useful check) to construct the dependency table first of all. The reader is referred to Exercise 7-9 parts (i) and (ii) for an example of a problem in this form.

A rather varied terminology has evolved concerning how to describe the lines representing the jobs. We have described them as 'arrows'. They are also sometimes called *directed edges* or *arcs*. This diagram form is called the *arc-node* diagram. One of the alternative forms of diagram has the length of arrows (always horizontal in this case) proportional to job time. This form is essentially a hybrid of the arc-node diagram and Gantt charts and can have

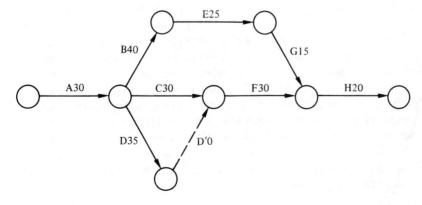

Figure 7-2

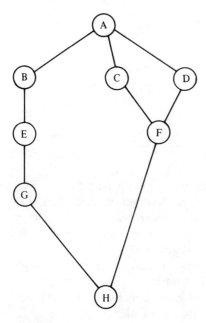

Figure 7-3

advantages for some purposes when constructed against a horizontal axis representing calendar date (see section 7-13).

The other principal form of diagram is called *activity on the node* or *precedence diagram form* where the 'nodes' themselves represent the jobs and the network logic is shown by the lines. In this form the project network would be as shown in Fig. 7-3. The activity on the node form has certain advantages (for example, dummies are not required) but is not in common usage. We shall, therefore, retain the arc-node form. The reader is referred to Exercise 7-6 and its answer for further practice with the activity on the node form.

Return now to the network as shown in Fig. 7-2. How long will it take to complete the maufacturing and assembly operation as a whole? The answer will be the longest path *in terms of time* through the network from start to finish. This is because each path through the network, following the direction of the arrows, represents a strictly ordered sub-set of tasks. Where two jobs lie on the same path they must be performed sequentially so the time taken for any path through the network will represent a *lower bound* on the time taken to complete the whole project. One way to ascertain this (in principle at least) is to enumerate the times taken on every path through the system. In the present case, with only three paths, this is no major task although more efficient methods (to be discussed later on) will be needed in more complex networks. In the present case the results are:

Path	Total time
ABEGH	130
ACFH	110
ADD'FH	115

Thus the path which effectively determines the completion time is ABEGH. This is the *critical path*, the path which sets the greatest of the lower bounds on project time. The whole cannot be completed in less than 130 days—as things now stand. The critical path is of particular importance, as we shall see, and is marked with double arrows throughout (to make it stand out) in Fig. 7-4. In Fig. 7-4 the nodes have also been numbered ① to ⑧. The numbering is in fact

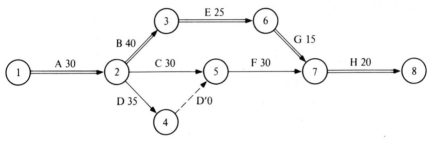

Figure 7-4

arbitrary—any system of numbering will do so long as each node receives a unique number. The critical path can now be represented by the nodes that it connects: ① ② ③ ⑥ ⑦ and ⑧. Incidentally, once the nodes are numbered the information in the dependency table could be presented in terms of the nodes as:

Job	Beginning and end events	Job time (days)
A	1–2	30
B	2–3	40
C	2–5	30
D	2–4	35
D'	4–5	0
E	3–6	25
F	5–7	30
G	6–7	15
H	7–8	20

It is not usual that the information on node numbering will be available prior to network construction, but the reader may gain more practice in drawing up networks by reconstructing the network from the above table. The critical path is sometimes referred to as the *bottleneck route*—a label which accurately identifies this sequence of jobs as those which must be affected if overall project time is to be reduced. There is no point whatever in trying to speed up jobs such as C, F and D which are non-critical. In larger networks, the vast majority of jobs are non-critical (perhaps over 90 per cent of all jobs) so knowing which jobs are on the critical path is priceless information. In large, complex projects also, the number of paths through the network can expand exponentially with the number of jobs so that means other than enumeration will be needed to find the critical path.

Before proceeding let us summarize the work done so far and gathering of information that is necessary:

1. Break down the overall project into distinct separate jobs.
2. Identify the order relationships between the jobs.
3. Form an initial estimate of the job times.
4. Construct the dependency table.
5. Draw the project network.
6. Identify the critical path.

The benefits resulting from this work will be:

1. The provision of a figure for overall project completion time and the identification of those jobs which are crucial to it.
2. The identification of the non-critical jobs—which are usually in the majority.
3. As a result of 1. and 2. proposals can be drawn up to shorten the critical path and reduce overall project completion time.

7-4 EVENT TIMES

The alternative method of finding the critical path requires some further work. The reaching of each node in the network represents an *event*, marking the completion of the immediately preceding job (or jobs in the case of nodes 7 and 5) and the simultaneous commencement of the immediately succeeding job (or jobs in the case of node 2).

For each node we shall now determine the *early event time* (EET); the earliest time by which that node can be reached. The EET for a node will depend upon all nodes that are strictly in sequence before it being reached at their EETs. This observation suggests the way in which EETs are determined.

Assume that the project may be started right away. The EET for node 1 will then be $t = 0$. Job A takes 30 days so that node 2 has an EET of $t = 30$.

Node 2 marks the start of Jobs B, C, and D. Thus since Job B takes 40 days, the EET for node 3 is 70. Continuing along the upper path, the EET for event 6 is 95. This is as far as we can go along this path at the moment since event 7 marks the completion of both Job G and Job F. Thus the EET for event 7 will be given by whichever of these two jobs finishes the later.

For a node which is on the critical path the critical route *must* represent the longest (in terms of time) way of reaching the node, and since, in this case, we already know the critical path, it is clear that the completion of Job G will set the EET of event 7. However, in general, event times are calculated prior to identification of the critical path so that we must return to the route through nodes 4 and 5.

Node 4 can be reached only by one route—AD—so that its EET is the EET for node 2 plus job time for D, giving 65. Now, node 5 can be reached from node 2 by going via C or D and D'. The longer of these paths sets the EET. Thus via job C, node 5 could be reached by $t = 60$, but via D and D' it is not reached until $t = 65$. This then is the EET.

Now we can return to node 7. This can be reached from nodes 5 or 6. Via job F node 7 could be reached by $t = 95$, but via job G it is not reached until $t = 110$; this becomes the EET. The EET for node 8 is $t = 130$ which marks the *early finish* time, F, for the entire project and completes the *forward pass* through the network. In general, call this F. The EETs are entered in squares above each node in Fig. 7-5.

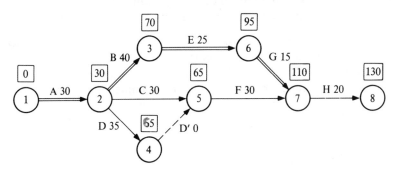

Figure 7-5

In addition to the EET for each node the early finish (EF) time for each job can be determined. EF for any job is the EET of the immediately preceding node plus job time. Thus EF for critical jobs will always be the EET of the succeeding node, but this will not always be the case for non-critical jobs. For example, EF for Job C is 60 and EF for Job F is 95. The EET of the immediately preceding node is called the *early start* time (ES) of a job. The subsequent analysis that we shall do with event times could also be conducted in terms of job start and finish time

Now as well as the early finish time for the project (F = 130 here) there will often be some deadline or *target time* for completion, T. For feasibility in the first instance, of course, we must have $T \geqslant F$. Suppose here that $T = 140$; the whole project must be completed in 140 days. This is the *late finish* time for the whole project. We are now to determine the latest time by which each node must be reached in order that the entire project is not pushed beyond the late finish time 140. These will be the *latest event times* (LETs).

The LETs are found by making a *backward pass* through the network working back from the final node 8 which we know to have an LET of 140. In order that node 8 is reached by this time and since Job H takes 20 days then node 7 must have been reached by $t = 120$. By a similar argument, since G takes 15 days node 6 must be reached by $t = 105$. This is the LET for node 6. Continuing this process we find that the LETs for nodes 3, 4, and 5 are 80, 90, and 90 respectively. Now node 2 marks the start of the three jobs which lead directly to these nodes. If node 5 is to be reached by $t = 90$, then since Job C takes 30 days, node 2 must have been reached by $t = 60$; but if node 4 is to be reached by $t = 90$ since Job D takes 35 days then node 2 must be reached by $t = 55$. It is evident that these times are too late, however, since node 3 must be reached by $t = 80$ and Job B takes 40 days then node 2 must be reached by $t = 40$ at the latest. This is the LET of node 2. It follows that the LET of node 1, the *late start* of the project, is $t = 10$. The LETs for each node are entered in triangles in Fig. 7-6. Late start (LS) and late finish (LF) times can be computed for each job. LS for a job is the LET of the immediately succeeding node minus job time. LF is the LET of the immediately succeeding node.

The formal rules for obtaining EET and LET can now be stated:

1. The EET for a node is the *greatest* of the times arrived at by summing EETs and corresponding job times for all immediately preceding nodes.
2. The LET for a node is the *least* of the times arrived at by subtracting the corresponding job times from the LETs of all immediately succeeding nodes.

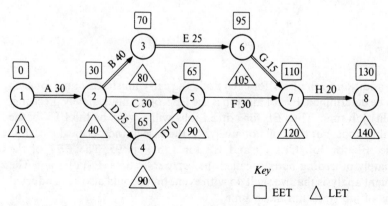

Key
☐ EET △ LET

Figure 7-6

The critical path is identified as passing through *all* those nodes for which LET *minus* EET equals T minus F. In this case critical jobs join nodes for which the LET exceeds the EET by 10 days. Notice that there are no other nodes with just this difference. All the other nodes (which of course will not lie on the critical path) have a greater difference. In a problem in which T = F the critical path would join all events where LET = EET.

7-5 FLOAT AND THE CRITICAL PATH

The EETs and LETs enable us to determine the maximum delays that are possible, individually, for each job in the project such that the target time, T, is not exceeded. Consider Job G. If node 6 has been reached by its EET then the start of Job G could be delayed by up to 10 days and node 7 could still be reached by its LET of 120. Alternatively, provided that a prompt start is made on Job G, it could be slowed down to take 25 days and still node 7 could be reached by $t = 120$. This maximum possible delay in the completion of Job G, 10 days, is called its *total float* (TF) or sometimes *total slack.*

It is clear that the total float in each job on the critical path is just 10 days. Of course, the critical jobs cannot be delayed by 10 days in every case. What of the non-critical jobs? Consider Job F. Assuming node 5 is reached by its EET time of 65, a maximum of 55 days may be taken for the completion of this job; an increase of 25 days over the original duration of 30 days. 25 is the TF of Job F. By a similar commonsense process the reader may verify that the total floats in the remaining non-critical jobs are 25, 25, and 30 for jobs D', D, and C respectively.

A formal procedure by which TF is calculated can now be stated:

1. For critical jobs $TF = T - F$.
2. For non-critical jobs TF = LET of immediately succeeding node minus the sum of the EET of the immediately preceding node and the job time.

If no separate target time is given, F is used instead of T. The critical jobs would then have precisely zero total float.

Total float is not the only concept of spare time in a job. Consider Job F again. If node 5 is reached by the EET of 65 then provided that Job F does not take longer than 45 days, node 7 can still be reached by its EET of 110. This delay of 15 days (45 − 30) is called the *free float* (FF) in the job. It will be seen that the only other job in the project with positive FF is Job C with 5 days. Free float is the maximum delay that is possible in a job without affecting the EET of the immediately succeeding node. This is in contrast to TF which is the maximum delay possible in a job such that the LET of the immediately succeeding node is not affected.

The formal procedure for determining FF is:

1. FF in all critical jobs is zero.

2. FF in non-critical jobs is the EET of immediately succeeding node minus the sum of the EET of the immediately preceeding node and the job time.

So long as the project is time-feasible ($T \geqslant F$) free float can never exceed total float. We can now present some definitions and results concerning criticalness and float.

1. A job is called critical if, when delayed by *any* amount of time $\Delta t \geqslant 0$, the whole project is delayed by Δt.
2. A critical job is a job having *minimum total float*, i.e., critical jobs have total float $= T - F$. This will be zero if $T = F$.
3. All non-critical jobs have total float $> T - F$.
4. A critical path consists entirely of critical jobs.
5. All critical jobs lie on a critical path (i.e., there can be no isolated critical jobs).
6. In any project network there will be at least one path from start to finish that contains only critical jobs, i.e., there will always be at least one critical path.

Result (6) above may require that we insert imaginary jobs 'start' and 'finish' (taking zero time) such that the job 'start' precedes all other jobs and 'finish' succeeds all other jobs. Where there are no real jobs fulfilling these roles it may be convenient in hand-solved problems to insert them, although this is not strictly necessary. Some computer routines require the insertion of such jobs.

We have mentioned in passing the consequences of slowing down of critical jobs—there will be the same delay in the project as a whole. But what if critical jobs are speeded up? How many time savings in general be effected? There are two ways in which F may be reduced:

1. Critical jobs may be speeded up.
2. The ordering of jobs may be changed.

Consider speedings up first of all.

7-6 JOB TIME IMPROVEMENTS

If it is our object to reduce F then clearly, in the first instance, *there is no point in speeding up non-critical jobs*. If a critical job is speeded up, then the consequent reduction in F *cannot exceed* the time saved in the critical job and may be less. When a critical job speeded up it is possible that the CP may change. In formal terms if a critical job is shortened by an amount Δt the reduction in F will be Δt *if the CP does not change* and will be $< \Delta t$ if a new path becomes uniquely critical.

Consider this point with reference to the example problem. Critical jobs are A B E G H. First note that Jobs A and H are on any path through the network. Suppose 1 day is saved in Job A so that only 29 days are now required. The reader will quickly verify that the EETs for node 2 and in fact all *subsequent* nodes are reduced by one. Thus the EET for node 8, which is the early finish time for the project as a whole, F is now 129. Each day saved in A will be fully reflected in F. Note what happens to TF in each job when 1 day is saved in A. Minimum TF (recall that this is T − F) now becomes 11 days and TF in all of the non-critical jobs goes up by one day also. Therefore, the jobs which were critical before the time saving (had minimum TF) remain critical afterwards. TF in Job A itself becomes 11 days (although LET of node 2 remains at 40 and EET of node 1 remains at 0). This is because job time is now 29. Note that the LET of node 1 is now 11 days.

If 1 day is saved on Job H, this too will be fully reflected in F. LETs for node 7 and all *preceding* nodes are increased by 1 day thus increasing TF in each job preceding node 7 by one day. Thus jobs which had the least TF before still have the least TF and the original path remains critical. In Job H itself TF increases to 11 since it now takes 19 days.

Jobs A and H were common to any path which may be critical. What if time is saved on B, E, or G? Consider the effects of 1 day saved on Job E. If this job is now done in 24 days the effects will be to reduce EET on nodes 6, 7, and 8 by 1 day and to increase LET on nodes 1, 2, and 3 by 1 day. Thus TF throughout the critical path is now 11 days. Note, however, that the nature of these changes in event times is such as to leave TF on Jobs C, D, D′, and F unchanged. Total float in D and D′ remains at 25 and in C it remains at 30.

Bearing this in mind, consider now *substantial* time savings in the section B E G. So long as the amount saved *in total* does not exceed 15 days (say 5 days in each of these jobs for the sake of argument) then the path A B E G H remains critical and the total saving is fully reflected in early finish time, F. If total savings amount to exactly 15 days, then the path A D D′ F H becomes critical also and any further savings in B E and G will leave A D D′ F H uniquely critical and will not be reflected in F at all. Unless time is saved in F and/or D the LET of node 2 cannot be increased beyond 55 since we are not at the moment considering a reduction in Job H time.

Thus if time savings are ruled out in Jobs A and H, once 15 days have been saved in section B E G additional reduction in early finish time can only be effected by cuts in time in at least two jobs; one in section B E G *and* either D or F. If D is the job that is reduced then once 5 days have been saved here (and in B E F) then further reductions in the early finish time would involve reducing Job C if savings in F are ruled out.

Let us review the picture. Time savings beyond certain amounts involved the 'picking up' of new critical paths when we ruled out savings on 'common' jobs. Thus it became necessary to work on several jobs to keep paths jointly critical. When one path becomes uniquely critical time savings elsewhere in the network will not be effective in reducing the early finish time overall. The results may be stated formally as:

1. When an amount of time Δt is saved in a critical job, the EETs of subsequent nodes in strict sequence with the job are all reduced by Δt provided that the original CP remains critical.
2. When Δt is saved in a critical job the LETs of preceding nodes in strict sequence with the job are all increased by Δt provided that the original CP remains critical.
3. When Δt is saved in a critical job, the TF in all critical jobs increases by Δt provided that the original CP remains critical.
4. When Δt is saved in a critical job, the TF in other sections of the network not in sequence with the job (i.e., not lying on the original CP) remains unchanged.

This last result gives the clue to the means by which we can determine the maximum time savings that it is worth making in a particular job (i.e. that will be fully reflected in early finish time) or indeed in a particular section of the project network. While TF has been defined in relation to particular jobs, it is for some purposes more convenient to think of it as belonging to sections of the network.

In Fig. 7-7, the network has been divided up into sections (one to six) and alongside each section number the TF for that section is given in brackets. For instance, section 2 comprises Jobs B, E and G and has total float of 10 days. This section is on the original CP and any time savings Δt in here will increase float here and in sections 1 and 6 (since they are in sequence). Total float in sections 3, 4 and 5, however, remains unchanged. Consider a particular

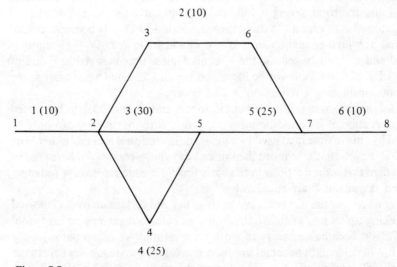

Figure 7-7

problem. Suppose target time T for the completion of the project is now 100 days instead of 140. With the original durations for each job this is not feasible. If LETs and EETs are re-calculated the EETs will *exceed* the LETs for all nodes. The new LETs with T = 100 will be 40 days less than the original values. TF in each section will also be 40 days less than originally. The new minimum value of TF will be *minus* 30. This situation is illustrated in Fig. 7-8.

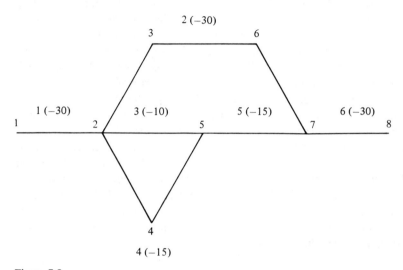

Figure 7-8

The problem is now to reduce job times so that minimum TF = 0. To make things awkward, suppose that no time savings may be effected in section 1, 5 and 6. Obviously, 30 days must be saved in section 2 and if this is done minimum TF in this section becomes 0 but minimum TF overall is − 15 since the CP now consists of sections 1, 4, 5 and 6. Overall, early finish is now 115 days. If 15 days are now saved in section four, the CP shifts again to comprise sections one, three, five and six. Minimum TF is now − 5 days and early finish is 105. When, finally, 5 days are saved in section 3, minimum *TF* becomes zero and early finish is the requisite 100 days.

7-7 NETWORK LOGIC VARIATION

In some projects, there is a certain amount of discretion as to the ordering of jobs. The order relationships between certain of the jobs may indeed be immutable but where some changes are allowed it may be possible to reduce *F* by varying the network logic.

To the extent that there is discretion in network logic, a combinatorial element is introduced. This can rapidly assume formidable proportions. For instance, if a project consists of 100 jobs (small by practical standards) 95 of which have a predetermined sequential relationship, while the remaining 5 can be fitted in anywhere, then in fact there are over eight thousand million possible arrangements of jobs! The rescheduling problem can therefore be formidable and some approximation approaches are discussed in the context of resource problems below. However, a few points relevant to limited discretion in small networks are appropriate here.

First, in order to be worth while, any rearrangement of jobs must affect the critical path. No time can be saved by rescheduling among non-critical jobs only. Secondly, some jobs must be taken *out* of the present CP. Now if any job is introduced into the CP then F is increased by the duration of that job. But if a job is removed from the CP then F will be reduced by the job time only if the original path (minus the one job) remains critical. Without study of a particular network all that can definitely be said (if the path is uniquely critical) is that the EET of all succeeding nodes is reduced and the LET of all preceding nodes is raised. In other words, TF in the CP is increased. The concept of TF in fact can be of value in a rescheduling context. If the position of a job is changed then the saving in project time will be the difference between the old value of minimum TF and the new value. More specifically, if the job is re-located in an 'independent' position—one that does not decrease the TF on any other branch—then the total time saved is the difference between the minimum TF and the next lowest level of TF or time on the re-positioned job, whichever is the smaller.

7-8 PERT/TIME

The original PERT/time system was developed by the United States Navy at around the same time the CPM was developed by the Du Pont Company. PERT/time has as its central feature the notion of a critical path, but differs from the CPM in respect of job time estimates. PERT is concerned with situations in which job times are *random variables*. It may be that job time is simply unknown in the case of an entirely new project or that the job times are influenced by uncontrollable variables (e.g., the weather).

Ideally, we should like to know the *probability distribution* of job times. The table below represents a simple discrete distribution of four specific times:

(1)	(2)	(3)
Time (t)	Probability (p)	$t \times p$
22	0.2	4.4
32	0.2	6.4
46	0.3	13.8
56	0.3	16.8
		expected time = 41.4

These times are listed in column (1). Probability of occurrence is given in column (2), and column (3) elements are summed to give the expected duration of the job. Things are rarely as convenient as this. The underlying probability distribution of job times will be more complicated in most instances. All is not lost, however, if we know the *type* of probability distribution (e.g., discrete (as above), normal, gamma, or beta) and the mean and variance of the distribution. It is rather unlikely that these parameters will be known in advance and PERT/time gives a simple and practicable means of obtaining reasonable estimates of mean and variance.

The person in charge of each job is asked to provide three estimates of job time: a 'pessimistic' estimate, an 'optimistic' estimate, and a 'most likely' estimate. The investigator may quantify 'optimistic' and 'pessimistic', for example, by defining the pessimistic time as one for which there are 95 chances out of 100 of getting the job done within this time. This statistic may be based on past experience with the job or may be an '*a priori* subjective estimate' (i.e., a guess) if the job has never been done before. 'Optimistic' would then be that time such that there were only 5 chances out of 100 of completing the job by this time. In non-quantitative terms, 'pessimistic' would be: 'the time taken to complete the job if everything goes wrong short of total disaster', and 'optimistic': 'everything goes well short of a miracle'. Figure 7-9 places these estimates and the most likely figure (m) on the graph of a possible underlying distribution of times.

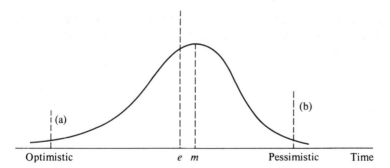

Optimistic e m Pessimistic   Time

Figure 7-9

The arithmetic mean time (expected time), e, can be approximated as a function of a, b, and m given the underlying distribution. For example, if the probability distribution is a beta distribution then e is given by $e \simeq \frac{1}{6}(a+b) + \frac{2}{3}m$. The coefficients $\frac{1}{6}$ and $\frac{2}{3}$ were weights derived from the particular beta distribution which is usually more appropriate than the normal distribution because it has maximum and minimum limits. Once the mean time has been determined this is used as in the CPM diagrams and analysis proceeds as for the CPM.

The job time variance can also be estimated from a, b, and m. In fact variance, σ^2, is given by $\sigma^2 \simeq \frac{1}{36}(b-a)^2$ where a beta distribution is appropriate.

Having obtained estimates of mean times and variances for individual jobs, the mean times and variances of strictly ordered sequences of jobs can be found. For instance, if a series of n jobs are in strict sequence the mean time for completion of the sequence $E(T)$, is the sum of the individual mean job times: $E(T) = \sum_{i=1}^{n} E(t_i)$. If the distributions of individual job times are *independent* of each other, then the variance of time for completion of the n jobs, σ_T^2, is the sum of the individual job time variances: $\sigma_T^2 = \sum_{i=1}^{n} \sigma_i^2$. Having found the expected completion time for a section of a system and the variance for that section, a *confidence interval* could be found for completion time for the section.

For instance, if individual job times in the branch are normally distributed, then it is known that for the i-th job there is a 95 per cent chance that the job time will actually lie in the interval: $E(t_i) \pm 1.96\sigma_i$. This is because 95 per cent of the area under a normal curve lies within 1.96 standard deviations of the mean. Each extreme tail contains only a $2\frac{1}{2}$ per cent chance that job time will take more than $E(t_i) + 1.96\sigma_i$. Equally, there is only a $2\frac{1}{2}$ per cent chance that completion time will be less than $E(t_i) - 1.96\sigma_i$. The 95 per cent confidence interval for the branch as a whole is given by:

$$C_{95} = E(T) \pm 1.96\sigma_T = \sum_{i=1}^{n} E(t_i) \pm 1.96 \sqrt{\sum_{i=1}^{n} \sigma_i^2}$$

As an example, suppose that a section of a network consists of five jobs with times and variances as given below, with each job time independently normally distributed.

t_i	σ_i^2
8.4	0.9
12.5	1.7
15.0	2.6
9.3	0.6
14.8	2.2
$\Sigma t_i = 60.6$	$\Sigma \sigma_i^2 = 8.0$

The 95 per cent confidence interval for completion time of the section is:

$$C_{95} = 60 \pm 1.96\sqrt{8} = 54.46 \text{ to } 65.54$$

If some of the job times are not independent of each other but are *jointly distributed* (i.e. the probability distribution of times for job i depends on the time taken for other jobs) the estimated variance of a sequence can still be found analytically although the situation is more complicated. Real difficulties arise when all jobs are not in strict sequence—as in the typical networks that have been considered so far—and a confidence interval for completion time for the whole project is desired.

To illustrate, when two or more branches join up, as do branches 2 and 5 in the network described earlier, then the EET for node 7 depends upon which of sections 2 and 5 is actually finished first. But completion times for these sections are now described by probability distributions. The expected EET for node 7 is the expected value of the maximum of T_2 and T_5 where T_2 is completion time for sections 1 and 2 and T_5 is completion time for sections 1 and 3/4 and 5.

A *simulation* exercise would often be more rewarding. In such a procedure, the estimated probability distributions of job times and network logic would be put into a computer and the distribution of F would then be determined empirically after many runthroughs of the system. Mean and confidence intervals could then be established for the project as a whole (or for particular non-strictly sequenced parts of the system).

7-9 CPM ALTERNATIVES TO PERT/TIME

Multiple time estimates in network analysis are not quite as fashionable nowadays as they were in the early and mid-1960s. This may be because the approach is over-sophisticated for some applications and because eventually a single figure is employed. Unless the complications of PERT produce a significantly better mean figure they will not be worth the cost and time involved. The choice of method should be determined by the particular problem at hand.

In fact, CPM itself can be used when job times are subject to variation. First is what might be called the 'levels of criticalness' approach. In this, critical jobs now become 'first level critical', and near-critical jobs become 'second level critical'. For instance, in a building operation, jobs with three days TF may be first level critical and jobs with four to six days TF second level critical. If all goes well the second-level critical jobs would not determine the minimum completion time for the project. But if some of these job times depend on extraneous factors (e.g., the performance of a sub-contractor) they may be 'unreliable' and become critical. If likely cases can be identified in advance, it would be useful to have some contingency plans worked out for speeding up of some of the subsequent newly critical jobs.

Secondly, it should be recalled that acquisition of information costs both time and money. An economical approach to information gathering and critical path determination is as follows. For each job a rough-and-ready (and presumably therefore quick and cheap) time study is done. With these approximate times critical and near critical jobs are identified. A detailed (and presumably more expensive and time-consuming) time study is then done only for these jobs. Time and money is thus saved by having only the rough study done for the 'far-from-critical' jobs.

Finally, if one wished to err on the side of caution, a fixed percentage could be added on to the initial time estimate for each job so that although single figure estimates are then used there is a built-in 'safety margin' for delays. This approach, along with the previous two, is one of approximation. The degrees of approximation are not specified but the methods should not be dismissed. It is modifications such as these that make theoretical models more useful in practice.

7-10 COSTS

To employ CPM methods in problems where cost as well as time is a relevant consideration, it is necessary to relate cost to time in a systematic manner. The complexity of the problem hinges a good deal upon how cost varies with time. If cost rises for a particular job as time taken increases, then minimization of job time will result in minimization of cost. For a project as a whole, in these circumstances, all time saved implies reduction of cost and the minimization of completion time overall is a necessary condition for the minimization of cost; but things are rarely so convenient. Time and cost on some jobs may have an inverse relationship—speedings up may imply increases in cost.

The problem that is most frequently faced is not overall minimization of costs but the problem of making costs as low as possible subject to getting the entire project finished within a given deadline. Consider an example.

A construction project consists of nine jobs. The list of jobs, the ordering and normal durations are given in the first three columns of Fig. 7-10. Column (4) gives the cost of each job *if it is completed in the normal time.* Some of the jobs may be speeded up. The minimum time in which each of the jobs can be done is given in column (5), and column (6) gives the job costs associated with the minimum times. It is assumed that for those jobs which can be speeded up any time between the extreme values may be taken and that time and cost are

(1)	(2)	(3) Normal time (days)	(4) Cost (£)	(5) Minimal time (days)	(6) Cost (£)
Job	Predecessors				
A		10	5 000	10	5 000
B	A	8	4 000	8	4 000
C	A	8	4 500	8	4 500
D	C	4	6 000	4	6 000
E	B	7	5 500	5	6 500
F	B	9	3 750	4	13 750
G	D	8	2 000	1	4 800
H	E, F, G	15	6 500	12	14 900
I	H	10	5 000	10	5 000

Figure 7-10

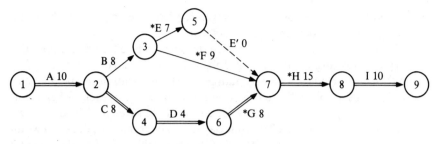

Figure 7-11

linearly related between these extreme values. The deadline time for the project is T = 48 days. What time should be taken on each job such that the project is completed in this time at least cost? Figure 7-11 shows the network and critical path for which normal time for each job is assumed. Jobs indicated with an asterisk* indicate the possibility of time savings but with the normal times assumed early finish, F, = 55. The table below shows the particular paths, completion time with normal job times and in the third column the requisite time reductions are shown. If the whole project is to be completed in 48 days then *all* paths must be done in this time. Column (4) shows the jobs within each path on which time may be saved.

(1) Path	(2) Duration	(3) Reduction	(4) *Jobs
A B E E' H I	50	2	E H
A B F H I	52	4	F H
A C D G H I	55	7	G H

Now consider the cost per day saved in each of the jobs where time reductions are possible. The cost per day saved is given by

$$\frac{\text{Cost (normal time)} - \text{cost (minimal time)}}{\text{normal time} - \text{minimal time}}$$

Results are as follows:

(1) Job	(2) CPDS	(3) MS
E	500	2
F	2000	5
G	400	7
H	2800	3

Column (2) shows the cost per day saved (CPDS) and column (3) shows the maximum possible time saving in each job.

Now consider how the requisite savings are to be effected. Suppose that we begin by making savings only in Jobs E, F, and G and consider variations from this starting point. The only manner in which variation can be effected is via reductions in Job H. Since H is common to all the paths then, to begin with at least, each day saved in H means one day less to be saved in E, F, and G. One day saved in H would cost £2800; one day less to be saved in E, F, and G would reduce costs in these jobs by $500 + 2000 + 400 = 2900$ so the first day saved in H is worth while. The same applies to the second day saved in H, but not to a third day. When two days have been saved in H the requisite time reduction has been made for the upper path. The third day saved in H would add 2800 to cost and only bring cost reductions of $2000 + 400 = 2400$ from lower time savings in F and G. The ideal arrangement is then to save 2 days in H, 2 days in F, and 5 days in G. The whole project can then be completed in 48 days at a total cost of £53 850 as against a total cost of £42 250 if 55 days had been allowed. What has been outlined here is an essentially commonsense way of tackling the problem but in large and complicated networks this may not always be practicable.

7-11 MINIMIZING OVERALL PROJECT COST

In considering project costs as a whole, it is useful to divide costs into those which increase with time and those which decrease with time. Into the former category would fall 'indirect' costs: costs of administration, financing, hire of plant and equipment, rent, etc. The 'direct' costs, attributable unambiguously to particular tasks would usually fall into the latter category. How can these different characteristics be optimally balanced?

First consider the direct costs (we shall include all costs with an inverse relationship to time under this heading) for the project as a whole. If we begin by doing each job the long, 'cheap' way, one pair of values for time and cost is obtained. The objective here is to obtain the graph of total direct costs against time and in principle we should like to find the cheapest way of saving each unit of time; but this problem can be enormous. Where this is the case, the following approximate procedure is suggested.

Consider just two possible times for each job—normal (cheap) time and 'crash' (costly) time. Begin by assuming that each job is to be done the normal way and find what would be total cost and the critical path. Now crash the cheapest (in terms of cost per day saved) job on the CP. Find the new level of total direct cost and time and the new CP. Now 'crash' the job with lowest cost per day saved on this path, and so on. This procedure will not necessarily give the cheapest time savings, but it should at least be near to optimal if computational expenses are taken into account.

We are thus able to obtain pairs of values of total direct costs for the project and overall time taken, so that a graph can be produced of total direct

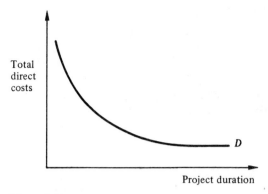

Figure 7-12

costs, D, against time. A plausible shape for such a graph is that shown in Fig.7-12 in which the cost per additional unit of time saved is rising. The end points of the graph mark, respectively, the shortest and cheapest (in terms of the direct costs only) ways of completing the project.

Now we are assuming that indirect costs for the project as a whole, I, will rise with project duration. A linear relationship is depicted in Fig. 7-13 although it is not necessary to assume this. As regards revenues, R, from the project, we shall assume here that these are unaffected by time taken. The idea is to choose the project duration such that profits, Π, are maximized. Profit overall is given by:

$$\Pi = R - (D + I)$$

and the full picture is shown in Fig. 7-14. The curve $D + I$ shows total costs and R indicates revenue. Since R is being assumed to be constant the duration that minimizes total costs will maximize profits. The profit graph is shown at the bottom of the diagram. $\bar{F}$ indicates the ideal duration while F_1 and F_2 are break-even durations. Note that the intersection of the D and I curves will not

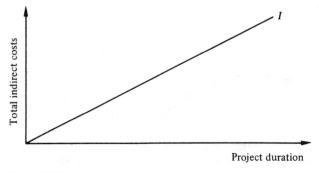

Figure 7-13

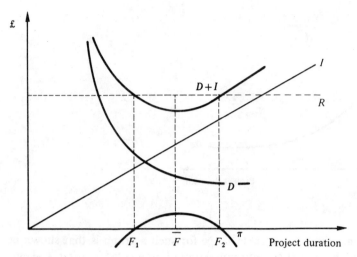

Figure 7-14

(except by coincidence) produce the minimum value of $D+I$. The minimum is obtained when the *rate* at which D is coming down is equal to the *rate* at which I is going up, i.e. when, ignoring signs, the slopes are equal.

The diagram of Fig. 7-14 can be put to further use. Suppose the company that would undertake this project is preparing a tender for the contract and in order to have a chance of obtaining the contract has to promise completion in some time, say F_3, where F_3 is less than $\bar{F}$. If a penalty clause is included in the contract, this will have to be taken into account but it will not necessarily mean that the tendering company should aim to finish by F_3. In Fig. 7-15 the line P represents penalty payments, which may be regarded as an additional cost. Π is shown as before, and the idea now is to determine the duration that maximizes profits *net of penalty payments*. This turns out to be $\hat{F}$ where the

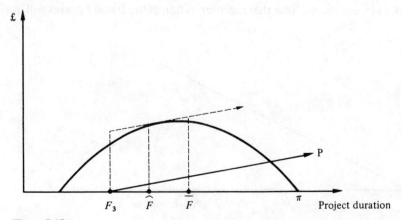

Figure 7-15

profit curve and P have the same slope. Costs come into the picture in other ways, too. We have been investigating cases in which we actively sought to minimize costs. Once the network has been laid out, we can use it to estimate the *cash flows* associated with a project (see Wilkes, 1983) and the capital that will be tied up at various stages. This is a *passive* use of the project network. Cost can also be used as a convenient although highly approximate measure of the non-financial resouces that are tied up in a job or a section of the network, but in this use, as in the other uses, there may be practical difficulties in allocating costs to particular jobs or collections of jobs.

The level of total expenditure on a project up to a particular time can give a rough guide to the progress that is being made on the project. A typical shape for the curve of planned expenditure, E, is shown in Fig. 7-16. A 'lazy S' shape would normally be expected. The graph may show either committed funds or spent funds. There are difficulties with this device, however. Unanticipated inflation may give a misleading picture. In Fig. 7-17 the curve, I, shows

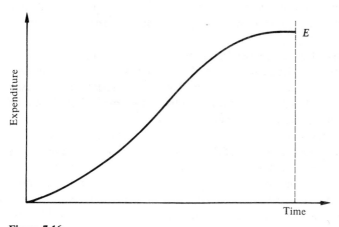

Figure 7-16

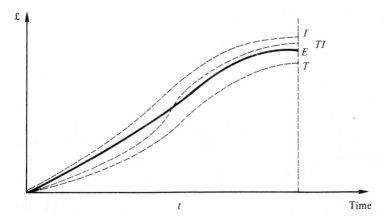

Figure 7-17

expenditure with the inflated costs; T shows a case of 'tardiness' without inflation; TI shows a possible 'tardy' project with inflation present. In this last case, note that at time, t, although the project is, in fact, running behind schedule, expenditure is as anticipated. The inflation problem (in terms of the expenditure graphs) is lessened if percentages of total expenditure are used on the vertical scale instead of units of money.

7-12 RESOURCE MANAGEMENT

Although the logic of a project network may allow varying numbers of jobs to be proceeding simultaneously, the implied patterns of resouces usage may not be practicable. For instance, it would be obvious nonsense to have a programme that called for 500 people in week 1, 20 people in weeks 2 and 3, 600 people in week 4, 10 people in week 5, etc. The project controller in this instance may have, say, 200 people available and although this number may be increased or decreased any substantial changes could be very costly if they were even possible in the short term. How can sensible patterns of resource use be guaranteed?

First we must distinguish two categories of resource and two types of situation. Resources are frequently divided into *pool resources* and *non-pool resources*. A pool resource is one which if not used today can be used tomorrow. Supplies of materials provide an obvious example. An example of a non-pool resource would be labour or machine time—today's labour time is not available tomorrow. Non-pool resources in general present more difficulties than do pool resources and it is in the context of non-pool resources that we shall set the discussion. Then there are those problems in which additional resources from outside of the project can be brought in, and those problems in which any further resources applied to a job must be taken from other jobs (unless currently idle). In the latter case the interrelationships are more involved.

Exact solutions are not generally obtainable and we shall be concerned with obtaining 'reasonable' solutions only. Let us make a start by seeing how Gantt charts can be useful in some simple cases.

Suppose that the initial arrangement of jobs on a project, based solely upon logical considerations, was as shown in Fig. 7-18(a). The numbers on the bars represent the numbers of units of a resource (say labour of a particular category) required throughout each job. Figure 7-18(b) is drawn to the same horizontal scale and shows the numbers of people required at various times. While Jobs A and B are proceeding 8 people are needed. This requirement rises to 10 when A, B, and D are being worked upon simultaneously. Then only 5 are needed when only A and D are proceeding, dropping to 2 then rising to 9, and finally falling to 7. This may be too erratic a pattern.

Suppose now that it is possible to reschedule Jobs B and D as shown in Fig. 7-19(a), albeit at the expense of pushing back the starts of C and E. The

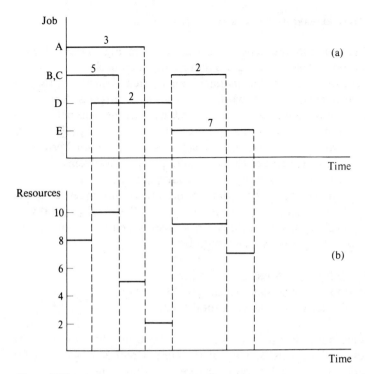

Figure 7-18

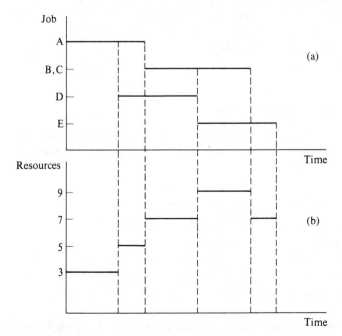

Figure 7-19

resulting pattern of resource requirements is shown in Fig. 7-19(b). This is altogether more desirable, showing a build-up and then decline.

The use of Gantt charts in this manner is an informal, *heuristic* method of resource management that can work well for small projects. The ideal approach is known as resources *smoothing* and involves the manipulation of jobs so that resource requirements over the duration of the project form smooth curves, something like flattened semi-circles. Computational problems restrict the use of this procedure to the smaller practical problems.

Next best to smoothing is the approach known as resources *levelling*. This involves the rearrangement of jobs so that pre-ordained limits on resources are not exceeded. *Priority rules* are employed when jobs that could logically be done simultaneously compete for limited resources. When two or more jobs conflict, examples of a priority rule would be:

1. Start that job first which has least duration.
2. Start that job first which has the earliest 'late finish'.
3. Start that job first which has least total float.

It cannot be determined in advance which of the above, or other, priority rules will work best and none is best all of the time. Computer packages for resources problems that use this approach generally allow considerable choice in priority rules. There are various ways in which the information about a network can be presented. Sections of the network can be printed out for people in control of parts of the overall project or the jobs can be printed out in order of total float so that critical jobs appear first on the list. This is a useful feature for updating networks. Notwithstanding these advantages, problems of practical size (up to around 500 jobs) can still be tackled efficiently by hand.

7-13 PLANNING AND REVIEW

In using a CP approach, it can be convenient to divide the exercise into two stages; the *planning* stage and the *review* stage. Each of these stages can be sub-divided thus:

Planning stage	Review stage
1. Construct network	1. Modify network and/or times
2. Estimate times and analyse	2. Re-analyse times
3. Modify	3. Re-modify
4. Schedule	4. Schedule

In this context 'schedule' means determine the actual starting dates of jobs (somewhere within their floats). This can be approached in the following manner:

1. Assign specific dates to each job.
2. Use a bar chart on a calendar time-scale along with a separate network diagram.
3. Relate events to calendar time in the usual network diagram.
4. Use a modified network diagram in which all of the job lines are drawn horizontally to a time-scale as in a bar chart. In this manner the various floats and interactions between jobs are clearly indicated.

An illustration of the latter method is given in Figs. 7-20(a) and (b). The alternative representation of the original project is shown in Fig. 7-20(a). Horizontal dashed lines show free float in jobs. The diagram is drawn against a time-scale of working days. Figure 7-20(b) shows the jobs in a possible scheduling that may be dictated by resources considerations. The diagram is drawn against a calendar time-scale for which five working days per week are assumed. Holidays during the project are assumed to cover three working

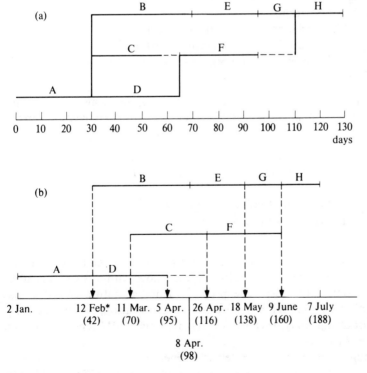

Note: *End of job A. Jobs B and D commence 13 Feb

Figure 7-20

days at Easter and one at the Spring Bank Holiday. The dates shown represent scheduled completion or start dates of jobs and the bracketed numbers beneath these dates show the numbers of days since the start of the project. Thus although only 130 working days are required, the project takes 188 days to complete.

7-14 CONCLUDING REMARKS

The earliest applications of CPM were in respect of manufacturing and assembly operations. In subsequent years, the area of application widened considerably to include more general administrative problems. Instances are:

1. The establishment of a new branch or department of a firm.
2. Introduction of a large-scale new procedure.
3. Planning and occupation of a new building.
4. The installation of major new equipment (e.g., a computer).
5. Large-scale movement of staff.
6. Planning provisioning procedures.
7. Contract preparation.
8. Control of research and development projects.
9. Planning and control of maintenance procedures.
10. Planning exhibitions, conferences, and training schemes.

An increasing number of administrative applications is also being found within the Government. Instances of actual or possible applications are:

1. Passage of a Bill through Parliament.
2. Putting into effect changes in legislation.
3. Planning a census.
4. Planning and control of publicity campaigns.
5. Planning and control of protocol procedures.

Although, as we have seen, CPM in its various guises is an immensely valuable technique, the widespread use of CPM-type methods within any organization can create some difficulties. The project-orientated nature of CPM may conflict with the functional structure of the organization, so that increased flexibility or change may be called for. By and large, CPM tends to facilitate *management by exception*.

Although conceived of separately from linear programming, since there is frequently a programming aspect of the problems to which CPM is addressed (e.g., minimization of cost subject to a constraint on completion time), it is not surprising that linear programming methods are being increasingly used in CPM problems (see Wilkes, 1983). There is also a tie in with capital budgeting methods as we have seen. The pattern and timing of cash flows associated with a project can be deduced from diagrams such as Fig. 7-20(b) and discounting can then be conducted.

Computer software is available for finding the critical path through networks and providing other important data. A typical print-out will state for each job the early start time (early event time for the start event), late start time (late event time for the end event less job time), early finish time (early start time plus job time), late finish time (late event time of end event), total float on the job and whether or not the job is on the critical path.

Computer output from typical PC software for the problem of section 7-3 might be arranged as follows:

Job	ES	EF	LS	LF	Float	Critical Y/N
A	0	30	10	40	10	Y
B	30	70	40	80	10	Y
C	30	60	60	90	30	N
D	30	65	55	90	25	N
E	70	95	80	105	10	Y
F	65	95	90	120	25	N
G	95	110	105	120	10	Y
H	110	130	120	140	10	Y

An example of a computer programme for critical path analysis is shown in Cohen (1985).

EXERCISES

7-1 Revision exercise
   (i) Explain the value of bar charts in macro-monitoring.
   (ii) By what means can the critical path be found?
   (iii) Define and distinguish between total float and free float.
   (iv) Explain the two main means by which project duration can be reduced.
   (v) How are the time estimates in PERT/time combined?
   (vi) How can the problem of minimization of project cost subject to a completion time constraint be approached?
   (vii) What balance is sought between direct and indirect costs in identifying the overall cost minimizing duration of a project?
   (viii) What problems may arise in using a comparison of planned and actual expenditures to gauge project progress?
   (ix) Explain how Gantt charts may be used in resources management.

(x) Show how network diagrams can be constructed to show job floats.

(xi) Give examples of administrative areas in which CPM methods can be applied

7-2 An assembly operation involves the completion of 11 jobs. The job labels, the time required to complete each one, and the necessary immediate predecessors of each job are shown in the table:

Job	Job time (days)	Immediate predecessors
a	13	—
b	8	a
c	10	b
d	9	c
e	11	b
f	10	e
g	8	d, f
h	6	e
i	7	h
j	14	g, i
k	18	j

(i) Draw the network. Which jobs are on the critical path?

(ii) Prepare a table of floats (free and total) on the non-critical jobs.

(iii) Outline ways in which reductions can be made in network completion time. Illustrate with an example from the network of (i).

7-3 A construction project is divided into seven activities:

Activity	Linking events	Duration (days)
A	1–2	2
B	2–3	7
C	2–4	9
D	3–4	4
E	3–5	10
F	4–5	5
G	5–6	4

(i) Construct the network.

(ii) Calculate the event times.

(iii) Identify the critical path.

(iv) Calculate total float and free float on each activity.

(v) How much time would be saved if the duration of activity E was reduced by three days?

7-4 The normal cost/duration and other relevant information for a project is given below:

Activity	Normal duration (days)	Normal total cost £	Minimum duration if accelerated	Cost per day accelerated £
1–2	3	140	1	110
2–3	2	200	1	175
2–4	3	160	1	125
2–5	2	300	1	200
3–6	2	250	1	175
4–6	6	400	1	70
5–6	5	230	1	70
6–7	5	230	1	90

There is a bonus of £100 per day for every day saved below the contract period of 15 days, and a penalty of £200 for each day after the 15 days.

(a) Calculate the normal duration and the normal cost of the project.

(b) Calculate the minimum cost of completing the project in 15 days.

(c) State the optimum plan for the company to attempt.

(d) Revert to the normal programme and normal costs and state what action you would recommend to ensure completion by the original date, if after the tenth day the actual situation was as follows:

(i) activities completed at normal cost: 1–2; 2–3; 3–6; 2–4; 2–5,

(ii) activities not yet started: 4–6; 5–6; 6–7.

What is the revised cost of the project in these circumstances?

7-5 The table gives estimates of the time and cost for activities involved in completing a contract.

Activity	Previous activities	Normal time (days)	Normal cost (£)	Minimum time (days)	Cost for minimum time (£)
A		12	10 000	8	14 000
B		10	5 000	10	5 000
C	A	0	0	0	0
D	A	6	4 000	4	5 000
E	B, C	16	9 000	14	12 000
F	D	16	3 200	8	8 000
		60	31 200	44	44 000

Minimum time represents the shortest time in which the activity can be completed gives the use of especially costly methods of operation. Assume that it is possible to reduce the normal time to the minimum time in small steps and that the extra cost incurred will be proportional to the time saved.

(a) draw a network diagram for the contract and identify the critical path assuming that normal procedures are adopted,

(b) recommend what programme should be followed if the job must be completed in 30 days, and calculate the total cost for that programme, and

(c) explain how you would modify your analysis if the estimates were subject to uncertainty. Illustrate your answer by assuming that estimates of the time required for E are uncertain. Normal time is expected to be in the range 12 to 20 days, but 2 days could still be saved by spending an extra £3000. You remain confident about the estimates for other activities. Target time for the contract is 30 days and there would be a penalty of £5000 for late completion.

(Institute of Chartered Accountants in England and Wales)

7-6 Consider the activities required to complete the processing of a customer's order:

Activity	Preceding activities	Average time in days	Normal variable cost per day £
1. Receipt of order, checking credit rating, etc.	—	2	5
2. Preparation of material specification, availability of material, etc.	1	4	10
3. Inspection, packing, etc.	2	1	7
4. Arrangement of transport facilities, etc.	1	5	5
5. Delivery	3, 4	3	2

The time for activities 1, 3, and 5 are fixed; for activity 2 there is a 0.5 probability that it will require 2 days and a 0.5 probability that it will require 6 days; for activity 4 a 0.7 probability of taking 4 days, 0.2 of taking 6 days, and 0.1 of taking 10 days.

(a) draw the network twice, first using an arrow diagram and secondly an activity-on-node presentation, clearly indicating the meaning of any symbols that you use;

(b) indicate the critical path, calculate average duration and variable cost under normal conditions;

(c) calculate the minimum and maximum times and the probabilities associated with them.

(The Chartered Institute of Management Accountants)

7-7 Consider the project which requires the following activities:

Activity		Activity time in days		Total cost (normal) £	Resources, normal number of men per day
Initial node	Terminal node	Normal	Crash		
0	9	6	3	480	4
0	10	10	5	900	5
10	7	7	4	490	5
7	8	9	2	540	4
9	2	8	4	560	6
3	4	5	2	300	4
7	3	6	3	500	4
6	11	6	3	520	6
1	6	7	4	510	5
8	4	10	5	920	6
4	5	8	4	580	6
2	8	10	5	940	5
0	1	9	6	560	4
11	4	8	4	480	4

The activities that can be crashed must either take the normal time or the crash time. There is no opportunity to reduce the time of an activity by one or two days. The cost of crashing any activity is £100 per day.

(a) calculate the normal duration of the project, its normal cost, and the critical path;

(b) state the number of different paths from start to finish;

(c) calculate the minimum time in which the project can be completed and state the critical activities;

(d) state the maximum number of men required to complete the project if all activities commence at the earliest start date.

(The Chartered Institute of Management Accountants)

7-8 Each autumn an Association prepares and distributes an annual programme. The programme gives dates of meetings and a list of speakers with summaries of their talks. Also included is an up-to-date list of paid-up members. The activities to be carried out to complete the preparation of the programme are as follows:

	Activity	Immediate predecessor	Estimated time (days)
A	Select dates for programme	—	4
B	Secure agreement from speakers and prepare summaries of their talks	A	12
C	Obtain advertising material for programme	A	11
D	Mail membership renewal notices	—	20
E	Prepare list of paid-up members	D	6
F	Send membership list to printer and read proofs	B, C, E	7
G	Print and assemble programme	F	10
H	Obtain computer-printed address labels of members	E	5
I	Send out programmes	G, H	4

(a) Draw a network for the scheme of activities set out above. Include full information on earliest and latest event times and indicate the critical path.

(b) Draw a bar chart for the scheme and state the total float for each activity.

(c) If each activity requires one member of the office staff of the Association, so that the activities may be completed in the estimated times, what is the minimum number of staff that should be allocated to the scheme?

(d) What would be the effect on the total time if one of the allocated staff was taken ill for the duration of the scheme and not replaced?

(Chartered Association of Certified Accountants)

7-9 A firm operates in a highly competitive fashion accessories industry where speed of response in adapting or extending the product range is essential. Management have, over time, developed a broad strategy for getting a new product on to the market rapidly and ahead of the competition. Once a possible 'trend' is recognized, in principle approval is sought from senior management (taking 4 days) to undertake the quick response process, but even while this approval is being sought it is already agreed that an initial design can be prepared (taking 7 days). When approval is received and the initial design is available, market research staff then sample representative potential customers for their reactions (12 days). As a result of the market research, design staff produce a final specification for the product (6 days), while other staff assess the strengths and weaknesses of the likely competition (10 days). When the finalized design is available, costings are prepared (5 days) and at the same time production equipment is set up (2 days). As soon as the costings are available and the likely competition has been weighed up, senior management approval is sought to proceed with manufacture (the approval process takes 5 days). As soon as approval to proceed has been given and the equipment has been set up, manufacture can commence (this takes 14 days). Meanwhile, on the basis of the costings and the survey of the competition (and without needing further managerial approval), the pricing and promotional strategy is set out (taking 7 days). When manufacturing is complete and when the promotional strategy has been decided the product is packaged and delivered (4 days).

    (i) Construct the dependency table for the entire process on the basis of the above information.

    (ii) Draw the network diagram.

    (iii) Calculate the early event time for each event and identify the critical path.

    (iv) How much longer would the survey of competitors have to take in order to have an adverse effect on overall completion time?

Solution guides

7-2 (i) The critical path consists of jobs A B E F G J K.

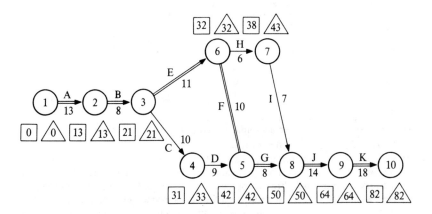

(ii)

Job	Total float	Free float
C	2	0
D	2	2
H	5	0
I	5	5

(iii) By changes of logic (repositioning jobs) or speedings up. In either case, the critical path must be affected. In the case of speeding-up, this usually requires further resources to be applied to the job. If these resources are drawn from outside the system, then there is only cost to consider. If the resources have to be drawn from other—presently non-critical—jobs, thus slowing them down, the problem is more complex. If time on job G is halved, the original path remains critical, 4 days are saved overall, and node 8 is reached after 46 days. However, if, in order to speed up G, resources are drawn from *I* with the effect that it is slowed down by 2 days, then the critical path switches to include EHI and only 3 days are saved overall, node (8) being reached after 47 days.

7-3 (i), (ii), (iii)

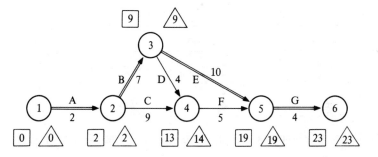

The critical path joins events 1-2-3-5-6 and consists of activities A, B, E, and G. It is shown as ⇒ above.

(iv) Activity	Total float	Free float
A	0	0
B	0	0
C	3	2
D	1	0
E	0	0
F	1	1
G	0	0

(v) One day. A B D F G becomes uniquely critical.

7-4 (a) 17 days. Cost £1910 + £400 penalty = £2310.

(b) Two days to be saved from critical path. CP consists of activities 1-2, 2-4, 4-6, 6-7. The *cost per day saved* is least (£70) in 4-6 and both days can be saved here. Check with the network to see that no other path becomes critical. Revised cost = £1910 + 140 = £2050.

(c) Here a trade-off must be made between the bonus payments on the one hand and the costs of time savings on the other. Overall time reductions that can be achieved for less than £100 per day will be worth while. It is soon evident that the optimal arrangement is 4-6 in 4 days and 6-7 in 1 day, other jobs at normal times. Duration 11 days, cost £2410 − £400, bonus = £2010.

(d) Save 4 days in 6-7, cost = 360
 2 days in 4-6, cost = 140
 1 day in 5-6, cost = 70

 570

∴ Total cost here = £1910 + 570 = £2480

7-5 (a)

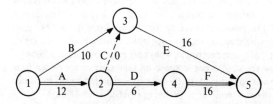

The critical path consists of A, D, F and takes 34 days at normal times.

(b) Prepare a table showing cost per day saved.

Job	Cost/day saved	Max. saving
A	1000	4
D	500	2
E	1500	2
F	600	8

All paths must be completed in 30 days. The only non-critical paths are BE and ACE which take less than 30 days even at normal times. Thus we need only be concerned with the critical path. The cheapest way of saving 4 days here is to save 2 days in D and 2 in F at an additional cost of £2200. Thus cost is now £31 200 + £2200 = £33 400.

The probability distributions (in full if discrete; type, mean, and variance if continuous) of the job times are needed to find a confidence interval for completion of the whole project. Statements would have to be in terms of probabilities and expected values. The problematical path is ACE which *could* take 32 days if E took 20 days. As no probabilities are given, no expected value calculations are possible. However, assume that it is desirable to avoid lateness with probability one. The cheapest way to do this is by saving 2 days in job A at a cost of £2000.

7-6 (a) The two variants of the network diagram are shown below. The arrow or more correctly the arc–node diagram is the earlier form and is still more widely used. The activity-on-the-node or precedence diagram form has advantages (dummies are never required, easier to construct networks from dependency tables) but has not really caught on.

Arc–node form:

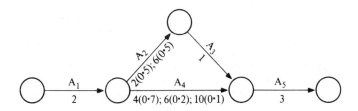

Activity on the node form:

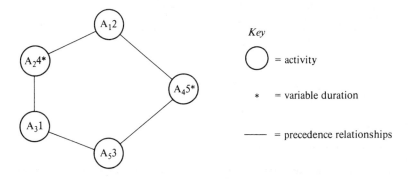

Key

◯ = activity

∗ = variable duration

—— = precedence relationships

(b) There are only two paths. If *average* times are used both are critical. After the event, of course, only one will have transpired to be critical. It is somewhat more likely that the $A_1 A_4 A_5$ path will be critical. The full range of possibilities is:

Path	Time	Probability
$A_1 A_2 A_3 A_5$	8	0.5
$A_1 A_2 A_3 A_5$	12	0.5
$A_1 A_4 A_5$	9	0.7
$A_1 A_4 A_5$	11	0.2
$A_1 A_4 A_5$	15	0.1

The only occasions when the $A_1 A_2 A_3 A_5$ path can be critical are when the 12-day time occurs and the $A_1 A_4 A_5$ path takes 9 or 11 days. The chance of this is $0.5(0.7 + 0.2) = 0.45$. Thus the probability that $A_1 A_4 A_5$ is critical is 0.55. The average or expected completion time for the network is 11.15 days. The workings are as follows:

(1) $A_1 A_2 A_3 A_5$ time	(2) prob	(3) $A_1 A_4 A_5$ time	(4) prob	(5) Max(1),(3)	(6) (2) × (4)	(7) (5) × (6)
8	0.5	9	0.7	9	0.35	3.15
8	0.5	11	0.2	11	0.10	1.10
8	0.5	15	0.1	15	0.05	0.75
12	0.5	9	0.7	12	0.35	4.20
12	0.5	11	0.2	12	0.10	1.20
12	0.5	15	0.1	15	0.05	0.75
					mean time =	11.15

Column (5) gives the larger of the times for the two paths and columns (6) is the chance of the particular situation arising. As to cost, the costs of $A_1, A_3,$ and A_5 are fixed and total 23. The average cost of A_2 and A_4 is 65 as shown below. Thus the average cost for the whole project is $65 + 23 = 88$.

(1) A_2 time	(2) A_4 time	(3) prob	(4) A_2, A_4 cost	(5) (3) × (4)
2	4	0.35	40	14
2	6	0.10	50	5
2	10	0.05	70	3.5
6	4	0.35	80	28
6	6	0.10	90	9
6	10	0.05	110	5.5
				65

(c) From the above workings the minimum time is 9 days with probability 0.35 and the maximum time is 15 days with probability 0.10.

7-7 The network for this project is:

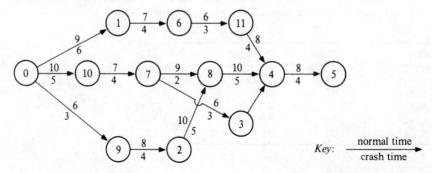

Key: $\dfrac{\text{normal time}}{\text{crash time}}$

(a), (b) There are just four paths, the longest of which at normal durations is 0–10–7–8–4–5 taking 44 days. The normal cost of the project is just the sum of the entries in the normal cost column; £8280.

(c) When crash times are used on all jobs the minimum completion time is 21 days. Two paths are now jointly critical: 0–9–2–8–4–5 and 0–1–6–11–4–5. Note that it is not necessary to crash both of 7–3 and 3–4; one of these could be left at the normal duration saving £300.

(d) Use of a bar chart shows that the maximum number of men required at any one time is 19.

7-8 (a) The network for the project is shown below. Note that two dummies are required. J is required because, by convention in this format, two nodes are joined by only one arc. K is required to ensure the correct precedence relationships. The critical path joins nodes 1 3 5 6 7 8 9 and comprises jobs D E (K) F G I.

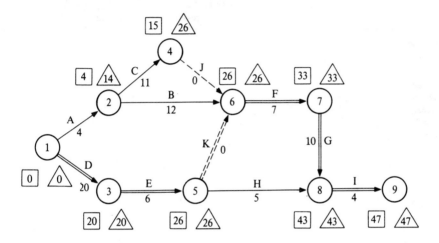

(b) A bar chart for the project is shown below:

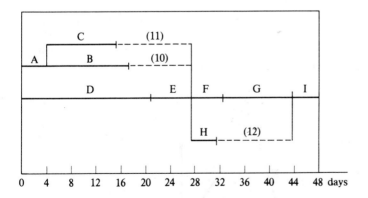

In this case the lengths of the activities (bars) correspond to duration. The figures in brackets after C, B, and H represent free float in those jobs. Note that no dummy activities are required in this format.

(c) Three. At no time are more than three activities being worked upon simultaneously. This is evident from the bar chart.

(d) One day's delay (48 now required). C can be worked on after B or B after C. This would delay the start of F by only one day.

7-9 (i) It is not difficult to write down the listing of jobs and attach alphabetical labels to them. Similarly, the job time estimates are simply entered directly into the final column. The more difficult part is in establishing the immediate predecessor (sequence) relationships. The key words to look for in the verbal description are words and phrases such as 'once', 'when', 'then', 'as a result of', 'as soon as', 'on the basis of' which imply strict ordering. A further key word in this context is 'and' which implies more than one job entering or leaving a node. Words such as 'meanwhile', 'while', 'at the same time as' mean that no order relationship exists between jobs involved. The resulting dependency table is:

Job	Job label	Immediate predecessor	Job time
Approval in principle	a	—	4
Initial design	b	—	7
Market research	c	a, b	12
Final specification	d	c	6
Assess competition	e	c	10
Costing	f	d	5
Production set-up	g	d	2
Management approval	h	e, f	5
Manufacture	i	g, h	14
Price/promotion strategy	j	e, f	7
Package/deliver	k	i, j	4

(ii) The network diagram for the process is shown below. Note that a zero-time dummy is required after Job a (as shown here) or after Job b.

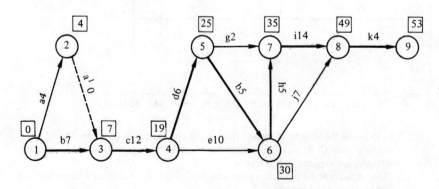

(iii) The early event times are shown at the nodes in the diagram. The critical path indicated with double arrows consists of Jobs b, c, d, f, h, i, k and takes 53 days to complete.

(iv) If surveying competitors (Job e) took more than one extra day, delay would follow since event 6 would be set back beyond 30 days. The change in the critical path would be that Jobs d and f were no longer critical while Job e would be critical. Other critical jobs are unchanged.

REFERENCES

Cohen, S. S. (1985), *Operational Research*, Edward Arnold.

Wilkes, F. M. (1983) *Capital Budgeting Techniques*, second edition, Wiley.

FURTHER READING

Anderson, D. R., Sweeney, D. J., and Williams, T. A. (1985), *An Introduction to Management Science*, fourth edition, West Publishing Company. Contains description of PERT/cost and links with linear programming.

Cook, T. M., and Russell, R. A. (1981), *Introduction to Management Science*, second edition, Prentice Hall. Links PERT to company cash flow and cumulative expenditures.

Littlechild, S. C. (1977), *Operational Research for Managers*, Philip Allan. Contains discussion of PERT/time and an application of network analysis to maintenance planning.

Monks, J. G. (1985), *Operations Management, Theory and Problems*, second edition, McGraw-Hill. Contains description of Gantt charts and PERT/time.

EIGHT

STOCK CONTROL

8-1 INTRODUCTION

As much as 20 to 25 per cent of the total assets of manufacturing industry take the form of stock. This proportion can rise to around 40 per cent in the retail sector. So more efficient inventory policies can bring major financial gains and improvements to overall company performance.

Inventory is classified into three main types dependent upon the stage of the production process at which it is held. Specifically distinguished are *pre-production inventory*, in-process inventory and *finished goods inventory*.

Pre-production inventory consists of raw materials and bought-in components or other inputs secured from outside the firm. In-process inventory is work-in-progress and may be held at several points in the production process. Finished goods inventory consists of the firm's products from which sales are drawn.

More generally *any* temporarily idle resource could be thought of an inventory. Stocks have been described as 'money in disguise'—indeed the stock may be of money itself as in the holding of cash. Some cash management problems can, in principle, fit the stock control framework.

The main purpose of inventory is to allow each stage of the production and sales process to operate economically by insulating them from different or varying rates of activity at other stages. Finished goods inventory, for example, acts as a cushion between production and sales. Even when demand is at a constant rate it may be uneconomical to produce continually at that rate. For example, if a manufacturer makes 50 different sizes of wheel, economies of scale can be gained by making a year's supply of each in 50 separate production runs, averaging one week. If sales are erratic or periodic, it would be hopelessly expensive to try to keep production in step with demand. Inventory is insurance against the inability to satisfy demand directly from current production. Similar considerations apply within the production process itself. If a product must be processed on several machines which operate at different rates or at different times then in-process inventory is desirable. Even if the different stages of production operate at the same rates and the same times, mechanical failures will not be simultaneous so that in-process inventory still has a useful function to perform.

The entire production process may need insulating from irregularities in the arrival of supplies. The price of this security is the cost of holding pre-production inventory. Where security of supply is not considered to be a problem (for example, when components come from other parts of the same organization), a just-in-time approach may save considerable sums.

Raw materials may also be held for speculative reasons if there are expectations of rising commodity prices. The role of inventories as buffers is shown schematically in Fig. 8-1 in which manufacturing takes place on two machines in sequence. There are valid and invalid reasons for holding stock. It has rightly been said that 'stocks buy organization' to the extent that inefficient production and distribution can be masked and sustained by excessive stock levels.

The stock control problem is to find the ideal balance between the costs and benefits of inventory. We shall be looking for the best obtainable stock control *policies* in a variety of situations. A stock control policy is a rule or collection of rules which determine:

1. the size of stock replenishments
2. the timing of replenishments
3. stock-out consequences

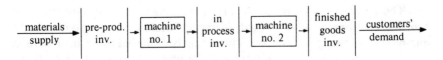

Figure 8-1

In the main, the models that follow are expressed in terms of finished goods inventory for a single product. Similar principles apply to in-process or pre-production inventory, although MRP methods (section 15) may be particularly relevant here.

8-2 THE CLASSICAL STATIC MODEL

This fundamental stock control model dates back over 70 years and has formed the basis of many more advanced models. The assumptions employed by the classical static model are:

1. A single item of stock.
2. All parameters known and constant.
3. Instantaneous replenishment of stock.
4. No variable re-order costs.

The parameters referred to in assumption (2) are data for costs and for the rate of demand (or in general, rate of depletion) of stock. Figure 8-2 shows the graph of inventory level against time and has the characteristic 'saw-tooth' shape. The problem is to determine the best value of q, the replenishment size. The diagram starts with inventory at its maximum level, q, which declines at the uniform rate. When stocks have fallen to zero level, it is assumed that they are immediately replenished in full.

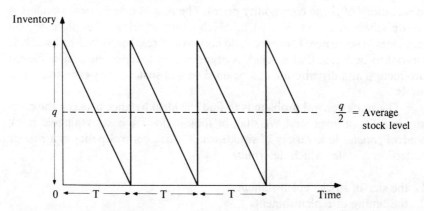

Figure 8-2

The length of time required for stocks to go from peak-to-peak (or equivalently from trough-to-trough) is one inventory *cycle*. We do not aim to minimize costs per cycle, however. This would be achieved by setting $q = 0$ and keeping no inventory at all. Rather it is the objective to minimize costs *per annum* (or some other suitable length of time). Now consider costs in more detail. The costs fall into two categories: (a) *holding costs* and (b) *replenishment costs*.

Under the heading of holding costs are included storage, insurance, deterioration, and interest charges. The second category relates to replacement of stock. There will normally be a fixed and a variable component here. The fixed component will include administrative costs of placing an order if supplies are brought in from outside or the set-up costs of machinery if the goods are produced by the firm itself. Variable costs depend on the amount re-ordered. The following notation will be employed:

C_m = the cost of procuring one unit of the item
$i \cdot C_m$ = the cost of holding one item in stock for one year
C_O = the fixed cost of a replenishment order of *any* size
A = the annual rate of demand

The use of the term $i \cdot C_m$ for the holding cost reflects the view that it is frequently the case that annual holding costs are proportional to the value (cost) of an item stocked. The factor of proportionality, i, might typically take values around 0.2 or 0.3.

First consider the annual holding costs. From the holding cost point of view it is as if half the maximum level of inventory was being constantly held throughout the year. This being so we can write:

$$\text{Total holding costs per annum} = \frac{q}{2} \cdot i \cdot C_m \qquad (8\text{-}1)$$

Assumption (4) of the basic model means that, for the moment, procurement costs will be ignored. They will be specifically brought into the model in section 8-3.

Costs arising from replenishment will be C_O times the number of stock refills needed. If annual demand is for A units of stock and replenishment size is q units then there will be A/q replenishments needed. Thus we can write:

$$\text{Total replenishment costs per annum} = \frac{C_O A}{q} \qquad (8\text{-}2)$$

So that, overall, total costs per annum, C, are given by:

$$C = \frac{q}{2} \cdot i \cdot C_m + \frac{C_O A}{q} \qquad (8\text{-}3)$$

The only unknown on the right-hand side of Eq. (8-3) is q, and we wish to determine the value of q which minimizes C. Figure 8-3 graphs the situation. Total costs and each component of costs are graphed against replenishment

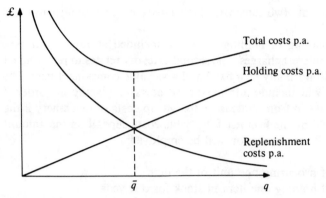

Figure 8-3

size q. The ideal value of q is that corresponding to the lowest point of the total cost curve; this is marked as $\bar{q}$. Although it so happens with this model that the minimum of the total cost curve is above the intersection point of the holding and replenishment cost curves, it is *rates of change* that are important. What is being sought is an optimal balance or trade-off between those costs which rise with q (holding costs) and those which fall with q (replenishment costs). The optimal balance is struck where the rate at which holding costs are going up is equal to the rate at which replenishment costs are coming down.

Minimizing C with respect to q in equation 8-3 requires that the first derivative be set equal to zero. Thus:

$$\frac{dC}{dq} = iC_m - \frac{C_oA}{q^2} = 0 \tag{8-4}$$

The second derivative requires that, for a minimum of C:

$$\frac{d^2C}{dq^2} = \frac{2C_oA}{q^3} \geq 0 \tag{8-5}$$

Since C_o and A are positive numbers, this condition will be fulfilled for any positive value of q. Returning to the first order condition (8-4).

The slope of the holding costs line is $i \cdot C_m/2$ and the slope of the replenishment costs curve is $-C_oA/q^2$. That is, replenishment costs are *coming down* at the rate of C_oA/q^2. So that to find the best value of q we set:

$$\frac{i \cdot C_m}{2} = \frac{C_oA}{q^2}$$

$$\therefore \ q^2 = \frac{2AC_o}{i \cdot C_m}$$

$$\therefore \quad q = \sqrt{\frac{2AC_O}{i \cdot C_m}} = \bar{q} \tag{8-6}$$

Equation (8-6) is most important. It is known as the *square root rule*. The best value of q, $\bar{q}$ is called the *economic lot size* (ELS), or *economic order quantity* (EOQ), or *economic batch size* (EBS). Generally we shall use the term EOQ here.

Inserting the EOQ value of q given by (8-6) into the cost expression (8-3) gives:

$$C = \sqrt{\frac{AC_O i \cdot C_m}{2}} + \frac{C_O A \sqrt{i \cdot C_m}}{\sqrt{2C_O A}} \tag{8-7}$$

$$= \sqrt{2AC_O i \cdot C_m} \tag{8-8}$$

The two components of (8-7) are equal as indicated by Fig. 8-3, while (8-8) shows the overall minimal achievable level of inventory costs. Note that as between (8-6) and (8-8) the optimal level of inventory varies inversely with $i \cdot C_m$ while the level of costs varies directly with the holding cost figure. In both cases, the effects of changing $i \cdot C_m$ are 'damped' by the square root.

Consider an example.

A company faces demand of 2000 items per annum. Stock replenishment costs are fixed at £100 irrespective of the scale of replenishment. It costs £2.50 to hold one item in stock for one year. Calculate the EOQ.

Clearly $C_O = 100$, $A = 2000$, and $i \cdot C_m = 2.5$. Thus substituting in the EOQ formula gives:

$$\bar{q} = \sqrt{\frac{2(100)(2000)}{2.5}} = \sqrt{160\,000} = 400$$

So the EOQ is 400 units and 5 replenishments will be needed each year.

Note that if annual sales double to 4000 units per annum with other parameters unchanged, the optimal level of inventory will increase by a factor $\sqrt{2}$ to 565.69. The square root rule confutes a commonsense 'rule of thumb' that if sales double so should stocks. Thus, if demand *did* double to 4000, optimal costs given by (8-8) would be £1414.21. If an EOQ of 800 had been used corresponding annual inventory costs given by (8-3) would be £1500.

Now consider a further example. A company's stock is depleted at the constant rate of 10 units per day. Storage costs per unit, per calendar month, are 40p. Cost per re-order is £150. At what intervals should replenishments be made?

On an annual basis $A = 3650$, $i \cdot C_m = 4.8$, and $C_O = 150$. First find the

EOQ. This will be:

$$\bar{q} = \sqrt{\frac{2(150)(3650)}{4.8}} = 477.62$$

Again, ignoring the problems of fractions for the moment, a replenishment size of 477.62 with an annual demand of 3650 means that there will be $3650 \div 477.62 = 7.64$ replenishments needed per annum which produces the interval between replenishments (as we should expect from the daily demand figure) of 47.76 days.

There would be no dramatic rise in costs if these figures were rounded off to $\bar{q} = 480$ ordered every 48 days as substitution in (8-3) will confirm. Annual costs C are not sensitive to small variations in q, in the neighbourhood of $\bar{q}$. The damping effect given by the square root means that the EOQ rule is robust with respect to minor errors or uncertainties in parameter values. The reader may confirm this fact by making a gross rounding of $\bar{q}$ to 500 and checking the still minimal effect on cost.

We shall now consider the effects of dropping the restrictive assumptions of the classical static model, beginning with re-order costs.

8-3 VARIABLE RE-ORDER COSTS

Re-order costs in practice will vary with the size of re-order due to the unit cost of the commodity. In this case in addition to the costs so far considered the firm has to pay C_m per unit to acquire the item for stock. If the firm is manufacturing the good itself, then C_m will usually be the unit variable costs of production. If the firm is a wholesaler or retailer then it will be charged C_m per unit ordered. It is assumed that C_m is a known constant. In this case, re-order costs for a re-order of size q will not be $C_o + C_m \cdot q$ and there will still be A/q re-orders necessary per annum. Total costs per annum are now given by:

$$C = \frac{q}{2} \cdot i \cdot C_m + (C_o + C_m \cdot q)\frac{A}{q} = \frac{q}{2} \cdot i \cdot C_m + \frac{C_o A}{q} + C_m \cdot A \qquad (8\text{-}9)$$

From Eq. (8-9) it is evident that the EOQ remains unchanged since $C_m \cdot A$ is a constant term. Annual costs themselves are increased but it still pays to replenish stock in the same quantities as before. All this assumes, of course, that the firm intends to satisfy fully the total annual demand. Thus the EOQ formula still applies. All this does not mean that the unit cost figure can always be ignored, as we shall shortly see. What it does illustrate is that the validity of a model cannot always be measured by the plausibility of its central assumptions.

Consider now the example of a builders supply merchants which holds stocks of a certain type of tap and demand for the taps is at the rate of 250 units per quarter. It costs £2 to hold one tap for a year and the merchant's administrative costs of placing a re-order with the manufacturer are £10. The manufacturer at present charges £3 per tap supplied plus a charge of £30 per re-order irrespective of re-order size.

The product manufacturer has, however, recently offered an alternative scheme of charges. The price per tap would come down to £2.50 but the charge per re-order would be increased by £120. Is this new arrangement advantageous?

In order to answer the question of EOQ and consequent annual cost figures must be worked out under each arrangement; that which produces the lowest cost being preferred.

In the first instance $i \cdot C_m = £2$, $C_o = £40$ (including the manufacturer's charge) $C_m = £3$ and $A = 1000$ units per annum. Thus the resulting EOQ is:

$$\bar{q} = \sqrt{\frac{2 \times 40 \times 1000}{2}} = 200$$

and the resulting annual costs are:

$$C = \tfrac{1}{2} \times 200 \times 2 + \frac{40 \times 1000}{200} + 3 \times 1000 = 3400$$

Under the alternative scheme the EOQ would be:

$$\bar{q} = \sqrt{\frac{2 \times 160 \times 1000}{2}} = 400$$

and annual costs would be:

$$C = \tfrac{1}{2} \times 400 \times 2 + \frac{160 \times 1000}{400} + 2.5 \times 1000 = 3300$$

so that the new arrangement would produce a saving of £100 per annum for the merchant. While both holding costs and re-order costs have increased this has been more than compensated for by the reduced value of C_m.

8-4 CASH MANAGEMENT MODEL

Certain cash management situations can be structured as inventory problems. Useful order-of-magnitude results can be obtained and insight gained into the structure of the problems. The following example also continues the theme of variable re-order costs and shows how the basic model can deal with inflows as well as outflows.

Ace Enterprises receives, at a steady rate, inflows of cash amounting to £350 000 per annum. The cash can be invested in securities to earn 12 per cent p.a. Each time that an investment is made there is a brokerage charge of £50 + 1 per cent of the sum invested. How many investments of cash should be made annually? An alternative scheme of brokerage charges is £100 + 0.8 per cent of the sum invested. Which scheme would Ace Enterprises prefer?

The reason that the cash is not immediately placed in securities is because of the fixed element in the brokerage charges. The company needs to ascertain the ideal size of investment and hence with the given annual inflow the number of investments to make each year. The situation is graphed in Fig. 8-4 with q representing the size of investment.

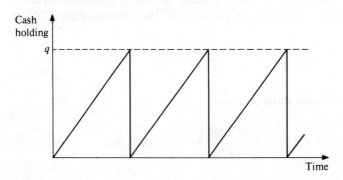

Figure 8-4

The average holding of cash is $q/2$ and the cost of holding £1 in cash for one year is £0.12, the forgone interest. In the original scheme $C_m = £0.01$ and with A at 350 000 and C_O at £50 the square root formula produces:

$$\bar{q} = \sqrt{\frac{2 \times 50 \times 350\,000}{0.12}} = 17\,078$$

so that the optimum number of investments per annum will be:

$$\frac{350\,000}{17\,078} = 20.49$$

or, for practical purposes, 41 in two years. Total cost works out at:

$$C = \frac{17\,078}{2} \times 0.12 + \frac{50 \times 350\,000}{17\,078} + 0.01 \times 350\,000 \simeq £5549$$

For the alternative scheme of charges we have:

$$\bar{q} = \sqrt{\frac{2 \times 100 \times 350\,000}{0.12}} \simeq 24\,152$$

and annual costs would be:

$$C = \frac{24\,152}{2} \times 0.12 + \frac{100 \times 350\,000}{24\,152} + 0.008 \times 350\,000 \simeq £5698$$

Thus Ace Enterprises should stay with the original scheme.

8-5 LEAD TIME

Having considered the consequences of relaxing assumption four of the classical static model let us turn our attention to assumption three—instantaneous stock replenishment—and determine the consequences of its removal.

Lead time, also known as *delivery lag*, is the delay between the time of placement of an order for replenishment of stock and the time of arrival of the goods in inventory. So far we have been assuming zero lead time (instantaneous replenishment). Let us now suppose that lead time is a known and fixed number of weeks, say L weeks. The effects of this change of assumption are minimal; the order for replenishment must simply be placed when the amount of inventory falls to the level of lead time demand. This gives us the *re-order level*, R. This is shown in Fig. 8-5.

Suppose for the data of the builders merchant example there is a lead time of 3 weeks ($L = 3$). Assuming a 50-week working year, weekly demand is for 20 units so that the re-order level would be 60 units, the EOQ remaining at 400. Of course, in order to operate this re-order level policy the amount of stock on

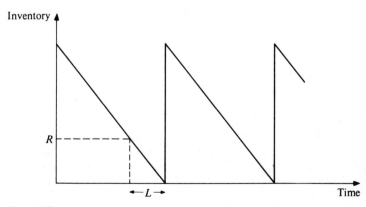

Figure 8-5

hand at any time must be known. The presence of lead time does not, therefore, alter the size of stock replenishment, its frequency or the costs as described by equation (8.9). However, it may increase other costs, as the implementation of a re-order level system requires constant monitoring of stock level. Also, in practice, lead time may be a random variable. This is a point to which we shall return later.

8-6 PRODUCTION RUNS

Many firms that produce a range of several similar products (e.g., different sizes and types of wheel) do not keep all items in continuous production. Rather they have production runs on each item lasting days, weeks, or months. Sometimes the entire anticipated annual demand is produced; on other occasions there may be a number of shorter 'runs' each year. This situation has features in common with both the 'inflow' cash management model of section 8-4 and the non-instantaneous replenishment introduced in section 8-5.

Consider the problem relating to one item produced by a firm (it will be assumed that there are no tight constraints on storage). The decision required is how much to produce at each run. Alternatively, given a steady rate of production, the problem could be re-expressed in terms of the *length of time* that each run should last.

The graph of inventory level over time in this case is shown in Fig. 8-6. Starting from zero level inventory steadily rises while the production run lasts (for time t). The rate of build-up of stock is the excess of the production rate over the demand rate. When the run is completed inventory declines at the demand rate. This model is sometimes called the *build-up model*.

Let the amount produced in time t be q. With the production rate at

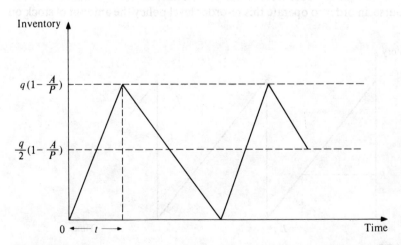

Figure 8-6

P units per annum then $t = q/P$. Demand during the production run is $tA = qA/P$. Maximum inventory will then be given by the total amount produced less demand during the production run. Thus maximum and average inventory are as shown in Fig. 8-6. Annual holding costs will be:

$$\frac{q}{2} i \cdot C_m \left(1 - \frac{A}{P} \right)$$

Replenishment costs per cycle (i.e., per production run) will, as before, be given by $C_O + qC_m$, where C_m is the unit variable production cost and C_O is the cost of setting up the equipment for the run. Total replenishment costs per annum will then be:

$$(C_O + qC_m) \frac{A}{q}$$

so that total costs to be minimized are:

$$\frac{q}{2} i \cdot C_m \left(1 - \frac{A}{P} \right) + (C_O + qC_m) \frac{A}{q}$$

and minimization produces the formula

$$\bar{q} = \sqrt{\frac{2AC_O P}{i \cdot C_m (P - A)}}$$

Note that the value of $\bar{q}$ in this case is the old EOQ formula multiplied by the factor $\sqrt{P/(P-A)}$ so that $\bar{q}$ will be larger than in the instantaneous production rate case. The faster the production rate the nearer is the result to the instantaneous case, since $\sqrt{P/(P-A)}$ approaches unity as P approaches infinity.

Consider an example. Each time that a firm starts a production run of a certain product there are set-up costs of £400. Production is at the rate of 12 000 units p.a. and demand is at the rate of 8000 units p.a. It costs £7.50 to hold one item for one year. How many production runs should there be each year?

Substitution into the formula for $\bar{q}$ gives:

$$\bar{q} = \sqrt{\frac{2 \times 12\,000 \times 400 \times 8000}{7.5(12\,000 - 8000)}} = 1600$$

Thus five runs would be needed each year.

8-7 BUFFER STOCKS

The classical static model assumes that all parameters are known and constant. It is a *deterministic model*. In due course, we shall explore substantial relaxation of this assumption and to lead into this the concept of *buffer stocks* is necessary. Buffer or *safety* stocks are additional inventory held against unforeseen contingencies such as a surge in demand or delay in arrival of replenishment stocks. In a deterministic world, represented by a classical model buffer stocks are never needed since by assumption nothing is unforeseen or stochastic. However, if buffer stocks *were* added in they would represent a level below which inventory would never fall. Both the average level of stock and the re-order level are shifted up by the amount of buffer stock, B. The situation is illustrated in Fig. 8-7. Once again the EOQ is unaffected. Lead time demand is $R - B$, the minimum level of stock is B and the maximum level is $B + \bar{q}$. Both holding costs per annum and total costs rise by $£Bi \cdot C_m$. The reason that buffer stocks are in fact held is that there *are* uncertainties particularly in respect of demand during any time interval and also in respect of the length of lead time itself.

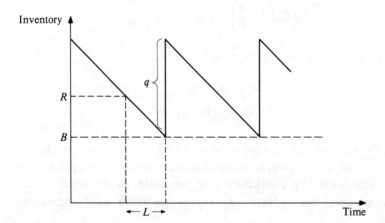

Figure 8-7

The amount demanded in any period is usually a random variable although the *average* rate of demand may be known. Thus instead of the 'sharp' sides of the saw-tooth diagrams we should have the rather ragged edges of Fig. 8-8. If the re-order is now set at *average* lead time demand and there is no buffer stock, then clearly if demand during lead time happens to be brisk all orders during this period cannot be filled at once—a *stock-out* situation occurs. Figure 8-8 has been drawn on the assumption that orders during the stock-out period may be filled as soon as supplies arrive. This is sometimes called the *backlogged demand* situation. This will not always be the case; some

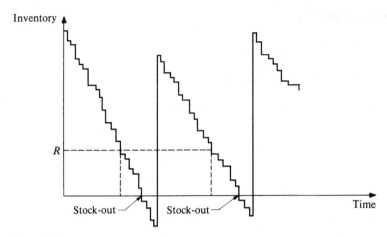

Figure 8-8

orders may be lost. In any event there will almost always be costs associated with stock-outs. These costs relate to lost custom in the future, possible failure to meet contractual liabilities, recompense for delay, etc. Any estimate of stock-out costs will be subject to uncertainty and account must be taken of this fact—it would be foolish to ignore these costs and thus implicitly assume that they are zero. If buffer stocks are kept, then the chance of a stock-out occurring is reduced. The larger the buffer stock the lower the probability of a stock-out each cycle. As buffer stock is increased, expected stock-out costs are reduced but, of course, holding costs increase. Once again the problem is one of finding the best balance—specifically the level of buffer stock which minimizes:

Buffer stock-holding cost (BSHC) + expected stock-out costs (SOC)   (8-10)

in which both BSHC and SOC are expressed on an annual basis. Expression (8-10) represents costs which are *additional* to the holding and re-order costs already determined and can be thought of as *uncertainty costs*. We shall examine two kinds of approach to the problem. The first seeks an overall optimum where there is a known discrete probability distribution of demand.

8-8 OPTIMIZATION WITH STOCHASTIC DEMAND

Consider the following problem in which the objective is to determine firstly the EOQ and the replenishment frequency and in addition to identify the optimal size of buffer stock and hence the re-order level that will minimize the uncertainty costs of 8-10.

A company stocking a single product operates a 50-week working year. Demand for the product in any week is described by the following discrete probability distribution:

Demand (X)	Probability (P)
0	0.07
1	0.10
2	0.11
3	0.13
4	0.15
5	0.17
6	0.13
7	0.08
8	0.04
9	0.02

Demand can only be satisfied (if at all) from stocks. The stock-holding costs are £2 per item per year. Fixed costs per re-order are £8 and the variable re-order costs are £15 per unit. Lead time is one week. The costs of being out of stock are £6 per unit short.

The first step is to determine average weekly demand and hence average annual demand. Multiplying each level of demand by its probability of occurrence and summing the results gives the arithmetic mean weekly demand. Thus a $P \cdot X$ column is formed, the elements of which are:

$$P \cdot X$$
$$0$$
$$0.10$$
$$0.22$$
$$0.39$$
$$0.60$$
$$0.85$$
$$0.78$$
$$0.56$$
$$0.32$$
$$0.18$$

$$\Sigma P \cdot X = 4.00$$

Thus the mean weekly demand is for four units and the mean annual demand $A = 200$. Employing this figure in the familiar square root formula produces

$$\bar{q} = \sqrt{\frac{2 \times 8 \times 200}{2}} = 40$$

So the EOQ is 40 units which would produce an average of *five* cycles per annum. This minimizes the costs of 8-9 (replenishment costs and non-buffer stock holding costs) and completes the first stage of the workings.

In the second stage in order to identify the best re-order level we need to determine the level of buffer stock which minimizes BSHC+SOC. The re-order level will then be $B+4$. Either re-order level, R, or buffer stock, B, can be taken as the decision variable in this stage. The relationship is:

Re-order level = mean lead time demand + buffer stock i.e.:

$$R = LW + B \qquad (8\text{-}11)$$

where L is the number of weeks lead time, W is the mean weekly demand (four units here) and B is buffer stock. Workings here will be expressed in terms of B. Since there is only a small number of possible levels of demand during any week, a process of *complete enumeration* is possible: that is, we shall determine BSHC+SOC for each possible level of buffer stock.

In order to get at the stock-out cost figure, we first need to find the extent of any possible shortages at the end of each cycle. This will vary with the buffer stock level.

Suppose to begin with that buffer stock was zero. Re-order level would then be set at mean lead time demand of four units and shortage would occur if demand during lead time was for five or more units. We must first determine the *expected shortage per cycle* at buffer stock zero. The requisite workings are:

		$B=0$	
Demand (X)	Shortage (S)	Probability (P)	$P \times S$
5	1	0.17	0.17
6	2	0.13	0.26
7	3	0.08	0.24
8	4	0.04	0.16
9	5	0.02	0.10
			$\Sigma PS = 0.93$

It emerges that the expected shortage per cycle, $\Sigma PS = 0.93$. This figure will be used to determine costs later on. The expected shortage per cycle must now be computed for the other possible levels of buffer stock for which workings are shown below. In each case shortage arises when lead time demand exceeds the mean value of four plus the buffer stock. With buffer stock set at five units there can be no shortage since maximum demand is for nine units. Obviously there would be no point in having buffer stock in excess of five.

		$B=1$				$B=2$	
X	S	P	PS	X	S	P	PS
6	1	0.13	0.13	7	1	0.08	0.08
7	2	0.08	0.16	8	2	0.04	0.08
8	3	0.04	0.12	9	3	0.02	0.06
9	4	0.02	0.08				$\Sigma PS=0.22$
			$\Sigma PS=0.49$				

		$B=3$				$B=4$	
X	S	P	PS	X	S	P	PS
8	1	0.04	0.04	9	1	0.02	0.02
9	2	0.02	0.04				$\Sigma PS=0.02$
			$\Sigma PS=0.08$				

Conceivably however buffer stock might be *negative*. If re-order level was set at three units this would correspond to $B=-1$. This situation would be 'desirable' if shortage costs were very low and storage costs high. As will be evident shortly, negative buffer stock is clearly non-optimal in the present case nor should we expect it to be so in practice. We are also taking a short cut in not working with expected surpluses when demand is low. The method can be modified but the effects on the final cost figures are negligible in no case exceeding $\frac{1}{10}$th of 1 per cent of the original value.

The next step is to compile a table in which costs associated with each level of buffer stock are deduced. Suppose that buffer stock is zero. The expected shortage per cycle is 0.93 but since there are on average five cycles per annum expected annual shortage is $5 \times 0.93 = 4.65$ units and, with a shortage cost of £6 per unit short, expected shortage cost per annum will be $6 \times 4.65 = £27.9$. Since there are no buffer stocks BSHC$=0$ and BSHC$+$SOC$=$ £27.9 for $B=0$ and $R=4$. Similar calculations are performed for each value of B and the results are detailed in Fig. 8-9.

(1) B	(2) ESPC	(3)$=5\times(2)$ ESPA	(4)$=6\times(3)$ SOC	(5) BSHC	(6)$=(4)+(5)$ BSHC$+$SOC
0	0.93	4.65	27.9	0	27.9
1	0.49	2.45	14.7	2	16.7
2	0.22	1.10	6.6	4	10.6
3	0.08	0.40	2.4	6	8.4*
4	0.02	0.10	0.6	8	8.6
5	0	0	0	10	10.0

*ESPC$=$expected shortage per cycle, ESPA$=$expected shortage per annum.

Figure 8-9

Entries in column (6) show that the optimal value of B is three units so that the re-order level should be $R = 7$. Clearly, however, there is little to choose between buffer stocks of three or four units and this suggests the question as to how sensitive are the results to variations in the original parameters of the problem. This is the field of sensitivity analysis. In particular there may be considerable uncertainty surrounding the shortage cost figure. We shall now determine the range of values of the shortage cost figure for which the original solution remains optimal.

If the shortage cost figure is S, then the entries in column (6) can be expressed as linear functions of S. The results are:

B	BSHC+SOC
0	$4.65S$
1	$2.45S + 2$
2	$1.1S + 4$
3	$0.4S + 6$
4	$0.1S + 8$
5	10

For the original solution to remain optimal, S must be such that the $B = 3$ cost figure of $0.4S + 6$ must not exceed any of the other values. As the value of S rises, the higher levels of buffer stock may become attractive and so the $B = 4$ and $B = 5$ cost figures will set *upper* bounds on S. Whichever sets the *least upper bound* (LUB) will determine the maximum value to which S can rise. Conversely, the lower values of buffer stock may become attractive as S falls. Each entry in the cost column for $B = 0$ to $B = 2$ will set a *lower* bound for S and the *greatest lower bound* (GLB) is the relevant one. The workings are

$$0.4S + 6 \leqslant 0.1S + 8$$
$$\therefore \ S \leqslant 6.67 \qquad \text{*LUB}$$
$$0.4S + 6 \leqslant 10$$
$$\therefore \ S \leqslant 10$$
$$0.4S + 6 \leqslant 1.1S + 4$$
$$\therefore \ S \geqslant 2.86 \qquad \text{*GLB}$$
$$0.4S + 6 \leqslant 2.45S + 2$$
$$\therefore \ S \geqslant 1.95$$
$$0.4S + 6 \leqslant 4.65S$$
$$\therefore \ S \geqslant 1.41$$

Thus provided that the true value of S lies in the range

$$2.86 \leqslant S \leqslant 6.67$$

none of the alternative values of B produces a lesser cost figure than $B=3$.

Sensitivity analysis on the other parameters—for instance C_O—can also be carried out. The workings in these cases are somewhat less straightforward as the EOQ value and hence the number of cycles per annum are affected by variations in C_O, A or iC_m. Consider the fixed cost per re-order C_O. As a function of C_O the EOQ is given by:

$$\bar{q}=\sqrt{\frac{2\times C_O\times 200}{2}}$$

$$=\sqrt{200}\sqrt{C_O}$$

Thus, the number of cycles per annum will be:

$$\frac{200}{\bar{q}}=\frac{\sqrt{200}}{\sqrt{C_O}}$$

In Fig. 8-10, the stock-out costs per cycle (the entries in column 2 of Fig. 8-9 multiplied by 6) and resulting total costs as a function of F are tabulated. For example, if $B=0$, SOC per annum will be:

$$\frac{5.58\sqrt{200}}{\sqrt{C_O}}=\frac{78.91}{\sqrt{C_O}}$$

B	SOC per cycle	SOC per annum	Total
0	5.58	$78.91/\sqrt{C_O}$	$78.91/\sqrt{C_O}$
1	2.94	$41.57/\sqrt{C_O}$	$2+41.57/\sqrt{C_O}$
2	1.32	$18.66/\sqrt{C_O}$	$4+18.66/\sqrt{C_O}$
3	0.48	$6.79/\sqrt{C_O}$	$6+6.79/\sqrt{C_O}$
4	0.12	$1.70/\sqrt{C_O}$	$8+1.70/\sqrt{C_O}$
5	0	0	10

Figure 8-10

The figure for total uncertainty costs in the final column is the SOC per annum plus BSHC as before.

For $B=3$ to remain optimal, the corresponding level of costs in the final column $6+6.79/\sqrt{C_O}$ must not exceed any of the other entries in the column. The resulting tolerance interval for C_O is:

$$6.48\leqslant C_O\leqslant 35.25$$

Clearly, the optimal level of buffer stock is more sensitive to downward movements in C_O from its original value of 8 than it is to increases. Tolerance intervals for iC_m and A could be calculated in a similar manner.

8-9 SERVICE LEVEL APPROACH

Practical objectives in stock control are often expressed in terms of *service level*. This may be defined in a number of ways, two of which we consider in this and the following section. Here we define service level as the probability expressed as a percentage of being able to fulfil an order from stock during lead time. This has been called the vendor service level by Lewis (1981). A 99 per cent service level corresponds to buffer stock and re-order level being set so as to achieve a 1 per cent lead time stock-out probability.

The level of service chosen in any particular case may be dictated by competitive conditions or selected from a range of alternatives to minimize estimated uncertainty costs for the vendor of the product. A service level approach is often indicated when demand is described by a continuous probability distribution rather than the more easily managed discrete case of section 8-8.

To see an example of the service level approach, suppose that a firm experiences demand for its single item of stock averaging W units per week. Demand in each week is independent of other weeks and is closely approximated by a normal distribution with variance of σ^2. Lead time is L weeks. During lead time as a whole average demand will then be LW units with variance $L\sigma^2$ and standard deviation $\sigma\sqrt{L}$. The distribution of lead time demand is graphed in Fig. 8-11.

As with any normal distribution, there is a 95 per cent chance that demand will be within 1.96 standard deviations of the mean. That is, 95 per cent of the area under the curve will be within the range $LW \pm 1.96\sigma\sqrt{L}$ and

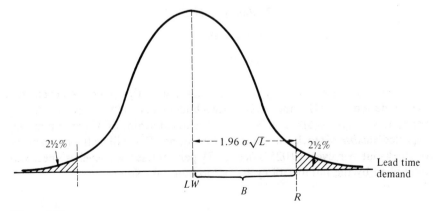

Figure 8-11

just $2\frac{1}{2}$ per cent of the area under the curve will correspond to extremely high demand or extremely low demand outside of this interval. Since it is only the occurrence of *high* demand that can lead to a stock-out, if at the beginning of lead time the re-order level R is set at

$$R = LW + 1.96\sigma\sqrt{L} \qquad (8\text{-}12)$$

this will correspond to a $97\frac{1}{2}$ per cent level of service. In (8-12) $1.96\sigma\sqrt{L}$ represents buffer stock B. High service levels correspond to greater buffer stock. Table 6 (page 494) shows the service level (as a decimal) achieved if buffer stock is set at Z standard deviations above the mean (i.e. $Z\sigma\sqrt{L}$). For example, with $Z = 1.81$ the chance that lead time demand will not be more than 1.81 lead time standard deviations greater than the mean is 0.9649 corresponding to a 96.49 per cent level of service and a 98.3 per cent level of service is achieved if buffer stock is set at $2.12\sigma\sqrt{L}$. If *no* buffer stock is held, Table 6 and Fig. 8-11 confirm that just 50 per cent customers will have orders fulfilled from stock during the lead time period. This also follows directly from the fact that LW is *average* lead time demand.

Consider a numerical example. A company has average annual demand for stock of 7500 units. The cost of holding one item of stock for one year is £3. Fixed costs per re-order are £200. Lead time is 4 weeks. There is a 50-week working/sales year. Standard deviation (σ) of demand in any week is 25 units. Demand in any week is normally distributed about the mean and is independent of demand in other weeks. Each stock-out (regardless of extent) is costed at £400. The company wishes to decide between $97\frac{1}{2}$ per cent and 90 per cent levels of service.

Annual demand of 7500 corresponds to weekly demand of $w = 150$ with a 50-week year. With $L = 4$ and $\sigma = 25$ the re-order level to give a $97\frac{1}{2}$ per cent service level is obtained by substitution in (8-12). So:

$$R = 600 + 1.96(25)(2)$$
$$= 600 + 98$$
$$= 698$$

Now consider the uncertainty costs associated with this policy. As ever, this will be the sum of BSHC and SOC. Since a buffer stock of 98 is kept, the BSHC per annum will be $98(3) = 294$. Now in order to determine SOC per annum the expected *number* of stock-outs must first be found. This will be the probability of stock-out per cycle (0.025 since a $97\frac{1}{2}$ per cent service level is specified) multiplied by the number of cycles per annum (n). Now

$$n = \frac{A}{\text{EOQ}}$$

where A is annual demand. The EOQ is given by the square root rule as:

$$EOQ = \sqrt{\frac{2(7500)(200)}{3}} = 1000$$

So that:

$$n = \frac{7500}{1000} = 7.5$$

with 7.5 inventory cycles per annum the expected number of stock-outs will be $7.5(0.025) = 0.1875$ and the expected stock-out costs per annum will be $0.1875(400) = £75$. So the uncertainty costs, u, with a $97\frac{1}{2}$ per cent of service level will be:

$$u = BSHC + SOC$$

$$= 294 + 75$$

$$= 369$$

Now consider the alternative 90 per cent service level. First note that the 'non-uncertainty costs'—the holding and replenishment costs—do not change with service level. The only difference is the uncertainty costs. With a 90 per cent level of service, buffer stock will be 1.28 standard deviations of lead time demand above the average (from Table 6, page 494). So:

$$B = 1.28\sigma\sqrt{L}$$

$$= 1.28(25)(2)$$

$$= 64$$

and buffer stock holding costs will therefore be $64(3) = 192$. A 90 per cent service level means a 0.1 probability of stock-out per cycle, so the expected number of stock-outs per annum will be $7.5(0.1) = 0.75$ with a corresponding level of expected cost of $0.75(400) = 300$. So uncertainty costs overall are:

$$u = BSHC + SOC$$

$$= 192 + 300$$

$$= 492$$

Thus the $97\frac{1}{2}$ per cent level of service is to be preferred by the vendor as well as the customer. The comparison is graphed in Fig. 8-12. An optimal trade-off is sought between SOC which declines with service level and BSHC which

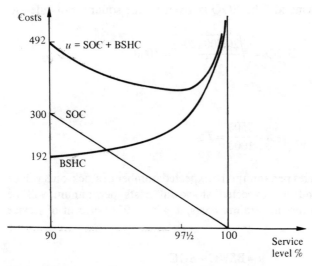

Figure 8-12

increases. $97\frac{1}{2}$ per cent is superior to 90 per cent. A finer gradation of choices is possible by calculating u for, to take an example, intervals of half a percentage point changes in service level. By this means, it can be confirmed that the overall lowest level is around 98 per cent. Sensitivity analysis in this context would centre around the stock-out cost figure. With a cost of £5 per stock-out, the costs as a function of S are given as follows:

Service level	BSHC	SOC	u
$97\frac{1}{2}$	294	$0.1875S$	$294 + 0.1875S$
90	192	0.755	$192 + 0.75S$

In order that the $97\frac{1}{2}$ per cent service level be preferred to 90 per cent it is required that:

$$294 + 0.1875S \leqslant 192 + 0.75S$$

which simplifies for the tolerance interval:

$$S \geqslant 181.\overline{33}$$

The situation is graphed in Fig. 8-13 with uncertainty costs, u, plotted against the stock-out cost figure.

8-10 THE SERVICE FUNCTION

We now turn to consider the second concept of service which some writers (e.g. Lewis 1981) have claimed gives a better guide to service quality from the customer point of view.

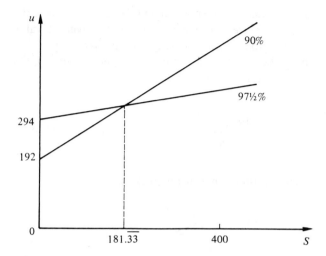

Figure 8-13

Again, we shall consider normally distributed demand in lead time. Now when we looked at cases involving discrete probability distributions of lead time demand we worked out the expected shortage. This is the average amount by which demand would exceed the re-order level quantity *when it did exceed it*. A similar concept in the continuous, normal distribution case is the *service function*. This plots the average excess of a normal variable when it exceeds its mean figure by more than z standard deviations. The service function is sometimes called the *unit normal loss integral*, $L(z)$. Values of $L(z)$ for values of z up to 3 are shown in Fig. 8-14. Thus if weekly demand D is independently normally distributed during L weeks of lead time the standard deviation of lead time demand is $\sigma\sqrt{L}$. Now when demand during the lead time exceeds

The unit normal loss integral

z	$L(z)$	z	$L(z)$	z	$L(z)$
0.0	0.398 9	1.2	0.0561 0	2.4	0.002 720
0.1	0.350 9	1.3	0.0455 3	2.5	0.002 004
0.2	0.306 9	1.4	0.0366 7	2.6	0.001 464
0.3	0.266 8	1.5	0.0293 1	2.7	0.001 060
0.4	0.230 4	1.6	0.0232 4	2.8	0.000 761 1
0.5	0.197 8	1.7	0.0182 9	2.9	0.000 541 7
0.6	0.168 7	1.8	0.0142 8	3.0	0.000 382 2
0.7	0.142 9	1.9	0.0110 5	3.1	0.000 267 3
0.8	0.120 2	2.0	0.0084 91	3.2	0.000 185 2
0.9	0.100 4	2.1	0.0064 68	3.3	0.000 127 3
1.0	0.063 32	2.2	0.0048 87		
1.1	0.068 62	2.3	0.0036 62		

Figure 8-14

LD by more than $0.5\,\sigma\sqrt{L}$ it has the average value $0.1978\,\sigma\sqrt{L}$. Similarly, when demand exceeds LD by more than $0.8\,\sigma\sqrt{L}$ it has the average value $0.1202\,\sigma\sqrt{L}$. So, if the buffer stock is set at $0.5\,\sigma\sqrt{L}$ units, since demand in each cycle must on average be equal to the economic order quantity $\bar{q}$, the percentage of demand that is not met from stock is:

$$\frac{19.78\,\sigma\sqrt{L}}{\bar{q}}$$

and the percentage of demand that is met from stock is:

$$G=\frac{100\bar{q}-19.78\,\sigma\sqrt{L}}{\bar{q}}$$

where G is the *customer service level*.

As an example, suppose that in some particular case $Q=350$, weekly demand $=100$ with weekly standard deviation 40 units, and lead time is two weeks. Then $\sigma\sqrt{L}\simeq56.57$ and in order to give a $97\frac{1}{2}$ per cent customer service level:

$$\frac{100\times350-5657\,L(z)}{350}=97.5$$

Solving gives $L(z)\simeq0.1547$ and so, using interpolation in Fig. 8-14 $z\simeq0.65$. This value would imply a buffer stock of $0.65\,\sigma\sqrt{L}\simeq37$ units, so that the re-order level would be set at $R=237$. Notice that with z as low as 0.65 there is (from Table 6, page 494) an over 25 per cent chance of a stock-out on each cycle. Does the reader think that customers would be likely to agree that they were getting '$97\frac{1}{2}$ per cent service'? With the data given, in order to produce a 'vendor' service level of $97\frac{1}{2}$ per cent the buffer stock would have to be $1.96\,\sigma\sqrt{L}\simeq111$ units, giving a re-order level of 311 with, of course, a $2\frac{1}{2}$ per cent stock-out probability per cycle.

8-11 STOCHASTIC LEAD TIMES

The delay between placing an order for replenishment of stock and the receipt of the new stock may also be subject to random variability.

Consider an example in which lead time follows a discrete probability distribution but where weekly demand is constant at the level $W=60$. In particular suppose that the length of lead time (L) follows the distribution:

L (weeks)	Probability (P)	PL
1	0.15	0.15
2	0.20	0.40
3	0.30	0.90
4	0.20	0.80
5	0.15	0.75
	Σ	3.00

so that the mean length of lead time is given by $\bar{L}=\Sigma PL=3$ weeks. Mean lead time demand will then be $\bar{L}W=180$ units. The analysis would then proceed in the same fashion as with fixed lead time and stochastic demand. The optimum level of buffer stock (or equivalently the re-order level) is sought which will minimize the uncertainty costs, buffer stock holding costs (BSHC) and stock-out costs (SOC):

$$BSHC+SOC$$

A process of enumeration is followed in the discrete case with the alternative of a service level approach in the case of continuously distributed lead time. In both the random lead time–fixed demand and fixed lead time–random demand cases the essential difficulty that arises is that of *lead time demand* being random. In the discrete case above, the enumeration procedure would compute annual uncertainty costs for buffer stock levels in units of 60, *viz.*:

$$R=60 \qquad B=-120$$
$$R=120 \qquad B=-60$$
$$R=180 \qquad B=0$$
$$R=240 \qquad B=+60$$
$$R=300 \qquad B=+120$$

which is an exhaustive list of the possibilities during lead time.

When both lead time and demand follow discrete probability distributions the problem is again one of demand during the lead time. Essentially we need to spell out the probability distribution of lead time demand. Consider a simple case. Suppose that there are just two values (independently determined) which both lead time and weekly demand may take. Specifically:

L	P	W	P
1	0.3	20	0.6
2	0.7	30	0.4

so that in passing we note that the mean length of lead time $\bar{L}=\Sigma LP=1.7$ weeks and the mean demand in any week is $\bar{W}=\Sigma PW=24$ units. There are five possible values of demand in lead time (LW) as follows:

	LW	Probability (P)	
$L=1$ {	20	0.180	$(=0.3 \times 0.6)$
	30	0.120	$(=0.3 \times 0.4)$
$L=2$ {	40	0.252	$(=0.7 \times 0.6 \times 0.6)$
	50	0.336	$(=2 \times (0.7 \times 0.6 \times 0.4))$
	60	0.012	$(=0.7 \times 0.4 \times 0.4)$
		1.000	

The arithmetic mean lead time demand will then be ΣPLW with workings:

P	LW	$P \times LW$
0.180	20	3.60
0.120	30	3.60
0.252	40	10.08
0.336	50	16.80
0.012	60	6.72
		$\Sigma = 40.80$

Mean lead time demand is 40.8 units. To complete an example let $C_O = 120$, $iC_m = 5$, $S = 7$ per unit short. With a 50 week year mean annual demand is $A = 50 \times \bar{W} = 1200$ so that:

$$\text{EOQ} = \sqrt{\frac{2(1200)\,120}{5}} = 240$$

which gives $n = A/\text{EOQ} = 5$ cycles per annum.

The alternative re-order levels are $R = 20$, 30, 40, 50 or 60 units corresponding to buffer stock of -20.8, -10.8, -0.8, $+9.2$ and $+19.2$ units respectively. First determine the expected shortage per cycle at each alternative value of R (we shall not consider expected surpluses). At $R = 20$:

Lead time demand (LW)	Shortage (S)	Probability (P)	PS
30	10	0.120	1.20
40	20	0.252	5.04
50	30	0.336	10.08
60	40	0.012	0.48
			16.80

the expected shortage per cycle (ESPC) is 16.80 units. At $R=30$:

LW	S	P	PS
40	10	0.252	2.52
50	20	0.336	6.72
60	30	0.012	0.36
			ESPC=9.60

At $R=40$:

LW	S	P	PS
50	10	0.336	3.36
60	20	0.012	0.24
			ESPC=3.60

At $R=50$:

LW	S	P	PS
60	10	0.012	0.12
			ESPC=0.12

While at $R=60$ there is no possible shortage. Now bringing in the cost data we obtain:

R	ESPC	ESPA	SOC	BSHC	SOC+BSHC
20	16.80	84	588	−104	484
30	9.60	48	336	−54	282
40	3.60	18	126	−4	122
50	0.12	0.6	4.2	+46	50.2
60	0	0	0	96	96

Where ESPA is expected shortage per annum (ESPC × 5 cycles) SOC is stock-out cost per annum (ESPA × £7) and BSHC is buffer stock holding cost per annum (negative for negative levels of buffer stock—a saving in holding costs). The optimum solution is thus to set $R=50$ and achieve uncertainty costs of 50.2. This is the minimum possible level of SOC+BSHC as shown graphically in Fig. 8-15.

8-12 PERIODIC REVIEW MODELS

The classical model with stochastic demand is an example of a *re-order level* model. The policy was to place an order for stock replenishment when stock on

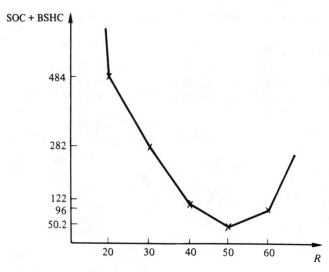

Figure 8-15

hand fell to or below the re-order level. The size of replenishment was fixed as given by the square root rule.

The disadvantage of re-order level policies is that they require continuous monitoring of stock level. This may be implemented as a very simple *two bin system* where two containers or 'bins' full of the item are used. When one bin becomes empty a replenishment order is placed. This should arrive before the second bin is emptied. Clearly in this system, while monitoring costs are low these are counterbalanced by the fact that average stock levels are probably higher than necessary. Monitoring in more sophisticated systems can be expensive.

The *periodic review* policy retains the concept of a re-order level but stock on hand is not constantly known; there are periodic *stocktakings*. If at the time of stocktaking inventory is at or below the re-order level a replenishment order, of fixed size, is placed. Otherwise there is no re-ordering. The operation of the policy is shown in Fig. 8-16. At time t_1 there is a stocktaking which reveals inventory level below R so that a replenishment order of size Q is placed. This arrives after the *random lead time*. At the next review at time, t_2, stock is above the re-order level so that there is no replenishment order placed at this time. The next review is at t_3 and an order is placed but a lead time stock-out arises. The next review is at t_4. The interval between reviews is fixed in this model and has to be determined as do both Q and the re-order level R. In comparison with the re-order level policy information costs are reduced, but this is at the expense of holding more stock on average or/and increased stock-out costs.

The *re-order cycle* policy dispenses with the re-order level and replenish-

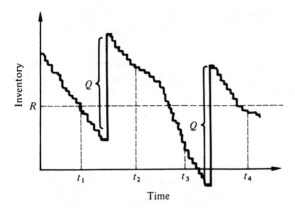

Figure 8-16

ment orders are placed at every review, but the size of replenishment order is now variable. The amount of stock ordered is the difference between a maximum inventory level S and the level of stock at review. The situation is illustrated in Fig. 8-17. In Fig. 8-17 at time t_1 the amount ordered is $Q_1 = S - I_1$ and at time t_2 the amount ordered is $Q_2 = S - I_2$.

In comparison with the periodic review policy there is less chance of a stock-out occurring with the re-order cycle policy. If the interval between reviews is similar in the two models (it may tend to be longer in the re-order cycle case) the average level of stocks and hence stockholding costs would tend to be higher, although strictly this would depend on the value chosen for S. If the interval between reviews is similar then re-order costs will be higher.

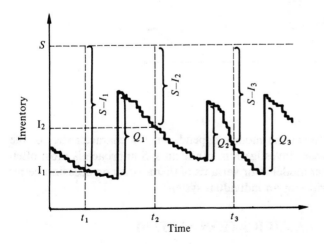

Figure 8-17

The *s, S policy* combines features of the periodic review and re-order cycle policies. In this case inventory is again reviewed at regular intervals but an order for replenishment is only placed if the stock level at review is at or below the level *s*. The amount re-ordered, if there is a re-order, is calculated as in the re-order cycle policy—an amount sufficient to bring the stock on hand at review up to the level *S*. So the amount re-ordered is given by the *decision rule:*

$$\text{Amount re-ordered } Q = S - I \text{ if } I \leqslant s$$

$$= 0 \quad \text{ if } I > s$$

The *s, S* model is illustrated in Fig. 8-18. It will be seen that no order is placed at time t_2. The classical static model is a special case of the *s, S* model with $s = 0$ and $S = \text{EOQ}$. In the *s, S* model if *backlogged demand* (in effect negative inventory) is allowed then a decision is required as to what negative level *s* should take. Again a balance has to be struck between holding costs which will diminish as *s* falls and shortage costs which will rise as *s* falls. In the stochastic case with lead time *s* would normally be positive.

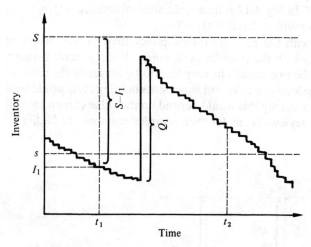

Figure 8-18

The choice between the models depends on the characteristics of the particular system under investigation. While an *s, S* approach is most often appropriate the other models—or variants of them—may on occasion better exploit the peculiarities of an individual system.

8-13 THE ABC CLASSIFICATION SYSTEM

In cases where more than one item is kept in stock, provided that the items do not compete for common scarce resources (e.g., storage space or management time), they can be optimized separately. If some goods *do* compete for (say) scarce storage space, if only a few products are involved, then methods of constrained optimization may be usable. The reader is referred to Wilkes and Brayshaw (1986) for discussion of such methods.

Where very many products are stored a quite different approach is called for. Some chemicals companies may have over 20 000 items in stock and in such cases detailed analysis of all products is quite impossible. One method that has been gaining popularity in recent years is the *ABC classification* method originally developed by the General Electric Corporation. The items of stock are ranked by turnover as follows:

Category A: Those items that account for most of the turnover (in value terms). It is often the case that just 10 per cent of the product range accounts for 70 per cent of total turnover.
Category C: A large part of the product range, perhaps 60 per cent, may account for only a small proportion of turnover, say, 10 per cent. These are category C items.
Category B: This is the intermediate section of the product range with, say, 30 per cent of the total number of items stocked accounting for 20 per cent of total turnover.

The classification scheme is graphed in Fig. 8-19. The curved line is called the *Pareto Curve* and the ABC method sometimes goes by the name of *Pareto Analysis* or *Grouping Methods*. The precise shape of the curve and the break points will vary between firms but the general point that a small percentage of items make up most of the value is generally true. The measure of value itself

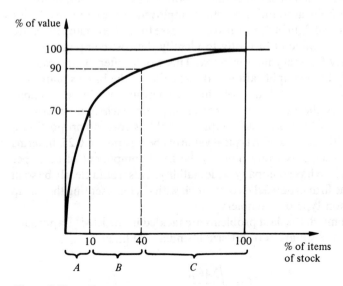

Figure 8-19

may be turnover—as we have shown here—profits, capital invested or some other concept of value that the company may decide.

The purpose of the classification method is to direct management effort (usually in limited supply) to where the best results will be obtained. So clearly, category A items should receive the greatest amount of control effort with sophisticated forecasting and recording systems and detailed analysis of order quantities and buffer stocks. Category B items would receive less detailed treatment with simpler forecasting methods and rougher estimates of EOQs. For the category C items only very simple treatment would be warranted. A possibility here is the *two bin system* (keep two bins of stock; re-order when one is empty, i.e., re-order level $= \bar{q}/2$). This would produce largish, infrequent orders with minimal cost consequences. No forecasting methods would be used—just an approximate estimate of annual demand. For category C there may not even be a formal system of recording stocks—with sample based estimates sufficing for audit purposes. There is also a simpler, two category version of the classification approach known as the '80/20' method. Also, if many products compete for scarce resources, then the LIMIT approach of the following section may help. Clearly, in the more complex cases computer-based systems will be used—at least for part of the stock range. So category A, and possibly category B items, would be included, but the nuts, bolts and slow moving items of category C might not.

8-14 LOT SIZE INVENTORY MANAGEMENT

A common difficulty in the implementation of EOQ-based systems is that of first identifying and then estimating the relevant cost data which go to make up the financial parameters of the model—re-order costs and holding cost. It may be that the normal accounting practices employed by the company do not throw up the required figures. It will also be the case that where many items are stored it will be too difficult or costly to identify the cost components with sufficient accuracy for every item in stock. This would often be the case for category C stock. So a simplification and re-casting of the basic square root rule which takes these cost data problems into account would be valuable. This is achieved by the *Lot size inventory management technique* or LIMIT.

The notation we have been using expresses holding cost as a proportion, i, of the unit cost of the stock with a typical value of i being approx. 0.25. In terms of the re-order costs, it is likely that C_O the fixed component of costs per re-order also tends to have company-wide stability. This would clearly be so in the case where the firm produced its own stock with C_O representing the set-up costs of a common type of machinery.

With this in mind, the data problems are tackled in the LIMIT approach by re-expressing the square root lot size formula. We had:

$$\bar{q} = \sqrt{\frac{2AC_O}{i \cdot C_m}}$$

Now define the parameter k as:

$$k = \sqrt{\frac{2C_O}{i}}$$

so that optimal lot size is:

$$\bar{q} = k \sqrt{\frac{A}{C_m}} \qquad (8\text{-}13)$$

So if the value of k is known for the company, or is set by it, all that is needed to use 8-13 are the values of demand and unit cost. These data are more readily accessible over a wider range of items that the original holding cost and replenishment cost data.

In fact, the whole approach can be re-cast with k as a *decision variable* rather than a given parameter. This is usually done in the following way. Letting N represent the number of re-orders per annum, we are already familiar with the relationship:

$$N = \frac{A}{\bar{q}}$$

and substitution into with re-arrangement gives:

$$k = \frac{1}{N} \sqrt{AC_m} \qquad (8\text{-}14)$$

In the use of this approach, company management is presented with a *range* of values of k averaged over many items of stock. The corresponding total inventory costs are also produced. Management can then select the best (usually the cost minimizing) value of k which will then be used to determine lot sizes from 8-13. The same value of k is used across items. Equivalently 8-14 can be re-arranged to determine the frequency of replenishment, viz.:

$$N = \frac{\sqrt{AC_m}}{k}$$

It is the use of this type of approach that is known as lot size inventory management. In practice it is used to ensure consistency of the numbers of replenishments (and hence set-ups) in the multi-item case where common facilities are used. The results in practice have been good—the technique has brought real cost reductions and has widened the area in which EOQ methods can be used.

8-15 MRP METHODS AND JIT MANAGEMENT

Where a finished product consists of numerous sub-assemblies and components manufactured and brought together in a number of stages in a multi-level production process, the method of *material requirements planning* (MRP) can bring about substantial reductions in stockholding costs. From the forecast demand for the final product, demand for the component parts is derived and projected over time. With these precisely stated requirements, stocks of components, materials and work-in-progress can be substantially reduced and eliminated altogether if the production plan shows up significant periods in which an item is not required.

Clearly for MRP to be effective a detailed production schedule is required, along with estimates of lead times for bought out components. The computer-based MRP package will derive orders for sub-assemblies, components and materials from the production schedule level by level. This operation—a requirement generation run—might be performed at monthly or even weekly intervals.

For *demand dependent* items such as components, MRP can bring up to 30 per cent reduction in inventories and considerable staff savings. Changes in the master production schedule or a separate demand for spare parts still call for a component inventory.

MRP has become central to *manufacturing resource planning* or MRP II, a more comprehensive, systems-oriented package taking in production, marketing and finance. All of this has been made possible by order-of-magnitude increases in computing power and corresponding reductions in cost. There have been difficulties with MRP II implementation on a day-to-day basis but such computer based systems are ideally suited to a *just-in-time* (JIT) management approach. JIT, developed in Japan, has had considerable success in simplifying production control methods and increasing overall efficiency.

JIT is more a *philosophy* of management than a set of specific techniques. It is a customer led, production to order approach, that has the objective of eliminating idle resources throughout the company. It is the antithesis of the 'just-in-case' school of management that would, for example, call for stock to be held just in case something goes wrong. The JIT view is that low or non-existent stock levels show up problems and areas of weakness that had been covered up by inventory. JIT is a philosophy that extends beyond the individual company, not just to the customer but to the suppliers—who may be 'helped' to be more efficient. The rapid response called for by a JIT company may lead to *higher* stock levels being held by suppliers and their re-location at short remove from the master company so some of the low stock benefits of JIT may be gained at others' expense.

Inventory is the first target of JIT and ideally would result in no component stock at all being held before it was needed for production. In the production process, JIT is implemented by a card system. The cards, called *kanbans* at Toyota (who have been using the system since 1981), are used to follow parts through the system and are returned to trigger more supply when the parts are used up.

MRP and EOQ-based techniques are not necessarily in conflict. Both approaches may be legitimately used within the same organization for different groupings of products. Those products with independent demand would be satisfactorily controlled with an EOQ-based system such as re-order level or periodic review. Even for raw materials inventory a re-order level or similar system would still be preferred if the final product was not unduly complex and had a fairly stable pattern of demand.

On the other hand, an MRP/JIT approach is indicated for products with highly involved production processes with consequent need for a large number of demand dependent items. On the downside, it should be noted that the JIT approach calls for a high degree of regimentation. Moving over to an MRP system also takes time. In large organizations, two years or more may be required for full implementation.

8-16 CONCLUSIONS

We have seen something of the range of EOQ-based stock control methods and how they are adaptable to a variety of circumstances. There are a number of more specialized models—for example, dynamic models—and more broad-brush approaches—such as the use of financial ratios that can at times prove to be of value. Increased power and availability of computer hardware and software has not only allowed the development of MRP and related methods but has also benefited smaller firms using EOQ-based PC packages. Computing developments have also benefited the whole range of methods by improved forecasting packages. For example, in terms of the ABC classification system, category A items will require good short-term demand forecasting with monitoring. Category B items warrant a less sophisticated adaptive forecasting method.

As we have seen, computer-based stock control and forecasting systems are particularly needed when there are many items of stock and where these are several stages of production. There may also be several *locations* at which the same type of stock is kept. Multi-plant organizations often use a *centralized store* at some location, thus enabling lower stocks to be kept at retail outlets. For example, some car manufacturers adopt this approach to spare parts inventory.

In multi-plant and conglomerate companies, the consequences of bad management of inventory are often experienced centrally at headquarters. The pressure on capital that is tied up in needlessly high levels of stock is not always felt by the individual plant but by the organization as a whole. This kind of situation can be addressed by *coverage analysis* where the object is to reduce capital tied up in inventory throughout the whole enterprise. This is usually subject to the provision that the number of replenishment orders placed by the firm remains the same (a number not determined by EOQ methods). Coverage analysis is often viewed as an alternative to LIMIT which tries to deal with similar multi-item situations. Coverage analysis has the advantages of speed and simplicity and the production of useful estimates of possible reductions in working capital. However, it has the drawback that in singling out a particular aspect of finance for special treatment some of the overall economies that might have been achievable with EOQ methods will be lost.

We have seen something of the value and use of EOQ-based stock control methods and the importance of inventory management in overall company performance. The advent of ABC classification, LIMIT, MRP and JIT approaches has benefited areas less well addressed by standard EOQ methods and provided a complementary range of techniques.

Finally we should note again the relation of stock control policy to other functions within the overall system. A full systems-based approach is the ideal with decisions on inventory being taken interdependently with production, finance and marketing decisions.

EXERCISES

8-1 Revision exercise
  (i) Distinguish the main types of inventory and the purposes for which each is held.
  (ii) Describe the classical static model and derive the EOQ rule. How are the different components of cost best balanced?
  (iii) Explain why the addition of a unit cost for stock re-ordered does not affect the EOQ.
  (iv) Show how constant lead time affects the timing but not the size of stock re-orders.
  (v) Show how the EOQ model can be adapted to determine the number of production runs needed per annum.
  (vi) Explain the functions of buffer stock and how a best balance is sought between buffer stockholding and stock-out costs.
  (vii) Describe the service level concept.
  (viii) What is shown by the service function?
  (ix) Explain how stochastic demand and lead time can be dealt with when both are discretely distributed.
  (x) Briefly describe the periodic review, re-order cycle and s, S models.
  (xi) Set out the ABC classification system.
  (xii) What advantages are offered by the lot size inventory management approach?
  (xiii) What are MRP methods and how does a just-in-time management approach complement them?
  (xiv) Are EOQ and MRP methods mutually exclusive?

8-2 A company experiences annual demand for 2500 units of the single product that it stocks. The replenishment cost for inventory is fixed at £400 regardless of the size of the replenishment. Annual holding costs are £8 per unit. What is the optimum number of replenishments per annum?

8-3 The annual demand for a company's single item of stock is 1000 units. It costs the company £6 to hold one unit of stock for one year. Each time that a replenishment order is made the company incurs a fixed cost of £75.
  (i) Determine the economic order quantity to two decimal places.
  (ii) Suppose that the company's supplier of stock introduces a condition that normally there shall be no more than five orders for replenishment per annum. How much would the company be prepared to pay in order to avoid having to meet this condition?

8-4 A company receives, at a steady rate, inflows of cash amounting to £250 000 per annum. Such cash can be invested to earn $12\frac{1}{2}$ per cent per annum. Each time the company makes an investment there is a brokerage charge of £25 plus 1 per cent of the sum invested (both sums payable at the time the investment is made).

    (i) How many investments of cash should be made per annum?

    (ii) If the brokerage charges were revised to £100 + $\frac{3}{4}$ per cent of the sum invested, in what amounts should investments now be made? Which scheme of brokerage charges would the company prefer?

8-5 Xerxes Holding Co. have a 50-week working year. The demand for a particular product stocked by Xerxes is subject to random variability. Demand for this product during any one week of the working year is described by the probability distribution:

Units demanded	Probability
0	0.03
1	0.06
2	0.07
3	0.09
4	0.11
5	0.21
6	0.17
7	0.12
8	0.08
9	0.06

Demand can only be satisfied (if at all) from stocks. The stock-holding costs are £40 per unit per annum. Each time that a re-order is made a cost of £50 is incurred irrespective of re-order size and the cost of the item is £180 per unit. There is a lead time of one week. The cost of being out of stock is estimated as £20 per unit short. Xerxes desires to minimize annual inventory costs.

    (i) Determine the economic order quantity.

    (ii) Find the optimal re-order level and size of buffer stock.

    (iii) For what range of values of the shortage cost figure would the re-order level found in (ii) remain optimal? (Assume all other data at their original values.) Could a similar sensitivity analysis be conducted on the holding cost figure?

8-6 Circa Holding Co. is examining its inventory policy in relation to one type of light-weight car wheel that it stores. Demand for the wheel runs at the average rate of 1000 units per quarter. It costs Circa £8 to hold one wheel for one year. When a re-order is necessary, Circa has fixed administrative costs of £40 irrespective of order size. The manufacturer charges Circa £12 per wheel supplied plus a charge of £120 no matter how large the order.

    (*a*)   (i) Determine the economic order quantity.

        (ii) An alternative scheme of charges would produce total costs per annum (including the £12 per wheel) of £52 000. Should Circa adopt the alternative scheme?

    (*b*) Assume a 50-week working year. Lead time is four weeks. Variance of demand in any week is 156.25 units. It can be assumed that demand in each week is normally distributed about the weekly average and is independent of demand in other weeks.

        (i) Determine the re-order level that would produce a $97\frac{1}{2}$ per cent 'service level'.

        (ii) Circa management, in an attempt to economize, is considering a reduction of the service level to 80 per cent. Each stock-out is estimated to cost Circa £120. Is the planned reduction in service level advisable?

8-7 Using the data of question 8-6, and the unit normal loss integral, confirm that:

(i) Zero buffer stock will meet the criterion of a $97\frac{1}{2}$ per cent *customer service level.*

(ii) A buffer stock of 49 units provides a customer service level in excess of 99.9 per cent.

8-8 A firm incurs costs of £600 each time that a production run is started and variable production costs are proportional to the quantity produced. The company operates a 50-week working year. When a production run is in progress, 500 units per week are made. Demand for the product is at the steady rate of 200 units per week throughout the working year. Stockholding costs are £5 per unit held per annum. How many production runs should be made each year?

8-9 In the context of a lot size inventory management (LIMIT) approach, the following data are given:

$$C_O = 50, \; i = 0.25, \; C_m = 4, \; A = 2500$$

(i) Using the data above find the value of k.

(ii) Use k to determine the optimal number of re-orders per annum.

8-10 A company faces variable lead time (L weeks) and demand (W per week) is also variable. L and W follow the discrete distribution below.

L	Probability	W	Probability
1	0.5	20	0.5
2	0.5	40	0.5

With $C_0 = £24$, $iC_m = £5$, $S = £2$ per unit short and assuming a 50-week year, determine the re-order level that minimizes uncertainty costs and the level of buffer stock to which this corresponds.

8-11 Electropoint Ltd has expanded the production of its domestic robots and now requires each year, and at a constant rate, 200 000 positronic circuits which it obtains from an outside supplier. The cost of placing each order for the positronic circuits is £32. For any circuit in stock it is estimated that the annual holding cost is equal to 10 per cent of its cost. The circuits cost £8 each. No stock-outs are permitted.

(a) What is the optimal order size, and how many orders should be placed in a year?

(b) What are the ordering and holding costs and hence what is the total relevant inventory cost per annum?

(c) If the demand has been underestimated and the true demand is 242 000 circuits per annum, what would be the effect of keeping to the order quantity calculated in (a) above and still meeting demand, rather than using a new optimal order level?

(d) What does your answer to (c) tell you about the sensitivity of your model to changes in demand?

(Chartered Association of Certified Accountants)

8-12 In an assembly process your company consumes annually 125 000 small screws at an even rate of 2500 per week. The cost of the screws is £4 per 1000. The cost of placing an order irrespective of the quantity ordered is £5. The risk of obsolescence is negligible and the cost of storage has been estimated at £1 per 1000 screws per year. The company's minimum required rate of return on capital is 20 per cent.

(a) calculate the order quantity and state the optimum ordering policy from a supplier who can guarantee immediate delivery;

(b) state the change required in the re-ordering policy if there were a lead time of two weeks;

(c) calculate the optimum production policy if the company decided that it could make the screw for £2 per 1000, plus an order cost of £5 and a set-up cost of £10, at a rate of 25 000 per week;

(d) state the considerations that should be taken into account if requirements fluctuated owing to changes in demand for the assembly;

(e) state the re-ordering considerations that should be taken into account if demand varies within the range of 1000 to 4000 screws required per week. A general stocking policy has now been agreed to ensure there is no problem if demand is 50 per cent higher than average. A stock-out owing to demand being 100 per cent higher than average will be tolerated.

(The Chartered Institute of Management Accountants)

Solution guides

8-2
$$EOQ = \sqrt{\frac{2 \times 400 \times 2500}{8}} = 500$$

$$\therefore \text{ no. of replenishments} = \frac{2500}{500} = 5$$

8-3
$$EOQ = \sqrt{\frac{2 \times 75 \times 1000}{6}} = 158.11$$

This calls for $1000/158.11 = 6.32$ orders per annum (view this as a *rate* of ordering). Total costs are

$$\tfrac{1}{2} \times 158.11 \times 6 + \frac{75 \times 1000}{158.11} = 474.33 + 474.35$$

$$= 948.68.$$

With only five re-orders p.a., re-order size would be 200. Putting this value into the cost expression gives

$$\tfrac{1}{2} \times 200 \times 6 + \frac{75 \times 1000}{200} = 600 + 375$$

$$= 975.$$

The absolute maximum that the company would pay is £975 − £948.68 = £26.32.

8-4
$$EOQ = \sqrt{\frac{2 \times 25 \times 250\,000}{0.125}} = 10\,000$$

$$\therefore \text{ 25 investments to be made per annum.}$$

Total costs here are

$$C = \tfrac{1}{2} \times 10\,000 \times 0.125 + \frac{25 \times 250\,000}{10\,000} + 0.01 \times 250\,000$$

$$= \quad 625 \quad + \quad 625 \quad + \quad 2500$$

$$\therefore C = £3750$$

With the revised scheme a new optimal size of investment is needed.

$$\text{EOQ (revised scheme)} = \sqrt{\frac{2 \times 100 \times 250\,000}{0.125}}$$

$$= 20\,000$$

Costs would then be

$$C = \tfrac{1}{2} \times 20\,000 \times 0.125 + \frac{100 \times 250\,000}{20\,000} + 0.0075 \times 250\,000$$

$$= \quad 1250 \quad + \quad 1250 \quad + \quad 1875$$

$$\therefore \ C = £4375$$

So that the company would prefer the original scheme.

8-5 Expected weekly demand is 5 units, so annual demand is 250 on average. Thus:

$$\text{EOQ} = \sqrt{\frac{2 \times 50 \times 250}{40}} = 25$$

$$\therefore \ 10 \text{ re-orders p.a.}$$

Now find expected shortages for the different levels of buffer stock. For $B = 0$ the re-order level is 5 so that expected shortage is 0.89 (workings below).

X	S	P	PX
6	1	0.17	0.17
7	2	0.12	0.24
8	3	0.08	0.24
9	4	0.06	0.24
			$\Sigma = 0.89$

Similar workings for other values of B produce the ESPC data in the table below:

B	ESPC	ESPA	SOC	BSCH	Total
0	0.89	8.9	178	0	178
1	0.46	4.6	92	40	132
2	0.20	2.0	40	80	120*
3	0.06	0.6	12	120	132
4	0.00	0.0	0	160	160

Hence the optimum size of buffer stock is two units. This gives a re-order level of 7. Now if the shortage cost was S the Total column would read:

B	Total
0	8.9S
1	4.6S + 40
2	2S + 80
3	0.6S + 120
4	160

For $B = 2$ to be optimal we must have:

$$2S + 80 \leqslant 4.6S + 40$$
$$\therefore S \geqslant 15.38 \quad \text{(greatest lower bound)}$$

$$2S + 80 \leqslant 8.9S$$
$$\therefore S \geqslant 11.59$$

$$2S + 80 \leqslant 0.6S + 120$$
$$\therefore S \leqslant 28.57 \quad \text{(least upper bound)}$$

$$2S + 80 \leqslant 160$$
$$\therefore S \leqslant 40$$

So, *ceteris paribus*, the solution is optimal for:

$$15.38 \leqslant S \leqslant 28.57$$

A sensitivity analysis *can* be conducted on the holding cost figure but it is rather more complicated than the above analysis on S as the EOQ depends on the value of iC_m.

8-6
$$EOQ = \sqrt{\frac{2 \times 160 \times 4000}{8}} = 400$$

so that there will be 10 cycles per annum. The total cost at present is:

$$4Q + \frac{640\,000}{Q} + 48\,000 = 51\,200$$

So that the alternative scheme should be rejected.

Now weekly demand is $4000 \div 50 = 80$ with variance 156.25 (i.e., standard deviation $= 12.5$). For a $97\frac{1}{2}$ per cent service level:

$$R = LW + 1.96\,\sigma\sqrt{L}$$
$$= 4 \times 80 + 1.96 \times 12.5 \times 2$$
$$= 369.$$

At $97\frac{1}{2}$ per cent service level the probability of a stock out each cycle is 0.025 so that the expected number of stock outs per annum is $0.025 \times 10 = 0.25$. The buffer stock is 49 here. At 80 per cent service level the buffer stock is:

$$B = 0.84 \, \sigma \sqrt{L}$$
$$= 21.$$

The expected number of stock-outs per annum is $0.2 \times 10 = 2$. So, at the 80 per cent level:

$$BSHC = 21 \times 8 \ = 168$$
$$SOC = 2 \times 120 = 204$$
$$\text{Total} \quad 408$$

Whereas at the $97\frac{1}{2}$ per cent service level:

$$BSHC = \ 49 \times 8 \ = 392$$
$$SOC = 0.25 \times 120 = \ 30$$
$$\text{Total} \quad 422$$

So that the reduction in service level is advisable on grounds of cost. Since stock out cost is difficult to estimate a sensitivity analysis of the result is worth while. Instead of £120 let the stock out cost be S. For the 80 per cent service level to be preferable, we require that

$$168 + 2S \leqslant 392 + 0.25S$$
$$\therefore \ S \leqslant 128$$

Thus only a $6\frac{2}{3}$ per cent increase in S is tolerable. The result should therefore be regarded with caution.

8-7 The *service function* or *unit normal loss integral* $(L(z))$ plots the average excess of a normal variable when it exceeds its mean figure by more than z standard deviations. The excess is measured in units of $\sigma \sqrt{L}$ where L is the number of weeks of lead time and σ is standard deviation demand in each week. If re-order level is set at:

$$LW + z\sigma \sqrt{L}$$

when demand in lead time exceeds $LW + z\sigma \sqrt{L}$ it will do so by an average amount of $L(z)\sigma \sqrt{L}$ which cannot, of course, be met from stock. So taking the inventory cycle as a whole (during which demand must average $\bar{q}$ the EOQ) the proportion of customer demand that is not met from stock will be:

$$\frac{L(z)\sigma \sqrt{L}}{\bar{q}}$$

So the percentage of customers that *are* satisfied from stock is G, where G is given by

$$G = \frac{100\bar{q} - 100L(z)\sigma \sqrt{L}}{\bar{q}} \tag{8.15}$$

This is the customer service level. Given the data of Question 6 $\sigma = 12.5$, $\bar{q} = 400$, $L = 4$ and with a buffer stock value of $z\sigma \sqrt{L} = 0$ so $z = 0$, the value of the unit normal loss integral $L(0) = 0.3989$.

Inserting this data into (8.15) gives the customer service level as:

$$G = \frac{100(400) - 100(0.3989)\,12.5(2)}{400} = 97.51\%$$

Zero buffer stock does in these circumstances (low lead time standard deviation relative to EOQ) meet a customer service level requirement of $97\frac{1}{2}$ per cent. For a buffer stock of 49 units $z\sigma\sqrt{L} = 49$ so that with $\sigma = 12.5$ and $L = 4$ this implies $z = 1.96$. Using linear interpretation $L(1.9) = 0.011050$ and $L(2.0) = 0.008491$ so that $L(1.96)$ is estimated as:

$$L(1.96) = 0.008491 + 0.4(0.011050 - 0.008491) = 0.0095146$$

Substitution in (8.15) gives:

$$G = \frac{40\,000 - 0.95146(25)}{400} = 99.94$$

so that the requisite criterion of a 99.9 per cent customer service level is met.

8-8
$$\bar{q} = \sqrt{\frac{2 \times 25\,000 \times 600 \times 10\,000}{5(25\,000 - 10\,000)}}$$
$$= 2000$$

So that one production run will satisfy ten weeks' demand and, with annual demand at 10 000, there will be five runs required per annum.

8-9 (a) The parameter k is defined as:

$$k = \sqrt{\frac{2C_o}{i}}$$

$$= \sqrt{\frac{2(50)}{0.25}} = 20$$

(b) The relationship between k and the number of re-orders per annum, N, is given by:

$$N = \frac{\sqrt{AC_m}}{k}$$

so that

$$N = \frac{\sqrt{4(2500)}}{20} = 5$$

There will thus be five re-orders per annum of size 500.

8-10 The distribution of lead time demand will be as follows:

	LW	P	PLW
$L=1$ $\begin{cases} \\ \end{cases}$	20	0.25	5
	40	0.25	10
$L=2$ $\begin{cases} \\ \\ \end{cases}$	40	0.125	5
	60	0.25	15
	80	0.125	10
			$\Sigma=45$

Mean lead time demand is 45 units as shown above. Mean *weekly* demand $\bar{W}$ is $20(0.5)+40(0.5)=30$ and with a 50 week year this gives annual demand $A=50(30)=1500$. So the EOQ is given by:

$$\bar{q}=\sqrt{\frac{2(1500)24}{5}}=120$$

And there will be $\frac{A}{\bar{q}}=\frac{1500}{120}=12.5$ cycles per annum.

The alternative re-order levels are 20, 40, 60 and 80 units. The expected shortage per cycle (ESPC) must now be calculated for each re-order level. For $R=20$ shortages would occur if lead time demand was 40 units or above. Workings are:

Lead time demand	Shortage (x)	Probability (P)	PX
40	20	0.375	7.5
60	40	0.25	10
80	60	0.125	7.5
		Expected shortage per cycle	25

With $R=40$ ESPC workings are:

Lead time demand	Shortage (x)	Probability (P)	PX
60	20	0.25	5
80	40	0.125	5
		ESPC=	10

With $R=60$

Lead Time Demand	Shortage (x)	Probability (P)	PX
80	20	0.125	2.5 = ESPC

The table of costs that results is:

R	ESPC	ESPA	SOC	Buffer stock	BSHC	Total
20	25	312.5	625	−25	−125	475
40	10	125	250	−5	−25	225
→60	2.5	31.25	62.5	15	75	137.5←
80	0	0	0	35	175	175

A re-order level of $R = 60$ is therefore indicated to produce lowest uncertainty costs. $R = 60$ corresponds to a buffer stock of $B = 15$ units, since lead time demand was found to be 45 on average and $B = R -$ average lead time demand.

8-11 (a) optimal order size $= \sqrt{\dfrac{2 \times 200\,000 \times 32}{8 \times 0.1}} = 4000$

∴ order frequency $= 200\,000/4000 = 50$ times a year.

(b) order cost $=$ order frequency $\times$ order cost per unit

$= £50 \times 32$

$= £1600$

holding cost $= \frac{1}{2} \times 4000 \times 0.1 \times 8 = £1600$

total relevant inventory cost per annum $= £1600 + 1600$

$= £3200.$

(c) Maintaining the same order level of 4000, the new order frequency $= 242\,000/400 = 60.5$ times a year.

Now order cost per annum $= £60.5 \times 32 = £1936$

Holding cost per annum as before $= £1600$

Therefore total relevant inventory costs per annum

$= £1936 + 1600 = £3536$

New optimal EOQ $= \sqrt{\dfrac{2 \times 242\,000 \times 32}{8 \times 0.1}} = 4400$

So new order frequency $= 242\,000/4400 = 55$

Order cost $= £55 \times 32 = £1760$

Annual holding cost $= £\frac{1}{2} \times 4400 \times 0.1 \times 8 = £1760$

So total relevant cost per annum $= £1760 + £1760 = £3520$

A decrease of just £16

(d) This example, in which an underestimate of demand of over 17 per cent gave a cost penalty (over the minimum value of 3520) of under $\frac{1}{2}$ per cent illustrates the robustness of the square root model.

8-12 (a) Storage costs are only a part of total holding cost. Here we must include the *opportunity cost* of money tied up in physical stock. This will be 20 per cent of £4 per thousand screws. So holding cost per unit per annum $= 0.001 + 0.0008$. So:

$$EOQ = \sqrt{\dfrac{2 \times 125\,000 \times 5}{0.0018}} = 26\,352$$

(b) Instead of ordering when stock level is zero, order when two weeks' supply remain, $R = 5000$. The EOQ is unchanged.

(c) The working year is inferred to be 50 weeks (from the first sentence of the question) so that $P = 1\,250\,000$. Note that holding costs will now be £1.4 per thousand. $C_0 = 5 + 10 = 15$.

$$EBQ = \sqrt{\frac{2 \times 125\,000 \times 15 \times 1\,250\,000}{0.0014(1\,125\,000)}} = 54\,554$$

In practice this might be rounded to 11 days' production (55 000) or even 2 weeks' production (50 000).

(d) When demand is deterministic the re-order level and periodic review approaches come to the same thing. When demand is stochastic a decision has to be taken as to which system to adopt. If the re-order level model was retained then the level of buffer stock would have to be decided on. How this was done would depend on the information available.

(e) Presumably 'no problem' means that a buffer stock of 2500 is being carried ($2500 = 2(3750 - 2500)$). The re-order level would be 7500. 'Tolerated' presumably means that stock outs can be ignored in the calculations. (Note: if stock outs are costless (e.g., if demand is merely backlogged) then advantage can be taken of this in determining the re-order level.)

REFERENCES

Wilkes, F. M., and Brayshaw, R. (1986), *Company Finance and its Management*, Van Nostrand Reinhold.

Lewis, C. D. (1981), *Scientific Inventory Control*, second edition, Butterworth.

FURTHER READING

Bennett, D., Lewis, C., and Oakley, M. (1988), *Operations Management*, Philip Allan. Contains good coverage of MRP and related methods.

Cook, T. M., and Russell, R. A. (1981), *Introduction to Management Science*, second edition, Prentice Hall. Shows use of simulation, links with accounting systems and MRP.

Littlechild, S. C. (1977), *Operational Research for Managers*, Philip Allan. Includes ABC classification system, the link with forecasting and an application in the welding industry.

Monks, J. G. (1982), *Operations Management*, second edition, McGraw-Hill. Shows use of statistical distributions in lead time demand.

Samuels, J. M., and Wilkes, F. M. (1986), *Management of Company Finance*, fourth edition, Van Nostrand Reinhold. Shows use of financial ratios, quantity discounts, production to order and more on cash management application.

NINE

QUEUEING THEORY

9-1 BACKGROUND

Queues are commonplace experiences, e.g.:

1. People waiting in shops and at service counters.
2. Cars waiting at traffic lights.
3. Aircraft waiting to land.
4. Ships waiting to enter port.

And, as less obvious examples of queues:

1. Machines waiting for repair.
2. Goods waiting in inventory.
3. Telephone subscribers waiting for a clear line.
4. Papers in an in-tray.

In principle, at least, these problems can be addressed by queueing theory methods. A theory of queues is possible because of certain regularities about the patterns of arrival and service of customers. These regularities can be described statistically and analytical results (formulae) sometimes follow. Queueing theory is about *delay* whether or not an actual queue is observed. Why does delay occur at all? The reason is that it is not possible or not worth while to tailor the supply of a service exactly to the demand for it. A *trade-off*

251

situation arises; delay can be costly but it is also costly to make provision to avoid or to reduce delay. However, the costs do not always fall on the same parties.

Sometimes a system of serving customers can be developed by *experimentation*, for example, changing the provision of cashiers at supermarket checkouts at different times of the day. In other cases such intervention in the real situation would be either impossible or prohibitively expensive. This is so where large or irreversible investments are involved—for instance, the number of lanes on a motorway cannot readily be changed. Very complex systems have to be *simulated* (an example is provided in the chapter on simulation). This was done in determining traffic flow arrangements in central London.

In principle, queueing theory can predict how systems will operate. Certain important measures of performance—system parameters—can be obtained, for example:

1. Average waiting time
2. Expected length of queue
3. Average number of customers in the system
4. Probability of experiencing delay.

The three main means of obtaining these parameters are:

1. Analytical results (formulae)
2. Real world experimentation
3. Simulation.

In practice, queueing theory in pure analytical form is employed relatively infrequently, but where it *is* used, it tends to be used extensively and to powerful effect. An analytical background is essential to understand and see the limitations of the other approaches. Also, some important qualitative conclusions can be reached—for example, that a single queue is superior to several queues.

Queueing systems—also known as waiting lines—are broadly characterized by the differing nature of five factors:

1. The arrival pattern of customers
2. The queue 'discipline'
3. The service mechanism
4. Capacitation
5. Population

1 Arrivals

The pattern of arrivals may be *deterministic* (e.g., items on a production flow line) or more usually random. 'Customers' may arrive one at a time or *en masse*. 'Customer' or 'item' are general words for the queueing elements: they do not have to be people. Arrivals may or may not depend on the state of the system (e.g., a customer may *balk* if he sees a large queue). The arrival rate may be constant or may vary over time. Customers may be identical or different (e.g., civil, military, private and distressed aircraft at airports).

2 Queue 'discipline'

The simplest arrangement is FIFO (first in, first out). There is also LIFO (last in, first out, as in items drawn from stock or redundancies in a workforce) or *random* (as with telephone callers trying to get a connection). Then there may be several queues; here customers may change from one to another (*jockey*). Some customers may join a queue and then leave before service (*renege*).

3 Service mechanism

There may be one or many servers, who may differ in speed of service. The speed of service at any service point may be constant or random and may vary with the time of day. Servers may be in *parallel* (as in a supermarket) or in *series* (as in a self-service cafeteria).

4 Capacitation

Some systems have a maximum number of customers that can be contained in the system. Where such a limit exists the system is said to be *capacitated*.

5 Population

The 'population' from which customers arrive may be infinite (effectively) or finite. The population is sometimes referred to as the *calling source*.

Clearly, a very large number of different queueing models can be constructed but all those of interest and practical relevance have patterns of arrival and service described by probability distributions rather than being deterministic. A purely random pattern of arrivals is described by the *Poisson distribution* and its continuous analogue the *negative exponential distribution*, which we shall now consider.

9-2 THE POISSON DISTRIBUTION

In any time interval, T, the probability that there are n arrivals into the queueing system is given by:

$$P(n \text{ arrivals in time interval } T) = \frac{(\lambda T)^n e^{-\lambda T}}{n!}$$

where λ is the mean rate of arrivals. Thus, the Poisson distribution is a single parameter (λ) discrete distribution (whole number values of n). The formula can look threatening but it is in fact simple to use. Consider some examples. Let $\lambda = 0.4$ arrivals per minute as the average rate in some case and let the time interval be $T = 1$ minute. The formula then becomes:

$$P(n \text{ in } 1) = \frac{(0.4)^n e^{-0.4}}{n!}$$

Now consider some specific values of n.

(i) $n = 0$. Quite possibly no one enters the system in some one minute intervals. The chance of this occurring is:

$$P(0 \text{ arrivals in } 1) = \frac{(0.4)^0 e^{-0.4}}{0!} = e^{-0.4} = 0.6703$$

In the above, note that $0!$ is defined as 1 and that $e^{-0.4}$ can be obtained from tables of e^{-x} or from scientific calculators.

(ii) $n = 1$. The chance of one person/item arriving in the system in a one minute interval is:

$$P(1 \text{ arrival in } 1) = \frac{(0.4)^1 e^{-0.4}}{1!} = 0.4 e^{-0.4} = 0.2681$$

(iii) $n = 2$. The chance of two arrivals in a one minute interval is given by:

$$P(2 \text{ arrivals in } 1) = \frac{(0.4)^2 e^{-0.4}}{2!} = 0.08 e^{-0.4} = 0.0536$$

(iv) $n = 3$. Here the probability is:

$$P(3 \text{ arrivals in } 1) = \frac{(0.4)^3 e^{-0.4}}{3!} = \frac{0.064 e^{-0.4}}{6} = 0.0072$$

As can be seen, it is not difficult to work the probabilities out given the particular value of $e^{-\lambda}$. However, Table 7 (page 495) gives values of Poisson probabilities for a range of values of n and λ and for $T = 1$. We shall shortly see how the table can be used for other values of T. Note that the sum of probabilities in each row is one. This is because there must be *some* number of arrivals. Note also that for values of $\lambda < 1$ the probabilities taper off across rows with $n = 0$ giving the highest value. However, as λ increases above 1 the spread of probability values across rows develops a roughly symmetrical build up and decline pattern.

Now consider some other uses of the Poisson formula. For example, what is the chance that at least two people arrive in a one minute interval? This is:

$$P(n \geqslant 2 \text{ in } T=1) = P(n=2) + P(n=3) + P(n=4) + \cdots$$

but since, as we have seen, the probabilities for all values of n sum to one, a more convenient way to obtain the result is:

$$P(n \geqslant 2 \text{ in } T=1) = 1 - [P(n=0) + P(n=1)]$$

$$= 1 - 0.9384$$

$$= 0.0616$$

Suppose that a three minute interval had been specified instead of one minute. The Poisson formula would, for $\lambda = 0.4$ then be:

$$P(n \text{ in } T=3) = \frac{(1.2)^n e^{-1.2}}{n!}$$

which is precisely the same expression as $P(n \text{ in } T=1)$ for $\lambda = 1.2$. Thus the chance of two people arriving in any three minute interval is found from Table 7 (page 495) in the $\lambda = 1.2$ row $n=2$ column to be 0.2169.

If the *number* of arrivals is described by the Poisson distribution it follows that the time between arrivals—a *continuous* variable—is described by the *negative exponential distribution*. This is written as:

$$f(t) = \lambda e^{-\lambda t}$$

The negative exponential distribution is graphed in Fig. 9-1. Probabilities correspond to areas under the curve. Thus, the chance of *up to* two minutes elapsing between arrivals is the hatched area between 0 and 2. The area can be worked out by definite integration. The probability is:

$$\int_0^2 \lambda e^{-\lambda t} dt = \left[-e^{-\lambda t} + K \right]_{t=0}^{t=2}$$

$$= -e^{-2t} - e^0$$

$$= 1 - e^{-2t}$$

which, with $\lambda = 0.4$ is $1 - e^{-0.8}$

$$= 1 - 0.4493$$

$$= 0.5507$$

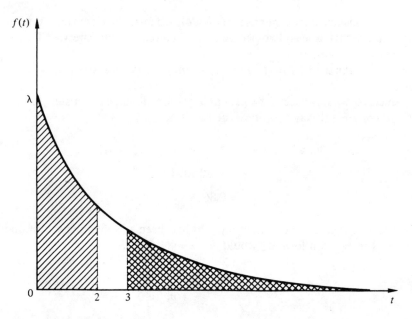

Figure 9-1

This value can be confirmed by use of Table 7 (page 495). The chance of up to two minutes elapsing between arrivals is the same as the chance that there is *at least* one arrival in a two minute interval. Now:

$$P(n \geqslant 1) = P(n=1) + P(n=2) + P(n=3) + \cdots$$

$$= 1 - P(n=0)$$

Since we are considering a *two* minute interval we must look in the $\lambda = 0.8$ row where we find that $P(n=0)$ is 0.4493. Thus $P(n \geqslant 1)$ is confirmed as 0.5507.

The reader may confirm by either use of the negative exponential distribution or appropriate use of Table 7 that the probability of at least three minutes elapsing between arrivals (the probability of no arrivals in a three minute interval) the cross-hatched area in Fig. 9-1 is 0.3012. The probability of between two and three minutes elapsing between arrivals is the unshaded area of Fig. 9-1. Since the total area under the curve is one, the required probability is most easily found as one minus the two probabilities already determined, i.e.,

$$1 - (0.5507 + 0.3012) = 0.1481.$$

The arithmetic mean inter-arrival time is $1/\lambda = 2.5$ minutes in the case of $\lambda = 0.4$. The standard deviation of inter-arrival time is also $1/\lambda$ minutes. Either the negative exponential or the Poisson distribution can be used to describe a random arrival pattern and extract desired probabilities. The basic model of queueing theory, to which we shall now turn, assumes a Poisson distribution of arrival probabilities.

9-3 SIMPLE QUEUES

Physically, a *simple queue* is observed as one line approaching one service point thus:

$$0 \quad 0 \quad 0 \quad 0 \quad 0 \quad 0 \quad 0 \quad \boxed{0}$$

However, to be described as a simple queue, twelve conditions need to be satisfied.

1. Random pattern of arrivals (i.e. Poisson distribution applies)
2. Random service times (i.e. negative exponential distribution applies)
3. Discrete customers (i.e. not continuous flow)
4. Large population (effectively infinite)
5. A single queue
6. No queueing capacity limit
7. FIFO queue discipline
8. No reneging
9. No balking
10. One service point
11. One-at-a-time service
12. Mean rate of service greater than mean rate of arrivals.

The standard notation of queueing theory represents the mean rate of service as μ and the mean rate of arrivals as λ. In condition 2, the fact that service times are negatively exponentially distributed means that the numbers being served in any T minute interval are described by the Poisson distribution i.e.

$$P(n \text{ served in } T) = \frac{(\mu T)^n e^{-\mu T}}{n!}$$

Given that the twelve assumptions are satisfied, important measures of the performance of the system can be derived analytically. The most commonly used of these system parameters are:

Traffic intensity:

$$\rho = \frac{\lambda}{\mu} \qquad (9\text{-}1)$$

Probability of system containing n customers:

$$P_n = \rho^n(1-\rho) \tag{9-2}$$

Probability that there are *at least* N customers in the system:

$$\rho^N \tag{9-3}$$

Average number of customers in the system:

$$\frac{\lambda}{\mu-\lambda} \tag{9-4}$$

Average length of queue (number of items in queue):

$$\frac{\lambda^2}{\mu(\mu-\lambda)} \tag{9-5}$$

Average length of queue (excluding zero queues):

$$\frac{\mu}{\mu-\lambda} \tag{9-6}$$

Average system process time (ASPT):

$$\frac{1}{\mu-\lambda} \tag{9-7}$$

Average queueing time:

$$\frac{\lambda}{\mu(\mu-\lambda)} \tag{9-8}$$

Average number of customers being served:

$$\frac{\lambda}{\mu} \tag{9-9}$$

The *traffic intensity* is a measure of use of the system and must be less than one. In the case of a simple queue, ρ is also the probability of an arrival having to wait. In other words it is the probability that there are one or more customers already in the system. Thus, since the system must be in some *state* (must contain *some* number of customers) $1-\rho$ is P_0, the probability that there are no customers in the system at any time. All the other states of the system (containing 1, 2, ..., n ... members) are related to P_0 by Eq. (9-2). Equation (9-3) results from the summation from N to ∞ of the P_n in Eq. (9-2).

The most important system parameters are Eqs (9-4)–(9-7) and we shall illustrate the use of these by example.

Example 9-1

On average, cars arrive at a petrol station every 3 minutes. The single attendant is capable of serving on average 30 cars per hour. Service times and inter-arrival times follow a negative exponential distribution.

 (i) What is the probability of a car arriving and having to wait for service?
 (ii) What is the probability of a car arriving and finding at least one car already at the petrol station?
 (iii) What is the average number of customers at the garage at any moment?
 (iv) What is the length of time that a customer would expect to have to spend at the garage?
 (v) What is the average number of customers in the garage who are not being served?
 (vi) The garage proprietor considers that unless customers can expect to be served immediately on arrival 40 per cent of the time, trade will eventually drop off. With the original demand pattern what percentage reduction in service time would be necessary to achieve this result?

ANSWER

If, on average, a car arrives every 3 minutes this means an average of 20 per hour; so, choosing an hour as the basic time unit, $\lambda = 20$. Clearly $\mu = 30$. The sentence 'service times and inter-arrival times follow a negative exponential distribution' suggests that simple queue conditions prevail, and that the formulae may be used. The results are as follows:

 (i) This is $\rho = \lambda/\mu = 20/30 = 2/3$.
 (ii) This is also $\rho = 2/3$.
 (iii) This is $\lambda(\mu - \lambda) = 2$. Note that 'in the system' means 'in the queue' or being served.
 (iv) This is the average system process time perhaps the most important of all parameters,

$$\frac{1}{\mu - \lambda} = \frac{1}{10} \text{ hour or } 6 \text{ minutes}$$

 (v) The average number in the queue ... $\lambda^2/\mu(\mu - \lambda) = 4/3$. If we had considered only those times when a queue actually existed, the average length would be $\mu(\mu - \lambda) = 3$.

(vi) The reduction in service time must be such as to produce $P_0 = 0.4$. A person will be served immediately only if there is no one already there. Thus $P_0 = 1 - \rho = 0.4$ so that $\rho = 0.6$. With a given arrival rate of $\lambda = 20$ we therefore require that $20/\mu = 0.6$ so that $\mu = 33\frac{1}{3}$. This value of μ implies a service time of $1/33\frac{1}{3} \times 60$ minutes $= 1.8$ minutes which is a 10 per cent reduction on the original time.

Example 9-2

Customers arrive in a shop at the average rate of 42 per hour. The shopkeeper takes on average one minute to serve each customer. Simple queue conditions prevail

  (i) What proportion of his time does the shopkeeper spend serving customers?

 (ii) What is the average queueing time for customers?

(iii) What is the probability that:

    (a) There are three customers in the shop?

    (b) There is one customer queueing?

    (c) There are four or more customers in the shop?

    (d) There are three or fewer customers in the shop?

Answer

We note that $\lambda = 42$ and $\mu = 60$ (both per hour).

  (i) This is the proportion of the time when there are one or more customers in the system. It is $P_1 + P_2 + P_3 + \cdots + P_\infty$. More conveniently this is $1 - P_0$, in fact it is ρ itself, the traffic intensity or the average number of customers being served. Thus the answer is $\rho = 42/60 = 0.7$.

 (ii) This is $\lambda/\mu(\mu - \lambda) = 42/60(60 - 42)$ hours $= 7/180$ hours $= 2\frac{1}{3}$ minutes.

(iii) (a) We shall assume here that 'being in the shop' means being in the system.

$$P_3 = (1 - 0.7)(0.7)^3 = 0.1029$$

(b) If one customer is queueing this must mean that one is being served so that there are two in the system. Thus

$$P_2 = (1 - 0.7)(0.7)^2 = 0.147$$

(c) Here we have simply:

$$P(4 \text{ or more}) = \rho^4 = (0.7)^4 = 0.2401$$

(d) To simplify workings we note that 'three or less' and 'four or more' cover all possibilities so that:

$$P(3 \text{ or less}) = 1 - P(4 \text{ or more})$$

$$= 1 - 0.2401 = 0.7599$$

Example 9-3

A telephone is used by eight people per hour on average and the mean call length is three minutes. A further instrument has been requested but this will only be installed if average queueing time is at least three minutes. Determine the percentage increase in demand necessary to produce this result.

Answer

We note that $\lambda = 8$. Clearly the 'service time' is the length of call so that with an average call length of three minutes, $\mu = 20$ per hour. Expected queueing time is given by $\lambda/\mu(\mu - \lambda)$ and with $\mu = 20$, queueing time is $\lambda/20(20 - \lambda)$ and we require this to equal 1/20 hour. Thus solving for λ

$$\frac{\lambda}{20(20 - \lambda)} = \frac{1}{20} \quad \therefore \quad 20\lambda = 400 - 20\lambda$$

$$40\lambda = 400$$

$$\lambda = 10$$

So that a 25 per cent increase in demand (measured by rate of arrivals) would be needed.

Example 9-4

A toll road is approached by a single line of traffic arriving Poisson fashion. There is one toll booth which on average takes six seconds to deal with each car. By taking various values of the mean arrival rate show how the queue length increases disproportionately as the traffic intensity rises.

Answer

Clearly, $\mu = 10$ per minute. Using this value Fig. 9-2 shows the results for values of λ ranging from 5 to 9.99.

λ	5	6	7	8	9	9.5	9.7	9.9	9.99
$\rho = \dfrac{\lambda}{\mu}$	0.5	0.6	0.7	0.8	0.9	0.95	0.97	0.99	0.999
Q_t	0.1	0.15	$0.2\overline{33}$	0.4	0.9	1.9	$3.2\overline{33}$	9.9	99.9
Q_l	0.5	0.9	$1.6\overline{33}$	3.2	8.1	18.05	$31.36\overline{33}$	98.01	998

Figure 9-2

The second row gives λ/μ, the traffic intensity, Q_t is the expected queueing time and Q_1 stands for the expected length of queue, all times considered.

As traffic intensity rises there is always a larger proportionate increase in both Q_t and Q_1. Even for $\rho=0.5$ a 20 per cent increase in traffic intensity to $\rho=0.6$ produces a 50 per cent rise in Q_t and an 80 per cent rise in Q_1. If we take a 20 per cent increase of ρ from 8 to 9.6 the resulting Q time goes up from 0.4 minutes to 2.4 minutes, an increase of no less than 500 per cent while Q length rises by 620 per cent. Now while queue length depends only on the traffic intensity (why?) the queueing *time* depends also on the absolute value of λ. In Fig. 9.3 both λ and μ have been doubled.

λ	10	12	14	16	18	19	19.4	19.8	19.98	
ρ	0.5	0.6	0.7	0.8	0.9	0.95	0.97	0.99	0.999	$\mu=20$
Q_t	0.05	0.075	0.11$\bar{6}$	0.2	0.45	0.95	1.61$\bar{6}$	4.95	49.95	
Q_1	0.5	0.9	1.63$\bar{3}$	3.2	8.1	18.05	31.363$\bar{3}$	98.01	998	

Figure 9-3

This leaves queue lengths unaffected but halves the queueing time (why?). However, it must be pointed out that as traffic intensity approaches one there is an increasing *variance* in both queue length and time.

The graph of queue length against traffic intensity gives a vivid impression of the results. In Fig. 9.4 the vertical scale has been compressed (try drawing the figure yourself) for convenience. As $\rho \to 1$ queue length 'takes off'. Above, say, $\rho = 0.7$ the effect is most marked; small increases in traffic intensity producing huge increases in queue length. You may have noticed this effect yourself on winter mornings. Only a slight deterioration in road conditions

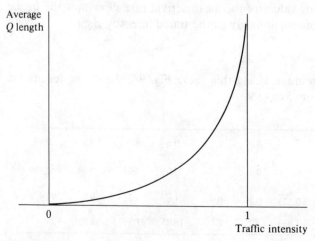

Figure 9-4

seems to cause huge traffic jams. This is because (although it is not of course a simple queue problem) the 'traffic intensity' is high. It only takes a slight slowing down (reduction in μ) to give a slight increase in intensity which causes huge increases in queues.

9-4 MULTIPLE SERVICE CHANNELS

There are many ways in which the rigid conditions of a simple queue can be relaxed. One of these concerns the number of service points that are operated. We shall now consider the consequences of having several service points instead of one. It will be assumed that these service points are approached by *one queue only*—the customer at the head of the queue going to the next sevice point or server that becomes free.

We shall see later on that a single queue gives the best theoretical performance (this is why we consider it first of all) and we shall endeavour to explain why multiple queues are nevertheless also commonly observed.

First, the single queue, multi-server case. We shall assume there are no other changes from the simple queue situation and the distribution of service time at each point is (the same) negative exponential distribution. The expressions for the system parameters are rather more lengthy than in the simple queue case. They are most economically expressed in terms of ρ, the traffic intensity, and P_0, the probability that the system is empty.

probability of a customer having to wait for service

$$= \frac{(\rho c)^c}{c!(1-\rho)} P_0 \tag{9-10}$$

average number of customers in the system

$$= \frac{\rho(\rho c)^c}{c!(1-\rho)^2} P_0 + \rho c \tag{9-11}$$

average number of customers in the queue

$$= \frac{\rho(\rho c)^c}{c!(1-\rho)^2} P_0 \tag{9-12}$$

average time a customer is in the system

$$= \frac{(\rho c)^c}{c!(1-\rho)^2 c\mu} P_0 + \frac{1}{\mu} \tag{9-13}$$

average time a customer is in the queue

$$= \frac{(\rho c)^c}{c!(1-\rho)^2 c\mu} P_0 \tag{9-14}$$

in which

$$P_0 = \frac{c!(1-\rho)}{(\rho c)^c + c!(1-\rho)\left\{\sum_{n=0}^{c-1} \frac{1}{n!}(\rho c)^n\right\}}$$ (9-15)

and where, most importantly, it should be noted that

$$\rho = \frac{\lambda}{c\mu}$$ (9-16)

The simple queue formulae can be obtained from those above by substitution of λ/μ for ρ and re-arrangement with $C=1$.

Equation (9-10) is the probability that there are c *or more* customers in the system (i.e., all the service points are occupied). This is the only circumstance in which waiting is necessary. It is usually best to begin any workings by calculating P_0 and to minimize rounding error it is best to leave things in fractional form until the end.

Example 9-5

A bank has arranged its services so that customers requiring cash only are served from any of 3 service points, there being one queue only. The average rate of arrivals is 72 per hour. Each cashier takes on average 2 minutes to serve a customer. Relative to the existing system, evaluate the following alternative arrangements in terms of the system parameters.

 (i) Installation of a cashpoint machine which would take an average 40 seconds to serve each customer.
 (ii) Altering the queueing arrangements so that each service point had its own queue.

First determine P_0 and the parameters for the original 3 service single queue system.

We observe that $\lambda = 72$ and $\mu = 30$ at each service point. Thus

$$\rho = \frac{\lambda}{c\mu} = \frac{72}{3(30)} = 0.8$$

Now find P_0. Spelt out in full it is

$$P_O = \frac{3 \times 2 \times 1(1-0.8)}{(0.8 \times 3)^3 + 3 \times 2 \times 1(1-0.8)\left[\frac{1}{1}(2.4)^0 + \frac{1}{1}(2.4)^1 + \frac{1}{2}(2.4)^2\right]}$$

Thus

$$P_0 = \frac{1.2}{21.36}$$

Notice that in the summation in the denominator $0! = 1$.
Now consider average systems process time, ASPT:

$$\text{ASPT} = \frac{13.824}{6(0.2)^2 90} \times \frac{1.2}{21.36} + \frac{1}{30}\text{hours}$$

$$= \frac{16.5888}{461.376} + \frac{1}{30}$$

$$= 0.069\ 288 \text{ hours or 4 minutes 9 seconds}$$

In ASPT, the 1/30 hour represents the average time spent (2 minutes) at the service point. The first component, 2 minutes 9 seconds, is the average queueing time.

Now ascertain the probability of a customer having to wait for service—this will make for an interesting comparison later on. Thus using Eq. (9-10)

$$P(n \geqslant c) = \frac{13.824}{1.2} \times \frac{1.2}{21.36} = 0.6472$$

Note that this value is less than ρ. Now consider the average number in the queue. From equation (9-12), this emerges as 2.59 and the average number in the system is $\rho c = 2.4$ more.

Having considered the main parameters of the original arrangement, consider the cashpoint machine alternative. This is a simple queue situation with $\lambda = 72$ as before but with $\mu = 90$. We could use the new formulae with $c = 1$ but it is much simpler to remember that

$$\text{ASPT} = \frac{1}{\mu - \lambda} = \frac{1}{90 - 72}\text{hours} = 3 \text{ minutes 20 seconds}$$

But with the machine the probability of having to wait $= \rho = 0.8$ which is *greater*. Under the old arrangements there was more chance of a customer getting served right away.

With the machine the average number in the system is 4 and of these 3.2 on average are in the queue. The 0.8 mean number at the service point means that the cash joint would be in use some 80 per cent of the time. Average queuing time would be two minutes forty seconds.

The other possibility would be to have three service points each with its own separate queue. To evaluate this last arrangement start by assuming no jockeying, no reneging, and no balking with random arrivals at the rate of $\lambda/3$ into each queue. We specifically assume that the rate of arrivals into each queue is *not state dependent*, viz, that a new arrival is equally likely to join any of the queues regardless of their relative lengths. This being the case we have the arrangement:

$$\lambda = 24 \quad \boxed{\mu = 30}$$

$$\lambda = 24 \quad \boxed{\mu = 30}$$

$$\lambda = 24 \quad \boxed{\mu = 30}$$

Clearly, for each of these three simple queue situations

$$\text{ASPT} = \frac{1}{30 - 24} = \frac{1}{6}\text{hour} = 10 \text{ minutes}$$

which is by far the worst performance of the three arrangements. The following ordering (by ASPT) is generally true:

1. Single queue single server operating at rate $n\mu$.
2. Single queue n servers operating at rate μ.
3. n queues n servers operating at rate μ.

A summary of the results of the comparative study is shown in Fig. 9-5. Generally, the deciding factor is ASPT. The separate queues arrangement is so bad on both time parameters that it can be ruled out of consideration. The cashpoint is superior on the crucial ASPT factor and has 20 per cent fewer in the system and would be preferred in most circumstances.

	Cashiers	Machine	3 sep. queues
Probability of having to wait	0.6472	0.8	0.8
Average number in the system	4.99	4	4
Average number in the queue	2.59	3.2	3.2
Average system process time	4' 9"	3' 20"	10'
Average queuing time	2' 9"	2' 40"	8'

Figure 9-5

The separate queue arrangement comes out badly from the comparison so why in practice is it still sometimes observed? Apart from cases where the servers perform different functions, in practice people join the shortest queue and 'jockeying' is allowed. This brings the performance of the multi-queue arrangement closer to the single queue.

Although it would be an unlikely arrangement within a bank, a further alternative in principle is to have multiple servers *in series* with each server performing part of the service. With the arrival and service rates above, the result would be:

$$\xrightarrow{\lambda=72} \boxed{\mu=90} \xrightarrow{\lambda=72} \boxed{\mu=90} \xrightarrow{\lambda=72} \boxed{\mu=90}$$

On the assumptions that (a) there is no interference between the stages (for example, lack of space to queue) and (b) all customers require all three parts of the service, we can compute the performance parameters for this arrangement. In terms of ASPT, this will be three lots of ASPT with $\lambda = 72$ and $\mu = 90$. Thus:

$$\text{ASPT} = 3 \left(\frac{1}{90-72} \right) 60 \text{ minutes}$$

$$= 10 \text{ minutes}$$

It is no coincidence that ASPT is the same as in the separate queues in parallel case. Both λ and μ are three times as large but the process has to be entered into three times over. The reader may confirm that under the series arrangement there are 9.6 in the queue and 12 in the system all told. Queueing time would be 8 minutes. Probability of delay is one minus the probability of not being delayed at any of the stages. This is

$$1 - (1-\rho)^3 = 0.992$$

The series arrangement would have advantages where the whole service is provided in stages and if early exiting and by-passing unwanted stages is made possible by the physical layout of the facility.

9-5 COSTS

Within queueing theory, analytical optimization of a financial objective function is rarely possible. Usually a number of discrete alternatives are set out and the best arrangement selected. The two examples to follow bring costs into the picture to help determine the best arrangement in financial rather than physical performance terms. This will mean that a price has to be put on factors such as time. Such valuations are generally subject to uncertainty and sensitivity analysis of the results is strongly indicated.

Example 9-6

The average rate of arrivals at a self-service store is 30 per hour. At present there is one cashier who on average can attend to 45 customers per hour. The store proprietor estimates that each extra hour of system process time per customer means the loss of £10 profit. An assistant can be provided for the cashier (to weigh and wrap goods, etc.) and in these circumstances the service point can deal with 75 people per hour on average. The wage rate of the assistant would be £4.00 per hour. Is it worth taking on the assistant?

Answer

$\lambda = 30$, $\mu = 45$ thus the average system process time originally is: $1/(\mu - \lambda) = 1/15$ hour per customer so that *per customer* there is an opportunity loss of £$1/15 \times 10 = £\frac{2}{3}$ but there are 30 customers per hour to consider so that the store's lost profit per hour is £$\frac{2}{3} \times 30 = £20$ per hour with the original arrangement. With the assistant provided, ASPT $= 1/(75 - 30) = 1/45$ hour per customer so that the opportunity loss per hour is $1/45 \times 10 \times 30 = £6\frac{2}{3}$, a reduction of £$13\frac{1}{3}$ on the original figure. If we now deduct the assistant's wages there is a net saving of £$9\frac{1}{3}$ per hour so that it is worth while having the assistant.

The question arises as to where the £10 per hour cost comes from. Such figures (rather like the shortage loss in stock control) are difficult to assess so it is advisable to conduct a sensitivity analysis. What is the least value of the lost profit per minute for which the assistant would be worth while? This is L such that:

$$\frac{1}{45} \times L \times 30 + 4 \leqslant \frac{1}{15} \times L \times 30$$

i.e.

$$\frac{2L}{3} + 4 \leqslant 2L$$

$$\therefore \ 2L + 12 \leqslant 6L$$

$$\therefore \ 4L \geqslant 12$$

$$L \geqslant 3$$

It may be that while the manager was by no means sure that £10 per hour was the correct figure he or she may be well satisfied that it is in excess of the required minimum of £3 per hour for the decision to be correct.

Example 9-7

The manager of a discount store is concerned about the delays that customers experience in the simple queue situation at the service counter. At present the average system process time is 6 minutes and the average queueing time is

$4\frac{1}{2}$ minutes. The manager estimates that each minute of system process time saved per customer would increase profit by 10p (not counting the cost of effecting the reduction). These are four possible ways of speeding things up. These are:

1. Increase the mean rate of service of the one attendant to 60 customers per hour on average. It would cost an extra £1.50 per hour to do this.
2. Have two attendants, working in parallel, each providing a mean rate of service of 50 customers per hour. There would still be one queue only and the extra cost of this arrangement would be £3 per hour.
3. Have two queues, each to its own server, with each server operating at the original service rate. The additional cost of this arrangement would be £2 per hour.
4. Split the payments procedure into two stages and have one queue with two servers in series, each server being able to process an average of 80 customers per hour. It would cost an extra £4 per hour to do this.

   (i) Which of the arrangements is to be preferred?
   (ii) Suppose that capital expenditure was required, in a differing amount in each case, to effect the arrangements above. Briefly explain how a selection between the alternatives could be made in the circumstances.

Answer

The values of λ and μ are implied by the original system parameters:

$$\text{ASPT} = \frac{1}{\mu - \lambda} = \frac{1}{10}; \quad \frac{\lambda}{\mu(\mu - \lambda)} = \frac{3}{40}$$

From ASPT, $\mu = \lambda + 10$ and substituting into the queueing time gives:

$$\frac{\lambda}{(\lambda + 10)10} = \frac{3}{10} \quad \therefore \ 40\lambda = 300 + 30$$

$$\therefore \ 10\lambda = 300$$

$$\therefore \quad \lambda = 30, \mu = 40$$

The lost profit due to system process time is £6 per hour per customer. Thus originally this lost profit amounted to

$$\frac{1}{10} \times 6 \times 30 = £18 \text{ per hour}$$

1. Here μ becomes 60 so the lost profit is:

$$\frac{1}{60-30} \times 6 \times 30 = £6$$

giving a gross saving of £12 and a net saving of

$$£12 - £1.50 = \boxed{£10.50}$$

2. In this case $\lambda = 30$, $\mu = 50$, $c = 2$,

$$\therefore \; \rho = \frac{\lambda}{c\mu} = 0.3$$

So that

$$P_0 = \frac{2(0.7)}{(0.6)^2 + 2(0.7)(1+0.6)} = \frac{1.4}{2.6}$$

So

$$\text{ASPT} = \frac{(0.6)^2}{2(0.7)^2 \, 100} \times \frac{1.4}{2.6} + \frac{1}{50} = 0.021 \, 978 \text{ hours}$$

Lost profit therefore equals £0.021|978(6)(30) = £3.96; so that there is a gross saving of £18 − £3.96 = £14.04 and a net saving of

$$£14.04 - £3 = \boxed{£11.04}$$

3. Here we must assume something about the arrival pattern. The simplest thing is to assume that the arrival rate into each queue averages $\lambda/2 = 15$. So

$$\text{ASPT} = \frac{1}{40-15} = \frac{1}{25} \text{hour}$$

giving a gross saving of £10.80 and a net saving of $\boxed{£8.80}$.

4. Here the arrangement is:

$$\xrightarrow{\lambda=30} \boxed{\mu=80} \xrightarrow{\lambda=30} \boxed{\mu=80}$$

in which we assume no interference between the queues and note that the rate of output from the first stage is equal to the rate of arrivals in the second (none leaves the system at this point). In this sort of arrangement

$$\text{ASPT} = 2\left(\frac{1}{\mu - \lambda}\right) = 2\left(\frac{1}{80 - 30}\right) = 0.04 \text{ hours}$$

giving a gross saving of £10.80 and a net saving of $\boxed{£6.80}$.

(i) So the preferred arrangement will be (2) with two service points in parallel producing a net saving of £11.04 per hour.

(ii) The problem now becomes a capital budgeting problem. The returns on the capital expenditures are the annual savings achieved. Thus assuming a 54-hour week (the norm for shops) and a 51-week year the *annual* saving under system (2) is £54 × 51 × 11.08 = £30 514. If there is a capital cost of K_2 needed to implement the system and a cost of capital of $100r$ per cent with a lifetime of n years the net present value of the type (2) arrangement (NPV_2) would be given by:

$$\text{NPV}_2 = \sum_{t=1}^{n} \frac{30\,514}{(1+r)^t} - K_2$$

This would be worked out for the given values of K_2 and r, with a similar calculation being performed for the other arrangements. Whichever gave the greatest NPV would be preferred.

9-6 GENERAL SERVICE TIME DISTRIBUTION

In most queueing systems, apart from obvious exceptions involving arrival *en masse*, the time between arrivals follows the negative exponential distribution to an acceptable degree of accuracy. Service times, however, may quite commonly follow distributions other than the negative exponential.

Rather surprisingly it turns out that the main parameters—number in the system, queue length, average system process time and queueing time—can be obtained if only the mean and variance of the service time distributions are known. With the mean service rate still represented μ, with variance of service time σ^2 and with the other conditions of a simple queue obtaining, the results are:

$$\text{Average queue length: } \frac{\rho^2(1 + \mu^2\sigma^2)}{2(1-\rho)}$$

$$\text{Average number in system: } \frac{\rho^2(1 + \mu^2\sigma^2)}{2(1-\rho)} + \rho$$

$$\text{Average queueing time: } \frac{\rho(1+\mu^2\sigma^2)}{2\mu(1-\rho)}$$

$$\text{Average system process time: } \frac{\rho(1+\mu^2\sigma^2)}{2\mu(1-\rho)}+\frac{1}{\mu}$$

These are the Pollaczek-Khintchine (P-K) formulae and are very powerful results as the *form* of the service time distribution is entirely arbitrary and may not even be known. The practical advantage here is that it is a good deal easier to obtain useful estimates of the mean and variance of service time from observation than it is to *fit* a distribution to the data.

Notice how the formulae reduce to the simple queue expressions. In the case of a negative exponential distribution with mean rate of service μ the variance of service times is $1/\mu^2$. Making this substitution for σ^2, the average queue length expression reduces to:

$$\frac{\rho^2}{1-\rho}=\frac{\lambda^2}{\mu(\mu-\lambda)}$$

A further important special case included in the P-K formulae is that of *constant* service time. With $\sigma^2=0$ the queue length becomes

$$\frac{\rho^2}{2(1-\rho)}$$

which is just half its value in the simple queue case. Thus we can think of half of the queue as being the result of service time variability and half results from the variability of arrivals.

In fact the P-K formulae have even more general applicability. The four system parameters are valid for *any* queue discipline that is independent of the service times. Thus queue discipline can be LIFO or random, as well as FIFO. Furthermore, it is only necessary that the system is single server with Poisson arrivals and is uncapacitated.

Consider the following example. Items arrive Poisson fashion into an uncapacitated single server system at the average rate of 9 per hour. The mean rate of service is $\mu=10$ per hour. Find the average queue length in the cases of:

(i) Negative exponentially distributed service time.
(ii) A service time distribution of unknown form with variance $\sigma^2=3/100$.
(iii) Constant service time.

In case (i) we know that $\sigma^2=1/\mu^2$ so $\sigma^2=1/100$ thus with $\rho=\lambda/\mu=0.9$ the average queue length is

$$\frac{\rho^2}{1-\rho} = \frac{0.81}{0.1} = 8.1 \text{ items}$$

In case (ii) variance $\sigma^2 = 3/100$ so that the P-K formula gives queue length as:

$$\frac{0.81(1+3)}{2(0.1)} = 16.2 \text{ items}$$

In comparison to case (i), note that a tripling of the variance of service time has resulted in a doubling of the expected queue length.

In case (iii) the service time is invariant with $\sigma^2 = 0$. The queue length is then simply:

$$\frac{0.81}{1(0.1)} = 4.05 \text{ items}$$

This confirms the halving of queue length in comparison to case (i).

9-7 CAPACITATED SYSTEMS

Suppose that simple queue conditions prevail except that the maximum number of items that can be contained in the system is $\bar{n}$. The system is said to be capacitated at $\bar{n}$ or have a *finite* or *truncated queue* (length $\bar{n}-1$). When the system contains $\bar{n}$ items, arrivals will *balk* (not enter the system). This is an example of a *non-captive system* or a *loss-delay system*. For low values of $\bar{n}$, it is useful to study such systems from 'first principles' using *state equations* which link, through λ and μ, the probabilities that the system contains the various possible numbers of items.

Formulae can also be obtained for some of the system parameters. In the capacitated case, care is required when considering average system process time as this must be conditional upon items entering the system in the first place. Here we shall examine the expression for the average number in the system. This is:

$$\text{Average number in system: } \rho \left[\frac{1 - (\bar{n}+1)\rho^{\bar{n}} \bar{n}\rho^{\bar{n}+1}}{(1-\rho)(1-\rho^{\bar{n}+1})} \right] \qquad (9\text{-}17)$$

In capacitated systems, $\rho = \lambda/\mu$ as before but λ represents the mean rate of *potential* arrivals. In this context, values of $\rho > 1$ are meaningful and (9-17) applies for *all* values of ρ except $\rho = 1$. The *actual* rate of arrivals will always be less than μ over any significant interval. In the case where $\rho = 1$ the average number in the system is $\bar{n}/2$.

Two special cases involving (9-17) are of interest. The first is the simple queue itself. In this case $\bar{n}$ is infinite and ρ must be less than one. The formula (9-17) then reduces to just $\rho/(1-\rho)$ which is the familiar simple queue result. The other special case is of queueless systems in which $\bar{n}=1$ and the average number in the system reduces to $\rho/(1+\rho)$.

Consider an example. A queueing system in which $\lambda=20$ and $\mu=15$ is capacitated at $\bar{n}=3$. Determine the average number in this system and the effect on the average number of doubling the mean rate of service.

In the original circumstances substituting $\rho=4/3$ and $\bar{n}=3$ in (9-17) produces a result of 1.85 in the system on average. If the mean rate of service is doubled to $\mu=30$ then substituting $\rho=2/3$ in (9-17) gives an average number in the system of 1.523. Note that the doubling of service rate resulted in a 17.7 per cent reduction in the number in the system but the throughput of the system will be greater as fewer potential arrivals will balk.

9-8 DISTRIBUTION OF SYSTEM PROCESS TIME

We have said much about the mean values of system parameters and ASPT was of particular importance. But, of course, not all customers will be served at or within the average time. A low ASPT represents good performance but a more refined concept of service quality would include the *distribution* about the mean. The narrower the spread of times the less is the chance that customers will experience very long process times and the better the system is performing.

It turns out that the distribution of SPT is negative exponential with the parameter $\mu-\lambda$. It is given by

$$\text{SPT}(t)=(\mu-\lambda)e^{-t(\mu-\lambda)} \qquad (9\text{-}18)$$

The mean of this distribution is of course $1(\mu-\lambda)$ and the standard deviation is also $1(\mu-\lambda)$. Surprisingly therefore, the distribution of system process time is the same for $\lambda=2$, $\mu=4$ and $\lambda=98$, $\mu=100$. The distribution is graphed in Fig. 9-5. In Fig. 9-6 the shaded area is the probability that system process time exceeds some particular value T. Integration of (9-18) with respect to t between the limits of T and infinity gives this probability as:

$$\text{P(SPT}>\text{T)}=e^{-t(\mu-\lambda)} \qquad (9\text{-}19)$$

There are two particularly interesting values of T. The first is where T represents the average time itself. Substituting $T=1/\mu-\lambda$ in 9-19 gives the result $e^{-1}=0.3679$. Thus, regardless of the particular values of μ and λ in a simple queue there is a 36.79 per cent chance of the process time exceeding the average. Note, however, that if μ increases relative to λ both the ASPT and the standard deviation will decrease and system performance improve on both counts.

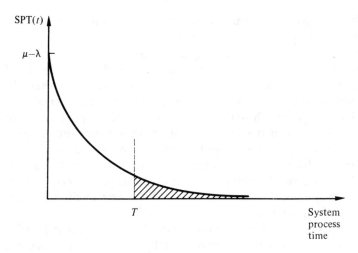

Figure 9-6

A second significant value of T would be the time within which there is a 95 per cent chance of being processed. From (9-19) we would have

$$e^{-T(\mu - \lambda)} = 0.05$$

From tables or a calculator $e^{-3} \simeq 0.05$ so the requisite value of T is $T \simeq 3/\mu - \lambda$. That is to say in a simple queue situation there is a 95 per cent chance of not experiencing a system process time exceeding three times the average. Put another way, if ASPT in some case was 40 minutes, only 1 in 20 customers would experience a process time of over two hours—but of course these are the customers who will complain!

9-9 CONCLUSIONS

We have examined a number of queueing systems in the light of performance parameters and shown how cost can be brought into the picture. There are many other models. A useful review of these is to be found in Murdoch (1978) and a classification scheme is described in Taha (1987). A simulation approach to queueing problems is described in Chapter Thirteen of this book.

The use of computers in queueing theory problems in practice is principally for simulation studies (see Chapter Thirteen). However, it is possible to produce computer programmes to solve the formulae for the various analytical queueing theory models. An example of such a programme is provided in Cohen (1985) which for a simple queue model will print out the state probabilities (P_0, P_1, etc.), and the main system parameters.

We have seen that altering the arrangements altered the system parameters. There are many ways (other than a change in the number of servers) of affecti.ag system performance. On the service side it may (at a price) be possible to speed up service; for example, by providing change-making machines for cashiers or by motion study of the operations involved.

A frequently encountered problem in connection with arrivals is one of *peak-loading*—uneven demand during the day (or week or year). For example, British Telecom attempts to smooth out demand for telephone services by differential charges and British Rail operates a system of 'off-peak' fares. An alternative possibility is to regulate demand by an appointments system. However, care must be exercised here for although visible queues may be reduced, there may be hidden queues (e.g. sick people waiting at home for appointments with a general practitioner). Monopolistic providers of services find it easier directly to regulate demand than do those in competitive industry where regulation by price is more common.

Even the simplest queueing system is so complex that it is rarely possible to optimize—to obtain ideal performance. Usually improved performance is sought from a limited range of alternatives rather than the unobtainable optimum. The move to a more customer-oriented management approach has given added emphasis to service delivery and efficiency within the organization. The important role of queueing theory in this context has been well pointed up by Murdoch:

> The basic concepts and an understanding of modern queueing theory are requirements not only in the training of operational research staff, management scientists, etc., but also as fundamental concepts in the training of managers or in management development programmes. The efficient design and operation of service functions is one of the main problems facing management today and the understanding obtained from a study of queueing theory is essential in the solution of these problems.

EXERCISES

9-1 Revision exercise
   (i) To what extent is queueing theory concerned with the study of *delay* whether or not an actual queue is observed?
   (ii) Give some examples of the differing character of arrival patterns, queue disciplines and sevice mechanisms in queueing systems. What other factors distinguish types of queue model?
   (iii) What is the relationship between the Poisson and negative exponential distributions in describing the nature of arrivals into a queueing system?
   (iv) What are the conditions necessary for a simple queue?
   (v) What are the most important parameters in measuring the performance of a queueing system?
   (vi) In a multi-server system what type of queue arrangement gives the best results?
   (vii) Show how costs can be included in evaluations of queueing arrangements and explain the value of sensitivity analysis in this context.
   (viii) Explain how present value methods can come in to the evaluation of queueing systems.
   (ix) What grounds are there for saying that half of the queue length in a system is due to sevice time variability and half is due to variability of arrivals?
   (x) In what sense is a simple queue a limiting case of a capacitated system?

    (xi) Why is the distribution of system process time a relevant consideration in judging the quality of service provided?

   (xii) Give two ways in which the arrival pattern into a system may be influenced.

9-2 The number of people arriving into a particular queueing system in a 'short' time interval is described by a Poisson distribution with mean 0.4 per minute. Use Table 7 (page 495), to obtain the following information:

    (i) The probabilities of no, one, and two customers arriving in any one-minute interval.

   (ii) The probability that more than one customer arrives in any one-minute interval.

  (iii) The probability that less than two customers arrive in any one-minute interval.

  (iv) The probability that two or three customers arrive in any one-minute interval.

   (v) The probability that two customers arrive in any *three*-minute interval.

9-3 Telephone calls arrive at a switchboard once every three minutes. The average call lasts two minutes.

    (i) Find the average system process time.

   (ii) Find the average queueing time.

  (iii) Suppose there is a 10 per cent increase in 'demand'. What per cent increase in expected queueing time does this produce?

9-4 The manager of a parts counter is comparing four possible queueing arrangements as shown below:

    (i) $\lambda=70 \rightarrow$ $\boxed{\mu=100}$

   (ii) $\lambda=70 \rightarrow$ $\boxed{\mu=50}$

                                 $\boxed{\mu=50}$

  (iii) $\lambda=35 \rightarrow$ $\boxed{\mu=50}$

             $\lambda=35 \rightarrow$ $\boxed{\mu=50}$

  (iv) $\lambda=70 \rightarrow$ $\boxed{\mu=200}$ $\lambda=70 \rightarrow$ $\boxed{\mu=200}$

In each case $\boxed{}$ indicates a service point and $\lambda=$mean rate of arrivals per hour (Poisson distribution) and $\mu=$mean service rate per hour (service time negative exponential distribution). Except for the structural differences shown in (i), (iii), and (iv) assume that simple queue characteristics obtain. For each case calculate the expected system process time in minutes and, making clear any necessary assumptions, the probability of having to wait.

9-5 A discount house at present has two service points. Customs form one queue and apart from the number of servers simple queue conditions obtain. The manager reckons that the hourly sales revenue (R) is

$$R = \bar{R} - 10p$$

where $\bar{R}$ is a constant and p is the probability of customers having to wait for service. The mean rate of arrivals is fixed at $\lambda=180$ and all servers operate at the rate of $\mu=100$. The manager is thinking of increasing the number of servers to three or four. To use three servers would increase hourly variable costs by £3.80. To use four servers would raise hourly variable costs by £6.00. In addition the capital cost of providing one more server than at present would be £3000 and two more servers would require capital expenditure of £6000. The cost of capital is 10 per cent and the new arrangements can be assumed to last indefinitely. The working week is 55 hours and there is a 50-week working year. What decision should be taken?

9-6 At the present time, a servicing department provides answers through one channel, which on average can deal with 24 enquiries per hour at a cost of £3 per enquiry. Increasingly the customers are complaining that they have to wait for a long time and the department is considering alternative arrangements. These are either a two-service channel system costing £100 per hour and service rate of 15 per hour in each, or a three-service channel system costing £125 per hour and a service rate of 10 per hour in each. Customers arrive at the rate of 20 per hour.

Calculate:
  (a) the average time a customer is in the system under the present arrangement;
  (b) the extra charges per enquiry that would need to be made to recover the extra cost of each of the two arrangements proposed;
  (c) the implied value of customers' time per hour if they agreed to pay the extra costs of the two channel system.

(The Chartered Institute of Management Accountants)

9-7 Your company is considering changing the present system of serving customers who arrive in person and wait for service. The existing single service channel can service ten people an hour at a variable cost of £8 per person. The service facilities have a fixed cost of £50 per hour. The demand for these services has increased from 4 persons per hour when first offered, to the current 8 per hour and is expected to increase to 15 per hour next year.

Alternative service patterns have been considered. Either a larger single service channel that would be able to service 20 people an hour at a variable cost of £7 per person and fixed costs of £120 per hour, or the addition of another single service channel which would still have a variable cost of £8 per person but additional fixed costs of £60 per hour. Customer time has been estimated to have a value of £25 per hour.

  (a) calculate the cost to the company of the optimum service system, ignoring customers' time, currently and next year;
  (b) calculate the cost in each system to the customer next year;
  (c) state which system the company should choose next year if it takes into account half the value of customers' time.

(The Chartered Institute of Management Accountants)

9-8 Items arrive Poisson fashion into an uncapacitated single server system at the average rate of 18 per hour. The mean rate of service is 20 per hour. Find the average queue length in the cases of service time distribution, being
  (i) negative exponential
  (ii) of unknown form but with variance 0.03,
  (iii) constant.

9-9 A queueing system in which $\lambda = 24$ and $\mu = 20$ is capacitated at $\bar{n} = 4$. Determine the average number in this system and calculate the effect on the number in this system of doubling the mean rate of service. Assume that, capacitation apart, simple queue conditions prevail.

9-10 For a simple queue system, calculate the probability that the system process time experienced by a customer will lie between one half and twice the average system process time.

Solution guides

9-2 The probability of n arrivals in a T minute interval with mean rate of arrivals λ per minute is given the Poisson probabilities. Table 7 tabulates these Poisson probabilities and is constructed for $T = 1$.

$$P(n \text{ in } T) = \frac{(\lambda T)^n e^{-\lambda T}}{n!}$$

  (i) Looking in the $\lambda = 0.4$ row and $n = 0$ column gives $p = 0.6703$. For the same row, with $n = 1$, $p = 0.2681$ and if $n = 2$, $p = 0.0536$. Note that the sum of the probabilities in any row is one since there must be *some* number of arrivals.

(ii) The probability that more than one customer arrives is one minus the chance that one or no customers arrive (using the fact that the probabilities in any row sum to one).

$$\text{Thus } P(n > 1 \text{ in } 1) = P(2) + P(3) + P(4) + \cdots$$
$$= 1 - [P(0) + P(1)]$$
$$= 1 - [0.6703 + 0.2681]$$
$$= 1 - 0.9384$$
$$= 0.0616$$

(iii) This has already been found in answering (ii). $P = 0.9384$.

(iv) $P(2) = 0.0536$, $P(3) = 0.0072$. Thus since two or three arrivals are mutually exclusive events the probabilities may be added: $P(2 \text{ or } 3 \text{ in } 1 \text{ min}) = 0.0536 + 0.0072 = 0.0608$.

(v) Now here we have to find some information where $T = 3$. A glance at the formula above shows that the same result is obtained for $\lambda = 0.4$ and $T = 3$ as is the outcome when $\lambda = 1.2$ and $T = 1$. Thus using the $\lambda = 1.2$ row of the table: $P(2 \text{ in } 3) = 0.2169$.

9-3 $\lambda = 20$ per hour, $\mu = 30$ per hour

(i) $\dfrac{1}{\mu - \lambda} \text{ hours} = \dfrac{1}{10} \text{ hour} = 6 \text{ minutes}$

(ii) $\dfrac{\lambda}{\mu(\mu - \lambda)} = \dfrac{20}{30(30 - 20)} \text{ hours} = \dfrac{1}{15} \text{ hour} = 4 \text{ minutes}$

(Note that this result could have been obtained by subtracting the mean service time (2 minutes) from the 6 minutes ASPT already obtained.)

(iii) λ now $= 22$. Queueing time now averages $5\frac{1}{2}$ minutes. This represents a 37.5 per cent increase.

9-4 In case (i) ASPT $= 1(\mu - \lambda)$ hours $= \frac{1}{30}$ hours or 2 minutes the probability of having to wait (call it $P(w)$) is $\lambda/\mu = 0.7$. In case (ii) the multi-server formula applies with $c = 2$. Note that $\rho = \lambda/c\mu = 70/(2 \times 50) = 0.7$.

$$P_0 = \frac{0.6}{1.96 + 0.6(1 + 1.4)} = \frac{0.6}{3.4}$$

Thus

$$\text{ASPT} = \frac{1.96}{2(0.09)2(50)} P_0 + \frac{1}{50} = 0.0392 \text{ hours or } 2.35 \text{ minutes.}$$

In this case the probability of having to wait is

$$P(w) = \frac{1.96}{2(1 - 0.7)} P_0 = 0.5765$$

In case (iii) assume that an arrival is equally likely to join either queue regardless of the lengths. So here ASPT $= 1/(50 - 35)$ hours $= 4$ minutes and $P(w) = 35/50 = 0.7$.

In case (iv) assume that there is no inference between the two stages and all customers go through both stages. So

$$\text{ASPT} = 2\left(\frac{1}{200 - 70}\right) \text{ hours} = 0.92 \text{ minutes.}$$

As regards the probability of having to wait, if this is interpreted as meaning waiting at the first service point then $P(w)=0.35$. The probability of having to wait at *either* point is $1-(0.65)^2 = 0.5775$.

9-5 First find the probability of having to wait, for the 2, 3, and 4 server alternatives. With the usual formula $P=0.8$; 0.382 677; and 0.147 621 respectively. In the 3-server case, the net hourly saving in comparison with two servers is

$$10(0.8-0.382\ 677)-3.80=0.373\ 23$$

Now, with a 2750 hour year the annual saving is

$$0.373\ 23(2750)=1026.4$$

This value constitutes the annual 'return' on the investment of £3000 that is required in this case. Since the project is a perpetuity at 10 per cent the net present value is

$$\frac{1026.4}{0.1}=3000=7264$$

In the 4-server case the net present value (in comparison with two servers) is

$$\frac{[10(0.8-0.147\ 621)-6]2750}{0.1}-6000=8404$$

Since both present values are positive, both the 3 and 4 server alternatives are superior to the 2-server case. Since the 4-server alternative provides the better NPV, this will be the alternative selected.

9-6 (a) The original $\text{ASPT}=\dfrac{1}{24-20}$ hour or 15 minutes.

    (b) The original average cost per hour $=20 \times 3=60$ with two channels it is £100; therefore, with 20 enquiries per hour an extra £2 per enquiry is needed. With three channels the additional cost is £125 − £60, i.e. £3.25 extra per enquiry.

    (c) An actual value of customers' time cannot be calculated, only a *lower bound* can be given. The ASPT in the two-channel case is 7.2 minutes. If customers prefer this situation they must value their time at at least $(£5-£3)/(15-7.2)$ per minute or £15.38 per hour.

9-7 (a) With $\lambda=8$:

larger service channel

$$\text{cost to company}=120+7(8)=£176 \text{ per hour}$$

extra small channel:

$$\text{cost to company}=50+60+8(8)=£174 \text{ per hour.}$$

Thus in the current year, the extra small service channel has a marginal advantage.

With $\lambda = 15$:

larger service channel

$$\text{cost to company} = 120 + 7(15) = £255 \text{ per hour.}$$

extra small channel:

$$\text{cost to company} = 50 + 60 + 8(15) = £230 \text{ per hour.}$$

So in this case the single, larger channel has the edge.

(b) Larger channel:

$$\text{ASPT} = \frac{1}{20 - 15} = 0.2 \text{ hours}$$

∴ value of customers' time per hour $= 0.2(15)(25) = £75$ per hour.
Extra small channel:

$$= 0.75, \ P_0 = \tfrac{1}{7}, \ \text{ASPT} = 0.228\ 57 \text{ hours}$$

∴ value of customers' time per hour $= 0.228\ 57(15)(25) = £85.71$.

(c) The larger service channel is selected since both the company's and the customers' costs are lower with this arrangement.

9-8 The Pollaczek-Khintchine formulae apply throughout. Traffic intensity $\rho = 16/20 = 0.8$

(i) Exponential service time $\sigma^2 = \dfrac{1}{\mu^2} = \dfrac{1}{400}$

∴ Average queue length $= \dfrac{0.64(1 + 1)}{2(0.2)} = 3.2$ items

(ii) Here $\sigma^2 = 0.03$.
So

$$\text{Average queue length} = \frac{0.64(1 + 400(0.03))}{0.4} = 20.8 \text{ items}$$

(iii) Here $\sigma^2 = 0$
So

$$\text{Average queue length} = \frac{0.64}{0.4} = 1.6 \text{ items}$$

9-9 In this capacitated model $\lambda = 24$, $\mu = 20$ ∴ $\rho = 1.2$ and with $\bar{n} = 4$

$$\text{Average number in the system} = 1.2\left[\frac{1 - 5(1.2)^4 + 4(1.2)^5}{-0.2[1 - (1.2)^5]}\right]$$

$$= \frac{0.702\ 336}{0.297\ 664}$$

$$\simeq 2.36$$

If mean rate of service is doubled $\mu = 40$ and $\rho = 0.6$ use of the formula for the capacitated case produces:

$$\text{Average number in the system} = 0.6\left[\frac{1.5(0.6)^4 + 4(0.6)^5}{0.4[1 - (0.6)^5]}\right]$$

$$= \frac{0.397\ 824}{0.368\ 896}$$

$$\simeq 1.08$$

9-10 The probability that system process time exceeds a given value T is given by:

$$P(SPT > T) = e^{-T(\mu - \lambda)}$$

In the case of half the average system process time $T = 1/2(\mu - \lambda)$ and substituting in the probability expression gives the result:

$$P(SPT > 0.5(ASPT)) = e^{-1/2} = 0.6065$$

In the case where process time is double the average $T = 2/(\mu - \lambda)$ and the probability is

$$P(SPT > 2(ASPT) = e^{-2} = 0.1353$$

The required probability of a system process time between half and double the average is the difference between the values above, i.e.

$$P(\tfrac{1}{2}ASPT \leqslant SPT \leqslant 2\ ASPT) = e^{-1/2} - e^{-2} = 0.4712$$

That is to say just under half the customers will experience a system process time within the given range.

REFERENCES

Cohen, S. S. (1985), *Operational Research*, Edward Arnold.
Murdoch, J. (1978), *Queueing Theory*, Macmillan.
Taha, H. A. (1987), *Operations Research*, fourth edition, Collier Macmillan.

FURTHER READING

Cook, T. M., and Russell, R. A. (1981), *Introduction to Management Science*, second edition, Prentice Hall. Includes a useful classification on queueing models.
Hillier, F. S., and Lieberman, G. J. (1974), *Operations Reseach*, second edition, Holden-Day. Contains technical background and description of more advanced models.
Littlechild, S. C. (1977), *Operational Research for Managers*, Philip Allan. Includes a case study of a queueing theory model of a telephone enquiry answering system.
Phillips, D. T., Ravindran, A., and Solberg, J. (1976), *Operations Reseach, Principles and Practice*, John Wiley. Contains discussion of Pollaczek-Khintchine formula, advanced models and classification system.
Wagner, H. M. (1972), *Principles of Operations Research*, Prentice-Hall. Contains good overview of queueing systems, Kendall's notation and advanced models.

EXPECTED VALUES, DECISION TREES
AND BREAK-EVEN ANALYSIS

10-1 EXPECTED VALUE ANALYSIS

Expected value analysis is an approach to business decision making under risk. *Risk* is defined as a situation where there may be a number of possible outcomes of a decision but where the probabilities of the different events can be reasonably estimated. Risk is distinguished from *uncertainty*, where again a multi-outcome situation is faced but where the probabilities are unknown. Some approaches to decision making under uncertainty are covered in Game Theory in Chapter Fourteen.

The expected value of a course of action is the sum of the monetary values of each possible result of that course of action weighted by the probability of occurrence. For example, if there are n outcomes to a course of action, giving monetary values x_1 to x_n with respective probabilities p_1 to p_n then the expected value will be given by:

$$EV = \sum_{i=1}^{n} p_i x_i \qquad (10\text{-}1)$$

(10-1) is sometimes called expected monetary value or EMV. The expected value decision rule chooses the course of action for which EV is greatest. Decisions based on expected value are particularly appropriate when the course of action being considered will be repeated many times, or is one of several similarly sized activities with independent probability distributions of outcomes. We shall now examine this decision rule in the context of a numerical example which illustrates the tabular layout involved.

10-2 PAY-OFF MATRICES

Consider the following problem. A clothing discount store advertises special sale items from time to time in the press. Only one item is advertised on each occasion. Experience with clothing in the price range £30 to £40 leads the management to judge that the probabilities of demand at various levels, after

Demand (units)	After advertising in	
	One newspaper	Two newspapers
30	0.10	0.00
40	0.25	0.15
50	0.40	0.35
60	0.25	0.40
70	0.00	0.10

Figure 10-1

each advertisement, are shown in Fig. 10-1. The next item to be advertised is to sell at £35, will cost £15 to buy in and can be disposed of to the trade, if unsold, for £10. There will be a charge of £37.50 for artwork and blockmaking for the advertisement and each newspaper will charge £50 for the insertion of the advertisement.

(i) How many units of the item should be bought in by the shop and in how many newspapers should advertisements be placed in order to maximize expected net profit?
(ii) Conduct a sensitivity analysis on the results.

The first step here is to construct a *payoff matrix* showing gross profit for all possible combinations of purchases and sales. The gross profit per unit sold over the counter is £35 − £15 = £20 and the gross profit per unit disposed of otherwise is £10 − £15 = − £5. Figure 10-2 shows the gross profits. If the shop purchases only 30 units then, since demand cannot be less than 30, exactly 30 units will be sold giving a gross profit of £20 × 30 = £600. If the shop buys in 40 units, if demand is for 40 or more, gross profits will be £800 (no more can be sold than have been purchased). If the shop buys 40 and demand is for only 30 units this means that 30 are sold at a gross profit of £20 per unit and 10 are disposed of at a loss per unit of £5, the net result is £550. It will be noted that

Demand (units)	Purchased by shop (units)				
	30	40	50	60	70
30	600	550	500	450	400
40	600	800	750	700	650
50	600	800	1000	950	900
60	600	800	1000	1200	1150
70	600	800	1000	1200	1400

Figure 10-2

entries below the main diagonal of Fig. 10-2 (top left to bottom right) are equal to the main diagonal entry in the same column and that those entries above the main diagonal reduce in steps of £250 from the main diagonal entry towards the top of the column. Now to calculate the expected gross profits the information in Fig. 10-2 (which will represent 'x' values) is combined with the probability data (the p values) and Σpx, the expected value of gross profit, is calculated for each possible level of purchases. A convenient layout is shown in Fig. 10-3.

Demand	Purchased by shop					Probability (P)	
	30	40	50	60	70	One paper	Two papers
30	600	550	500	450	400	0.10	0.00
40	600	800	750	700	650	0.25	0.15
50	600	800	1000	950	900	0.40	0.35
60	600	800	1000	1200	1150	0.25	0.40
70	600	800	1000	1200	1400	0.00	0.10
Σpx (one)	600	775	887.5	900	850		
Σpx (two)	600	800	962.5	1037.5	1012.5		

Figure 10-3

In Fig. 10-3 expected gross profit of £887.5 corresponding to a purchase of 50 units and advertisement in one newspaper is the sum of products of elements in the 50 column multiplied by the 'one paper' probabilities, viz., 887.5 = 500(0.1) + 750(0.25) + 1000(0.4) + 1000(0.25) + 1000(0). From the Σpx values produced it is evident that sixty units should be bought *irrespective of the number of newspapers in which the advertisement is placed.*

The expected net profit figures are now readily obtained. If the advertisement is placed in one newspaper the costs of this will be:

Cost of block	£37.5
Cost of one insert	£50
Total	£87.5

Thus (assuming the optimal purchase of sixty units is made) expected net profit will be $£(900-87.5)=£812.5$. For two newspapers the advertising costs would be:

Cost of block	£37.5
Cost of two inserts	£100
Total	£137.5

So that the expected net profit in this case would be (again assuming 60 units purchased) $(£1037.5-137.5)=£900$. Thus the optimal course of action is the purchase of 60 units and advertisement in two newspapers.

There is an alternative layout for the calculations of expected gross profit. For each possible level of purchase, the expected revenue can be found and the cost subtracted. For instance for an advertisement in one newspaper and 40 units purchased the expected gross profit is given by

$$0.10(1050+100)+0.25(1400)+0.40(1400)+0.25(1400)-600=775$$

where the bracketed figures are the revenues achieved at each possible level of demand, so that if demand is at 30 units then 30 of the 40 items are sold at £35 giving £1050 revenue and 10 are sold at £10 giving £100 revenue. Expected gross profit with 60 units purchased by the store would be

$$0.10(1050+300)+0.25(1400+200)+0.40(1750+100)+0.25(2100)-900=900$$

The correct answer can be obtained by proceeding in this fashion.

However, it is *not* correct to work with the expected level of demand. For one newspaper advertisement this would be obtained as 48, viz.

D	P	PD
30	0.10	3
40	0.25	10
50	0.40	20
60	0.25	15
70	0	0
		48

Working with 50 (to the nearest multiple of 10) or, even worse, with 48 itself will produce the wrong result with an expected gross profit of under £900. This approach would work only if profit was always strictly proportional to the value of D, which is not the case here.

10-3 SENSITIVITY ANALYSIS

As in all management science techniques applied to problems where the values of certain parameters may be subject to doubt, it is a valuable exercise to express the ultimate decision in terms of the range of values of the parameter to which it applies. We begin the sensitivity discussion with the following question: *Given* a decision to advertise in two newspapers, for what range of values of selling price is it optimal to purchase 60 units?

Working with a selling price of £p instead of £35, the expected gross profit, $E(\pi)$, with 60 units purchased is $53(p-15)-32.5$. The workings are

$$E(\pi)=0.15[40(p-15)-100]+0.35[50(p-15)-50]$$
$$+0.4[60(p-15)]+0.1[60(p-15)]$$
$$=53.5(p-15)-32.5$$

For instance, there is a 0.15 chance of demand being only 40 units. In this event 40 are sold at a margin of $p-15$ and 20 are sold at a loss of £5, thus giving the bracketed term $[40(p-15)-100]$. By a similar process the expected gross profit on 70 units bought, $E(\pi)70$, is:

$$E(\pi)70=0.15[40(p-15)-150]+0.35[50(p-15)-100]$$
$$+0.4[60(p-15)-50]+0.1[70(p-15)]$$
$$=54.5(p-15)-77.5$$

and also in similar fashion we obtain:

$$E(\pi)50=48.5(p-15)-7.5$$

$$E(\pi)40=40(p-15)$$

$$E(\pi)30=30(p-15)$$

Note that the purchase of 30 units can never be optimal in the two-paper case.

Now for 60 units to give at least as much expected profit as 70 we require:

$$53.5(p-15)-32.5\geqslant54.5(p-15)-77.5$$

which re-arranges to give $p\leqslant60$. *This is the upper bound on price.* In comparison with the 50 unit alternative, again there must be no less expected profit with 60 bought. Therefore:

$$53.5(p-15)-32.5 \geqslant 48.5(p-15)-7.5$$

giving $p \geqslant 20$.

Comparing the 60 and 40 alternatives:

$$53.5(p-15)-32.5 \geqslant 40(p-15)$$

i.e., $p \geqslant 17.\overline{407}$.

Thus, *given* a decision to use two newspapers the policy of buying 60 units is optimal provided that:

$$20 \leqslant p \leqslant 60$$

This is a broad range and the original value of $p = 35$ falls near the middle. So even if there is some uncertainty about the final price to be charged, the shop can be confident that the correct purchasing decision has been made.

Now the 'artwork and blockmaking' cost is common to all cases and so does not affect the final decision. However, the newspaper insertion charge might. The insertion charge, I, cannot influence the number of units that the shop buys in but it *might* cause a switch to one-newspaper advertising. With one newspaper the expected net profit is:

$$E\pi(60) = 900 - 37.5 - I$$

and with two newspapers:

$$E\pi(60) = 1037.5 - 37.5 - 2I$$

Thus two newspapers will only be chosen if:

$$1037.5 - 37.5 - 2I \geqslant 900 - 37.5 - I$$

that is if:

$$I \leqslant 137.5$$

Thus, provided that the insertion charge remains below £137.50 per paper, then it is best to use two papers.

Finally, consider again the question of the selling price, p; by an extension of the earlier workings to allow for a switch in the number of newspapers (given the original insertion charge) we obtain the following results:

Price range	Optimal decisions
$p \leqslant 15.556$	30, one paper
$15.556 \leqslant p \leqslant 17.692$	40, one paper
$17.692 \leqslant p \leqslant 22.5$	50, one paper
$22.5 \leqslant p \leqslant 60$	60, two papers
$p \geqslant 60$	70, two papers

In fact, it is better not to do business at all if $p < 17.372$ as the expected profit is negative. On this account it would *never* be worth buying 30 units. Note that the switch from two to one newspaper would occur at $p = 22.5$ and that the original, composite, decision of 60 bought *and* two newspapers is optimal if $22.5 \leqslant p \leqslant 60$.

10-4 EXPECTED VALUE ANALYSIS AND DCF

Frequently decisions to be taken on the basis of expected values will involve cash flows over a period of time sufficiently long for discounting to make a significant difference to the results and indeed the expected value approach can be applied to the assessment of investment projects under conditions of risk. For example, suppose that the returns to an investment in any year, t, may take a number of values each with known probability. The *expected return* for the year, $\bar{R}_t$, is found as per equation (10.1) and the expected returns are then discounted in the usual way to give the *expected net present value* or ENPV. That is:

$$\text{ENPV} = \sum_{t=1}^{n} \bar{R}_t(1+r)^{-t} - K \qquad (10\text{-}2)$$

where K represents the initial outlay (which may itself be an expected value) and $100r$ per cent is the discount rate. The simplest decision rule involving ENPV is that the project is worthwhile if ENPV is positive and not worthwhile otherwise. More sophisticated rules would take into account the spread of possible values of NPV, interactions with other projects and the decision maker's attitude to risk (see Wilkes, 1983). Consider an example. A project would run for three years with the distribution of returns in each year as shown

Year one		Year two		Year three	
Return	Probability	Return	Probability	Return	Probability
10 000	0.1	20 000	0.4	10 000	0.3
12 000	0.6	30 000	0.6	16 000	0.5
16 000	0.3			20 000	0.2

Figure 10-4

in Fig. 10-4. The initial outlay K is a certain £42 000 and the appropriate discount rate is 10 per cent. Is the project worthwhile on the basis of ENPV? The first step is to find the expected value of return in each of the years. For Year 1 the workings are:

$$
\begin{array}{ccc}
R_{1i} & p_{1i} & p_{1i}R_{1i} \\
10\,000 & 0.1 & 1000 \\
12\,000 & 0.6 & 7200 \\
16\,000 & 0.3 & 4800 \\
\hline
& & 13\,000 = \sum^{3} p_{1i}R_{1i} = \bar{R}_1
\end{array}
$$

Similar calculations for Years 2 and 3 give expected returns of £26 000 and £15 000 respectively. Insertion of these results into 10-2 gives:

$$
\text{ENPV} = \frac{1300}{(1.1)} + \frac{26\,000}{(1.1)^2} + \frac{15\,000}{(1.1)^3} - 42\,000
$$

$$
= +2576
$$

So that on the basis of ENPV alone, the project would be worthwhile.

For an individual investor, it may also be appropriate to consider the spread of possible outcomes. ENPV may be positive but it may include some very bad outcomes that the decision maker would prefer to rule out by not selecting the investment despite the positive ENPV. In the present case, with independence between years there are 18 possible values of NPV as detailed in Fig. 10-5. The decision maker, if assessing this project in isolation would make a judgement on the basis of the results in Fig. 10-5 or determine the *variance* of NPV from the table in a rule which combines expected value and variance (we shall return to this subject later on). Inspection of Fig. 10-5 shows that the overall probability of achieving a positive NPV is 0.714. Note also that only the cash flow pattern 10, 20, 10 would produce an accounting loss (returns, undiscounted, less than initial outlay) with probability 0.012. The expected value approach can also be used when the returns in years are contingent on

Cash flow pattern (£1000)			Probability (p)	NPV (10%)	p × NPV
10	20	10	0.012	−8.867	−0.106
10	20	16	0.020	−4.359	−0.087
10	20	20	0.008	−1.354	−0.011
10	30	10	0.018	−0.603	−0.011
10	30	16	0.030	+3.905	+0.117
10	30	20	0.012	+6.911	+0.083
12	20	10	0.072	−7.049	−0.508
12	20	16	0.120	−2.541	−0.305
12	20	20	0.048	+0.464	+0.022
12	30	10	0.108	+1.216	+0.131
12	30	16	0.180	+5.724	+1.030
12	30	20	0.072	+8.729	+0.628
16	20	10	0.036	−3.412	−0.123
16	20	16	0.060	+1.095	+0.066
16	20	20	0.024	+4.101	+0.098
16	30	10	0.054	+4.852	+0.262
16	30	16	0.090	+9.360	+0.842
16	30	20	0.036	+12.365	+0.445
			1.000		+2.576

Figure 10-5

returns in earlier years. This generates a *tree structure* and is described in the following section.

10-5 DECISION TREES

Decision processes under risk often involve one or more decision points interspersed with chance outcomes. Subsequent decisions may be contingent upon the chance determined results of previous stages of the process. *Decision trees* are often useful ways to structure such problems, organize the information and determine the best initial decision. The use of decision trees is best illustrated by example. Figure 10-6 shows the *tree* (defined as a branching diagram without loops) for a firm's problem in deciding whether to launch its new product with a TV advertising campaign or a newspaper and poster campaign. The square boxes represent *decision nodes* where a choice has to be made. The first box D_1 is the initial choice between the types of campaign. If the TV campaign was chosen there is an equal chance of a good or poor market response. This is shown by the 0.5 probabilities on the *branches* emanating from node E_1 shown as a circle. This is called a *chance node* or a *state-of-nature node*. A good response would lead to an outcome of £9m profit for the firm. However, if the response is poor, a further decision has to be faced. The alternatives are to cut losses and sell the manufacturing rights to the product—with a profit of £1m resulting—or whether to re-design and

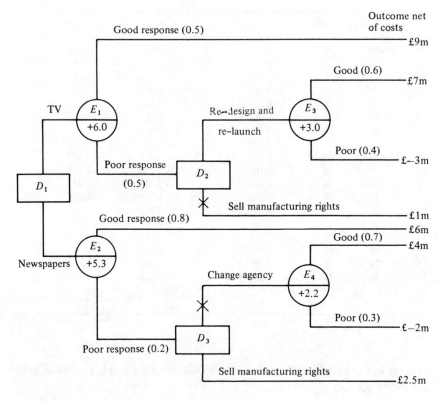

Figure 10-6

re-launch the product. These are the branches emanating from decision node D_2. If the re-design/re-launch option is taken there is a 0.6 probability of a good response and a 0.4 probability of a poor response to the re-launch with outcomes of £7m and £−3m respectively shown at the end of the branches from chance node E_2. This completes the branching process on the TV option.

If the newspaper campaign is selected initially there is a 0.8 chance of a favourable outcome and a 0.2 chance of a poor one as shown by the branches from chance node E_2. In the event of a poor outcome a decision is required as to whether to sell the manufacturing rights (net result £2.5m) or change the advertising agency. If the agency is changed there is a 0.7 chance of a good result netting £4m and a 0.3 chance of a poor result with a loss of £2m as shown at the end of the branches from chance node E_4.

We shall now use the decision tree diagram to make the decision between TV and newspaper campaigns on the basis of expected value. To do this, the diagram is used from right to left. The expected value is calculated at each chance node. Consider E_3. The expected value at this point is 0.6(7m)+ 0.4(−3m) = +3.0m and is shown below the line in the chance node circle. This is the expected value of the re-design and re-launch option should this point be reached. Clearly this is higher than the loss-cutting option of selling the manufacturing rights (value 1m) and this branch would not be selected—as indicated by the cross below D_2. We can now find the expected value at E_1. This will be $0.5(9m)+0.5(3.0)m = +6m$. This figure £6m is the expected value of the TV option.

The next step is to work back through the tree beginning at E_4. At E_4 the expected value is $0.7(4m)+0.3(-2m) = +2.2m$. This is the figure for the expected value of the agency change. This is less than the net £2.5m resulting from the sale of manufacturing rights so that the agency change branch will not be followed—as shown with the cross above D_3. Incidentally, the difference in values (£1m and £2.5m) of the sale of manufacturing rights options results from the different costs—the TV campaign being more expensive.

We can now obtain expected value at E_2. This will be $= 0.8(6m)+0.2(2.5m) = 5.3m$ and this figure is the expected value of the newspaper campaign option. The decision then, would be to go for the TV campaign and, should the initial response be poor, to redesign and relaunch the product. The method of working backwards through the decision tree is known as the *roll-back procedure*.

10-6 THE VALUE OF INFORMATION

The decision tree approach lends itself well to assessing the value of market research or any other information relating to the outcomes from chance nodes. To see how this arises consider the situation shown in the decision tree of Fig. 10-7. A firm introducing a new product has to decide on the scale of its

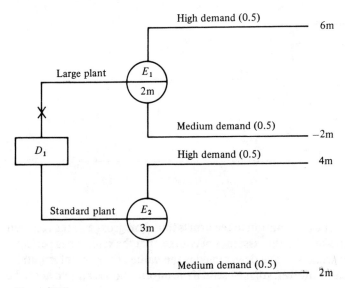

Figure 10-7

production facility. This can be standard size or large size. Subsequent demand for the product (which is independent of the plant size chosen) may be at high or medium levels with equal probability. As can be seen from Fig. 10-7, expected value is maximized by selection of the standard size plant which would give £3m EV in comparison to the £2m EV for the large plant. Note also that the large plant has a much wider spread of outcomes including a substantial loss. This would count against the larger plant if a decision criterion involving the range of outcomes was being used. The decision then is quite definitely for the standard size plant.

Now suppose that the company has the opportunity to have a detailed accurate market research carried out by a professional agency at a cost of £0.25m. The purpose of the research would be to establish conclusively whether demand was going to be high or low. The decision faced now is whether the market research contract should be taken. The problem is shown in Fig. 10-8. The 'no research' branch from D_1 is the £3m best expected result from the earlier problem of Fig. 10-7. In the event that the research is carried out and shows demand to be at medium level, the firm would build the standard size plant and obtain £2m gross of the market research costs. But if the market research showed that demand would be high the firm would build the larger plant and achieve the £6m outcome. The expected value at E_1 is then £4m gross of the market research costs or £3.75m with the research costs netted out.

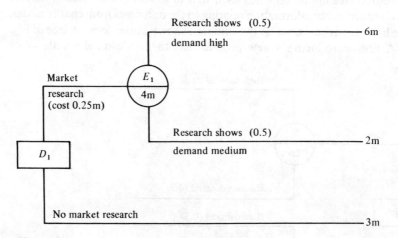

Figure 10-8

The value of the information to the firm is thus £1m gross and the research should be undertaken. All this assumes of course, that the research is perfectly accurate so that what we have determined is the value of *perfect* information. The approach can, however, still be useful if the information is known *not* to be perfect. For example, the £1m difference in EV represents an *upper bound* to the value of information and would rule out any investigations costing more than this figure. Also, if probabilities were available regarding the accuracy of the information, a more complicated tree structure could incorporate these.

10-7 DECISION TREES AND ENPV

When it is necessary to take into account the time value of money this can be accommodated within the decision tree framework. One way of doing this is shown in Fig. 10-9. A project is to be accepted or rejected in its entirety. If it is accepted there is a certain initial outlay of 150. Return after one year (R_1) may be 130 with probability 0.7 or 90 with probability 0.3. If the 130 return materializes at $t = 1$ the second-year return (R_2) could be 120 with probability 0.4 or 70 with probability 0.6. Should the year one return of 90 materialize, then the second year return could be 130 with probability 0.5 or 100 with probability 0.5. A discount rate of 10 per cent is appropriate.

In Fig. 10-9, all chance nodes associated with acceptance of the project are labelled E^A. Those chance nodes associated with rejection are labelled E^R.

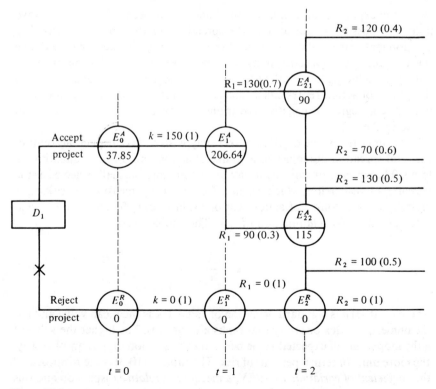

Figure 10-9

Node E_{21}^A gives the expected value (at $t=2$) of the contingent returns 120 and 70. E_1^A gives the expected value (at $t=1$) of the returns 130 and 90 at $t=1$ and the E_{21}^A value discounted for one year. Thus

$$E_1^A = 130(0.7) + 90(0.3) + \frac{90}{(1.1)} = 206.64$$

E_0^A gives the present value of the whole project being E_1^A, discounted for one year minus the initial outlay of $K=150$. Thus:

$$E_0^A = \frac{206.64}{(1.1)} - 150 = 37.85$$

Since this, the expected value of the whole project in present terms, is positive it is preferred to the 'null' project of the lower branch.

10-8 EXPECTED VALUES AND RISK

When the expected value of a course of action has been calculated, we have noted the possible importance of the spread or distribution of returns. The decision maker may take note of the dispersion of possible outcomes and take this into account informally along with the expected value. A wide spread of outcomes including losses will be less significant to a decision maker for whom the course of action represents a small part of his overall activities and who may seek a degree of negative covariance between various projects—as in portfolio theory.

At other times, the decision maker may wish to take explicit account of the total spread of outcomes to a course of action and do so in quantitative terms. The *variance* or *standard deviation* of outcomes is usually selected as the measure of dispersion which is, in effect, a proxy measure of risk. The desirability of a course of action will be an *increasing* function of expected value and a *decreasing* function of risk. The simple ratio:

$$u = \frac{\text{EV}}{\sigma} \tag{10-3}$$

where in (10-3) σ is standard deviation of value, EV is the mean value and u is the numerical index or *utility* that ranks alternatives. The higher the value of u the more units of expected value per unit of dispersion or, put another way, the more units of return per unit of risk. The ratio in (10-3) is the reciprocal of the *coefficient of variation*, $c = \sigma/\text{EV}$, a measure of *relative* dispersion and this approach represents the coefficient of variation decision rule.

The *expected value–variance* criterion forms the expression

$$u = EV - k\sigma^2 \tag{10-4}$$

where σ^2 is variance of the outcomes and the value of the coefficient k reflects the decision maker's attitude to risk in the form of dispersion of outcomes. The higher the value of k, the more averse is the decision maker to risk. k is sometimes called the *risk aversion factor*. The expressions (10-4) and (10-3) are sometimes called *utility functions* or *preference functions*. The intended effect of using them is to make a uni-dimensional measure out of the two components— expected value and dispersion. The measure is further discussed in Taha (1987).

In assessing a single course of action, some threshold level of u would have to be predetermined. In comparing alternatives, that with the greater value of u would be preferred under either (10-3) or (10-4). Consider an example. Suppose that a choice is to be made between two alternative courses of action. The first gives an expected value of 10 with standard deviation 5 and the second gives an expected value of 18 with standard deviation 8. On grounds of expected value alone the second alternative would be preferred. On criterion (10-3), the alternatives give $u = 2$ and $u = 2.25$ respectively so that again the second alternative is superior. With the expected value-variance criterion let $k = 0.3$. For the first project we would then have a variance (standard deviation squared) of 25 and u would emerge as:

$$u = 10 - 0.3(25) = 2.5$$

For the second alternative variance is 64 and u emerges as:

$$u = 18 - 0.3(64) = -1.2$$

So that the first alternative is preferred by this criterion.

A sensitivity analysis on the value of k would be appropriate here. The first alternative would be preferred by the expected value–variance criterion so long as:

$$10 - 25k > 18 - 64k$$

so:

$$39k > 8$$

$$k > 0.205$$

The coefficient k shows the significance that the decision maker attaches to departures from mean value. Note that the expected value criterion itself is a special case where $k=0$ and no significance is attached to departures from the mean. Low or zero values of k would be appropriate when the same choice situation arises repeatedly.

10-9 BREAK-EVEN ANALYSIS

Break-even analysis is a simple and very useful means of determining the level of output for which revenue (income) for a period covers the costs (outgoings) for the same period. Costs consist of fixed and variable components and we may write:

$$C = F + V \qquad (10\text{-}5)$$

where C = total costs, F = fixed costs and V = variable costs. Which costs are fixed depends on the length of time considered. A typical period for break-even analysis might be a month. In this case items, such as rent, leases, administrative costs, interest charges would be invariant under normal circumstances. Variable costs would include wage costs, materials, fuel and power etc., and we shall take these to be proportional to output level. That is:

$$V = bq \qquad (10\text{-}6)$$

where q is output level and b is unit variable costs. Thus $C = F + bq$.

Revenue or income is also proportional to output level. Specifically:

$$R = p \cdot q \qquad (10\text{-}7)$$

where p represents product price and R is sales revenue. (10-7) is again defined for a specific period of time.

Break-even occurs at that output level for which revenue equals costs—that is where $R = C$. For break-even we require:

$$R = C$$

$$\therefore \quad pq = F + bq$$

$$\therefore \quad (p - b)q = F$$

$$\therefore \quad q^* = \frac{F}{p - b} \qquad (10\text{-}8)$$

Equation (10-8) is the break-even formula expressing break-even output level q^* in terms of the three parameters. The situation is graphed in Fig. 10.10. In Fig. 10-10 q_c represents maximum plant capacity. Note that profit, the difference between revenue and costs, increases up to plant capacity in this

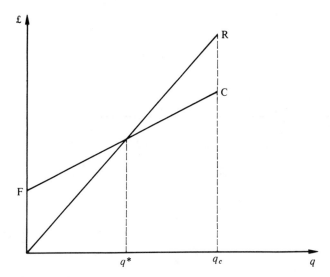

Figure 10-10

linear model. Consider a numerical example. Let $p = £10$, $b = £6$, $F = £10\,000$ and $q_c = 4000$ units of output. Substitution in (10-8) gives:

$$q^* = \frac{10\,000}{10-6} = 2500$$

so that the break-even output level of 2500 units per month represents usage of plant at 62.5 per cent capacity. Clearly there are potential difficulties if break-even output level is not reached until very near to the plant capacity limit. Measures of capacity utilization have their limitations as we saw in Chapter Two, but they are often used in industry and commerce (proportion of seats filled on aircraft is one example).

A *profit-volume chart* is another way of presenting the same information. The profit-volume chart for the numerical example above is shown in Fig. 10-11. Profit π, is expressed as:

$$\pi = -F + (p-b)q$$

The profit line in Fig. 10-11 measures the difference between R and C in Fig. 10-10 and its slope, the rate of increase of profit with respect to output level, is the difference between price and unit variable cost. This difference, $p-b$, is the limit that *unit profit* approaches in Fig. 10-12. In Fig. 10-12, notice how unit profit or 'profitability' increases beyond the break-even point as capacity utilization rises. By thinking in these terms, industrialists become concerned with the extent of plant usage.

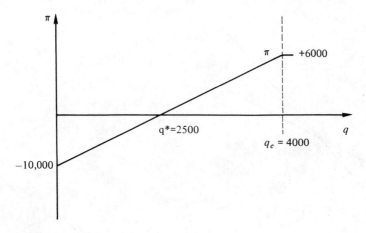

Figure 10-11

Now consider sensitivity analysis in a break-even context. The measures of cost in (10-8) are more likely to be subject to estimation problems than is price. With the values given for p and b we obtain:

$$q^* = \frac{F}{10-6}$$

Although q^* is always an increasing function of F, its rate of change is the lesser the greater is the excess of price over unit cost. Now consider price with the

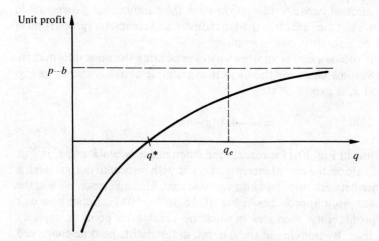

Figure 10-12

other values given:

$$q^* = \frac{10\,000}{p-6}$$

and we may ask for what range of values of p is break-even output level less than plant capacity? This will be p such that:

$$\frac{10\,000}{p-6} < 4000$$

So that:

$$4000(p-6) > 10\,000$$

$$\therefore \ p > 8.5$$

If price falls below 8.5, break-even output level cannot be reached unless plant capacity is expanded.

The cost parameters may vary abruptly as a result of interest rate changes or new wage agreements. For example, if unit cost rises 5 per cent to 6.3 this raises break-even output level by over 8 per cent to 2703 units.

Break-even analysis can be extended in a number of ways. *Cost-Volume-Profit* analysis (CVP) considers the relationship between output level and financial variables such as expenses, as well as profit and revenue and can be helpful in addressing such questions as the means of remuneration of sales staff salary or commission (i.e. volume related). CVP analysis is covered in detail in Drury (1988). The analysis can be extended to the multi-product case. A further example is provided by non-linear revenue and cost functions. These arise when the firm faces a downward sloping demand curve for its product or when economies (or diseconomies) of scale cause unit variable cost to change with output level. The achievement of break-even output level is usually a significant milestone on the build-up of production and sales of a new product. It is not in itself an objective for but is a useful benchmark and can point up the value of efforts to reduce fixed costs and increase profitability.

EXERCISES

10-1 Revision exercise
   (i) What is the expected value decision rule and under what circumstances is its use appropriate?
   (ii) Show how expected net present value can be calculated when a project's returns follow discrete probability distributions.
   (iii) When are decision trees helpful in calculating expected values?
   (iv) Explain what is meant by the roll-back procedure.

(v) How can decision trees help in gauging the value of information?
(vi) Can the time value of money be taken into account in a decision tree structure?
(vii) What is the expected value-variance criterion? In what other way can dispersion of outcomes be taken into account?
(viii) Explain what is meant by break-even analysis and profit-volume charts. In what ways can the analysis be extended?

10-2 Each day a department store purchases for £30 per unit a product which it sells for £55 per unit. For each item sold a 'selling cost' of £5 is incurred. Units unsold at the end of the day are returned to the supplier who refunds £20 for each returned item. Daily customer demand experienced by the store is a random variable described by the probability distribution

Units demanded	Probability
1	0.1
2	0.4
3	0.3
4	0.2

(i) What amount should the store order each day?
(ii) Given the order size determined in (i) and with all other data unchanged, what is the minimum selling price that the store can set without sustaining a loss?
(iii) A newspaper advertisement costing £10 per day would alter the probabilities of each level of demand to 0.1, 0.1, 0.4, 0.4 respectively. Would this be worth while?
(iv) As an alternative to the newspaper advertisement the store is considering a price-cut to £50. This would cause the probabilities to alter to 0, 0.1, 0.3, 0.6. Would this policy be preferable to the advertisement?

10-3 Once each year, Chaos Limited buys a quantity of perishable commodity. It processes and packages the commodity immediately and holds the cartons for sale one year later. Purchases have to be made in units of 100 kg; the current buying price is £30 per 100 kg. Each 100 kg yields sufficient output for a batch of 100 cartons and the processing and packaging of each batch costs £70. Storage costs, excluding interest, amount to £25 per 100 cartons per annum, payable at the end of the year. Chaos incurs fixed operating costs, i.e., costs which arise independently of the output level, of £70 000 per annum, payable at the end of the year.

Market conditions are such that Chaos takes its selling price as fixed by competitive considerations. Sales are made in cases of 100 cartons. The selling price, next year, for current output is estimated at £200 per 100 cartons. The probabilities of different volumes of sales have been estimated as follows:

Cases of 100 cartons	Probability
2000	0.2
2500	0.5
3000	0.3
	1.0

The directors are considering what quantity of the commodity should now be purchased for sale next year. Assume that the quantity to be purchased will be 200 000 kg, 250 000 kg, or 300 000 kg.

Any output that is not sold next year will have to be scrapped and will have no scrap value. The cost of capital is 25 per cent per annum.

(a) calculate the quantity which should be purchased in order to maximize the expected value of cash flows from the year's operations, and

(b) comment on the limitations of the criterion that the expected value of cash flows from operations should be maximized.

Ignore taxation.

(Institute of Chartered Accountants in England and Wales)

10-4 Every day a shop purchases, for £2 per unit, a product which it sells for £4 per unit. For every unit of product sold, a wrapping cost of £0.20 is incurred. Since the product is perishable, units remaining unsold at the end of the day are returned, without wrapping, to the supplier who refunds £1 for each returned item. The probability distribution for daily demand is as follows:

Possible number of units demanded daily	Probability that X units will be demanded daily
(X)	P(X)
0	0.1
1	0.4
2	0.3
3	0.2

(a) Draw up a table showing the profit earned for different order and demanded levels. Your profit table should be in the form:

Order level

N \ Q	0	1	2	3
0				
1				
2				
3				

Demand level

where Q is the order level.

(b) Let the profit figures in your table be the elements of a matrix **A**. If the probability vector **P** is given by (0.1, 0.4, 0.3, 0.2) calculate the matrix product **PA**.

(c) Interpret the entries in the matrix **PA** and hence determine the optimal order level that the shop should place each day.

(d) If the wrapping cost per unit increases dramatically to £1, write out the additional cost matrix and determine the effect upon the order level policy.

(Chartered Association of Certified Accountants)

10-5 A publishing company have carried out a market survey estimating future demand for a new book and have produced the following probability estimates:

Year 1		Year 2		Year 3	
Likely sales	Probability	Likely sales	Probability	Likely sales	Probability
5 000	0.2	5 000	0.4	5 000	0.8
10 000	0.5	10 000	0.6	10 000	0.2
20 000	0.3				

(a) Calculate the expected total sales (i.e., number of books) over the three years.
(b) The book's price is fixed at £10 and the variable cost of producing each book will be £2 in year 1, £3 in year 2 and £4 in year 3. Calculate the present value of the contribution as at the beginning of the first year, using a discount rate of 10 per cent per annum. (Assume that all cash flows take place at the end of the year concerned.)
(c) There is a possibility of an updated soft-backed version of the book being published at the beginning of year 2 (the original hard-backed version would then be taken off the market at the end of year 1) with the following estimates of sales:

Year 2		Year 3		Year 4	
Likely sales	Probability	Likely sales	Probability	Likely sales	Probability
20 000	0.5	10 000	0.8	5 000	0.9
30 000	0.5	20 000	0.2	10 000	0.1

(The sales will be extended by one year due to the updating.)
The soft-backed book will be priced at £5 and the variable cost of producing each book will be £1 in year 2, £2 in year 3, and £3 in year 4. Should the option to produce the soft-backed edition be taken up?

(Chartered Association of Certified Accountants)

10-6 An investment proposal has the following probability distribution of returns:

Year one		Year two		Year three	
Return	Probability	Return	Probability	Return	Probability
6000	0.2	8 000	0.5	7 000	0.3
8000	0.4	12 000	0.5	11 000	0.5
9000	0.4			17 000	0.2

The events of each year are independent of other years. The outlay on the project is fixed at 22 000 and the appropriate discount rate figure is 10 per cent. Find:
(a) The expected net present value
(b) The probability that the project yields less than 10 per cent.

10-7 A project has an initial outlay fixed at 1500. Return in year 1 could be 1350 with probability 0.4 or 900 with probability 0.6. If in year 1 the 900 return transpires then in year 2 there can be 1200 ($p=0.2$) or 1050 ($p=0.8$). If the first-year return had been 1350, then in the second year there is a seven-tenths chance of 600 and a three-tenths chance of 150. The interest rate is 10 per cent. Find the expected net present value of the project.

10-8 An oil company can purchase exploration rights in either of two blocks of the North Sea. If it acquires block A there is a 0.4 probability of striking oil which would give a profit of £14m. If it fails to strike oil, it can relocate the rig within the block and drill once more when there would be an even chance of an oil strike with a net profit of £12m. Failure to strike oil at the second attempt would mean a loss of £5m. Alternatively, having failed to strike oil first time the company could opt to cut its losses and lose £3m. If the company acquires block B there is an even chance of striking oil first time. If it has no success, it can pull out (losing £3m) or relocate the rig once with a 0.7 chance of striking oil and an £8m profit or a 0.3 chance of a dry well at the second attempt and an overall £5m loss. Which block should the company acquire?

10-9 A company introducing a new product can construct a large plant or a standard size plant. If it constructs the large plant and demand for the product is subsequently high, a profit of £10m is made. There is, however, a 0.6 probability of low demand and a loss of £3m. If the firm chooses the small plant and demand is high (probability 0.4) it will make a profit of £3.5m. If on the other hand, demand was low a profit of £2m would follow. Which size of plant should be built?

10-10 Assess the value of perfect market information to the company of question 10.9.

10-11 A choice is to be made between two alternative courses of action on the basis of the expected value-variance criterion with $k = 0.2$. Alternative one has an expected value of 20 with standard deviation 8. Alternative two has expected value 26 with standard deviation 10. Find out which alternative is selected and conduct a sensitivity analysis on the value of k. Which alternative would have been selected on the basis of units of return per unit of risk?

10-12 A plant has been constructed to manufacture a new product. Fixed costs amount to £8000 per week. The unit variable cost of the product is £7 and the selling price is £12. Maximum plant capacity is an output of 3200 units per week. Find:
  (i) The break-even output level and associated capacity utilisation.
  (ii) For what values of price does break-even output level not demand more than 75 per cent capacity utilization?
  (iii) What is the maximum weekly profit?

10-13 A firm can choose between two types of plant to produce a new product. The product will sell at a price of £25. Plant A has fixed costs per month of £20 000 and a unit variable cost of £15. Plant B has a monthly fixed cost of £15 000 but has a unit variable cost of £17. The maximum capacity of either plant is 3000 units of output per month. Find out which plant has the lower break-even output level. Which has the greater profit potential if full capacity can be used? What is the minimum value of monthly demand for the product that would result in the choice of plant A on profit grounds? Illustrate with a profit-volume chart.

Solution guides

10-2 (i) The profit per item sold is £20. The loss per item unsold is £10. In table form the results are:

Demand (X)	Units purchased				P(X)	P(X, ADVT)
	1	2	3	4		
1	20	10	0	−10	0.1	0.1
2	20	40	30	20	0.4	0.1
3	20	40	60	50	0.3	0.4
4	20	40	60	80	0.2	0.4
EXP Π	20	37	42*	38		
EXP Π(ADVT)	20	37	51	53*		

Thus in the original circumstances
- (i) three units should be ordered.
- (ii) This is £37.50. The expected profit on three units bought is given by:

$$0.1[(p-35)-20]+0.4[2(p-35)-10]+0.3[3(p-35)]+0.2[3(p-35)]$$

Equating this expression to zero and solving for p gives $p = 37.50$.
- (iii) Yes, provided that the store now orders four units per day. As can be seen from the table above, expected profit on four units is £53. After paying £10 for the advertisement, an increase of £1 remains.
- (iv) Yes. As can be seen from the table below, a profit of £47.50 could be made.

| | Units purchased | | | | |
Demand X	1	2	3	4	$P(X)$
1	15	5	−5	−15	0
2	15	30	20	10	0.1
3	15	30	45	35	0.3
4	15	30	45	60	0.6
EXP Π (PRICE CUT)	15	30	42.5	47.5*	

10-3 (a) It is not convenient to work in units of 100 kg/cartons. Thus 'one unit' will mean 100 kg and one batch of 100 cartons. First consider the costs per unit.

Source of cost	Cost (£)	When incurred
Buying in price	30	$t=0$
Processing & packaging	70	$t=0$
Storage	25	$t=1$

and on the revenue side:

Selling price	200	$t=1$

Now construct a table or revenues. This will enable expected revenue to be calculated for each possible level of purchases.

In the 2500 column of Fig. 10-13, if 2500 units are purchased and demand is for 2000 units then 2000 will be sold producing revenue of 400 000. If demand is for 2500 units, this will be the level of sales, and revenue of 500 000 is produced.

Finally, if demand is for 3000 units only, 2500 will be sold (since sales are purchases or demand, whichever is the smaller) again giving revenue of 500 000. Each of these possible levels of revenue is multiplied by the chance of it arising (the corresponding figure in the probability column). After summing up, the result is an expected revenue of £480 000 at the end of the year if 2500 units are purchased at the beginning of the year.

	Units purchased			Demand probability
Demand	2 000	2 500	3 000	
2000	400 000	400 000	400 000	0.2
2500	400 000	500 000	500 000	0.5
3000	400 000	500 000	600 000	0.3
Expected value	400 000	480 000	510 000	

Figure 10-13

Now we are asked to maximize 'the expected value of cash flows from the year's operations'. With the *timing* of each cash flow then being given explicit mention in the earlier part of the question as well as a cost of capital figure being provided it seems likely that it is expected *present* value that is the criterion. With such a high cost of capital figure a company in practice would be unlikely to ignore differences in timing of one year. However, an alternative interpretation of the questions is possible and although we shall start with present value workings a 'non-present value' calculation will be given subsequently.

First consider the expected cash flow resulting from 2000 units being purchased initially. At time $t = 0$ there is a cash flow out of 200 000 resulting from purchase expenses of 60 000 ($= 2000 \times 30$) and processing and packaging costs of 140 000 ($= 2000 \times 70$). At $t = 1$ there is an expected net cash flow in of £280 000 being composed of expected revenue of £400 000 less the storage costs of £50 000 ($= 2000 \times 25$) and less the fixed costs of £70 000 which are payable at this time. The expected net present value that results is $+£24 000$ which is obtained thus

$$-200\,000 + \frac{280\,000}{(1.25)} = +24\,000$$

These results and those for the other possible levels of purchase are shown in Fig. 10-14.

	Net cash flow		
Purchased	$t = 0$	$t = 1$	ENPV at 25%
2000	− 200 000	280 000	+ 24 000
2500	− 250 000	347 500	+ 28 000
3000	− 300 000	365 000	− 8 000

Figure 10-14

In Figure 10-14 $347\,500 = 480\,000 - (62\,500 + 70\,000)$
and $365\,000 = 510\,000 - (75\,000 + 70\,000)$
Thus the level of purchases which maximizes expected net present value is 2500 units.

An alternative construction on question (*a*) would be to assume that interest at 25 per cent is charged on the cash flow out at $t = 0$, and that interest due on the storage costs comes to £6.25. This would produce the following results:

200 units purchased:
$$-200\,000(1.25)-70\,000-2000(1.25)25+400\,000=+17\,500$$
2500 units purchased:
$$-250\,000(1.25)-70\,000-2500(1.25)25+480\,000=+19\,375$$
3000 units purchased:
$$-300\,000(1.25)-70\,000-3000(1.25)25+510\,000=-28\,750$$

Thus the optimal number to be purchased, as it happens, is still 2500 units.

(b) In simply choosing the course of action that maximizes expected value no explicit account is taken of risk. For example, with 2500 units purchased there is a 0.8 probability that revenue will be 500 000 and a 0.2 chance that revenue will be only 400 000. Thus, in terms of the present value approach, there are two possible figures for NPV: $+44\,000$ with probability 0.8 and $-36\,000$ with probability 0.2 (note that 28 000 = 0.8 × 44 000 − 0.2 × 36 000). In other words there is a one in five chance of a substantial loss.

Figure 10-15 gives for each level of purchases the possible values of NPV and the associated probabilities.

No. purchased	NPV	Probability
2000	+24 000	1.0
2500	+44 000	0.8
	−36 000	0.2
3000	−96 000	0.2
	−16 000	0.5
	+64 000	0.3

Figure 10-15

Few companies would opt for the 3000 level of purchases since it has the largest spread of possible outcome and the lowest, indeed negative, expected figure. The real choice is between the first two possibilities. The investor has to decide whether the greater risk is compensated for by the increased expected return. Quite possibly, purchase of 2000 units with its guaranteed return of $+24\,000$ would be selected.

10-4 (a)

Order level

| | Q | 0 | 1 | 2 | 3 |
X					
	0	0	−1.0	−2.0	−3.0
	1	0	1.8	0.8	−0.2
Demand level	2	0	1.8	3.6	2.6
	3	0	1.8	3.6	5.4

(b), (c) This is simply a roundabout way of saying calculate the expected profits. In previous questions we have adopted the form of putting the probabilities on the right of the table and the expected profits below. The expected profits emerge as 0, 1.52, 1.92, 1.48. The maximum daily profit is £1.92 when the order level is two units. In matrix form we could write:

$$PA = (0.1 \quad 0.4 \quad 0.3 \quad 0.2) \begin{pmatrix} 0 & -1.0 & -2.0 & -3.0 \\ 0 & 1.8 & 0.8 & -0.2 \\ 0 & 1.8 & 3.6 & 2.6 \\ 0 & 1.8 & 3.6 & 5.4 \end{pmatrix}$$

$$PA = (0 \quad 1.52 \quad 1.92 \quad 1.48)$$

(d) The changes to be made to the profit table, A, are

$$\begin{pmatrix} 0 & 0 & 0 & 0 \\ 0 & 0.8 & 0.8 & 0.8 \\ 0 & 0.8 & 1.6 & 1.6 \\ 0 & 0.8 & 1.6 & 2.4 \end{pmatrix}$$

This array is subtracted, element from corresponding element, from the original profit table/matrix to give the new profit table/matrix:

$$\begin{pmatrix} 0 & -1.0 & -2.0 & -3.0 \\ 0 & 1.0 & 0 & -1.0 \\ 0 & 1.0 & 2.0 & 1.0 \\ 0 & 1.0 & 2.0 & 3.0 \end{pmatrix}$$

The new expected profits are

$$0 \quad 0.8 \quad 0.8 \quad 0.2$$

so that the optimum order level is either one unit or two units.

10-5 (a) The workings here are as follows:

	Sales (000)	Probability	Expected value (000)
Year 1	5	0.2	1.0
	10	0.5	5.0
	20	0.3	6.0
			12.0
Year 2	5	0.4	2.0
	10	0.6	6.0
			8.0
Year 3	5	0.8	4.0
	10	0.2	2.0
			6.0

so that the expected sales each year are:

Year	Expected sales
1	12 000
2	8 000
3	6 000
Total expected sales	26 000

(b) Three-figure discount factors were given in the question. Workings are:

Year end	Expected sales (000)	Profit contribution (£)	Expected contribution for year (£000's)	Discount factor	Present value (£000's)
1	12	8	96	0.909	87.26
2	8	7	56	0.826	46.26
3	6	6	36	0.751	27.04
					160.56

So that the expected value of contributions is £160 560.

(c) For the expected sales of softback version of book, the workings are:

	Sales (000)	Probability	Expected value (£000's)
Year 2	20	0.5	10
	30	0.5	15
			25
Year 3	10	0.8	8
	20	0.2	4
			12
Year 4	5	0.9	4.5
	10	0.1	1.0
			5.5

For the expected present value of the softback alternative the workings are:

Year end	Expected sales (000)	Contribution (£)	Expected contribution for year (£000)	Discount factor	Present value (£000)
1	12	8	96	0.909	87.26
2	25	4	100	0.826	82.60
3	12	3	36	0.751	27.04
4	5.5	2	11	0.683	7.51
					204.41

This option, therefore, has an expected present value of contribution of £204 410. Note that the first-year sales and contribution of the hardback version are included.

We have now to advise on which option is preferable. No mention is made of the size of initial outlays necessary in the two schemes. Let K_H represent the outlay required for the hardback project and K_S be the further outlay on the softback. We then have the following:

Expected NPV (hardback only) $= £160\,560 - K_H$

Expected NPV (softback alternative) $= £204\,410 - (K_H + K_S)$

So, for the softback alternative to be preferable:

$$204\,410 - (K_H + K_S) > 160\,560 - K_H$$

i.e. $$K_S < 43\,850$$

That is, the outlay on the softback project must be less than £43 850. One last point: we have made no measures of the *spread* of possible NPV values. This would normally be considered in respect of sizeable projects.

10-6 (a) The expected return in year 1, $\bar{R}_1$, is 8000. The workings are:

Return (R)	Probability (p)	pR
6000	0.2	1200
8000	0.4	3200
9000	0.4	3600
		8000

and the expected returns in years 2 and 3 are (by similar arithmetic mean calculations) found to be $\bar{R}_2 = 10\,000$ and $\bar{R}_3 = 11\,000$. Thus ENPV is given by:

$$\text{ENPV} = -22\,000 + \frac{8000}{(1.1)} + \frac{10\,000}{(1.21)} + \frac{11\,000}{(1.331)} = 1801.65$$

(b) An exact answer here requires investigation of the full spectrum of possibilities. These, and the corresponding probabilities and present values, are:

Cash flow	Probability (p)	NPV	pNPV
6, 8, 7	0.03	−4674.68	−140.24
6, 8, 11	0.05	−1699.42	−83.47
6, 8, 17	0.02	2838.47	56.77
6, 12, 7	0.03	−1368.90	−41.07
6, 12, 11	0.05	1636.36	81.82
6, 12, 17	0.02	6144.25	122.89
8, 8, 7	0.06	−2856.50	−171.39
8, 8, 11	0.10	148.76	14.88
8, 8, 17	0.04	4656.65	186.27
8, 12, 7	0.06	449.29	26.96
8, 12, 11	0.10	3454.55	345.46
8, 12, 17	0.04	7962.43	318.50
9, 8, 7	0.06	−1947.41	−116.84
9, 8, 11	0.10	1057.85	105.79
9, 8, 17	0.04	5565.74	222.63
9, 12, 7	0.06	1358.38	81.50
9, 12, 11	0.10	4363.64	436.36
9, 12, 17	0.04	8871.53	354.86
	1.00		1801.65

The cash flow elements in the table are given in units of one thousand. The pNPV column total provides a check on the previous ENPV result (the exact total is shown—rather than the total of pNPV values already rounded to two decimal places).

The probability that the project yields less than 10 per cent can now readily be ascertained. If and only if NPV is negative is yield less than 10 per cent. Simply sum the probabilities corresponding to negative values of NPV. Thus:

$$\text{probability of yield} < 10\% = 0.03 + 0.05 + 0.03 + 0.06 + 0.06 = 0.23$$

So there is a 23 per cent chance of the project failing to yield 10 per cent.

10-7 An alternative form of the tree diagram is shown below. The column headed 'p' shows the probability of each stream of returns. Thus the stream −1500, 900, 1200 has probability 0.12 of arising. The next column shows the NPV of each stream. Note that the probability of the project making a loss is 0.12.

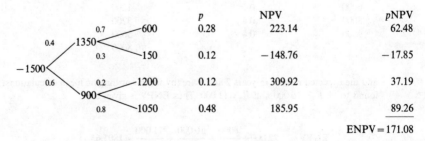

	p	NPV	pNPV
600	0.28	223.14	62.48
150	0.12	−148.76	−17.85
1200	0.12	309.92	37.19
1050	0.48	185.95	89.26
			ENPV = 171.08

10-8 The decision tree is shown in Fig. 10-16. Block A which would produce an expected value of profit of £7.7m should be selected.

10-9 The decision tree is shown in Fig. 10-17. Construction of the small plant is indicated by the greater expected value of £2.6m.

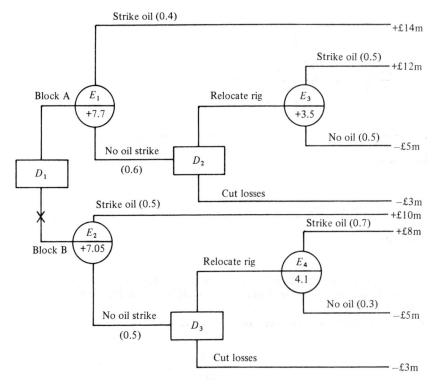

Figure 10-16

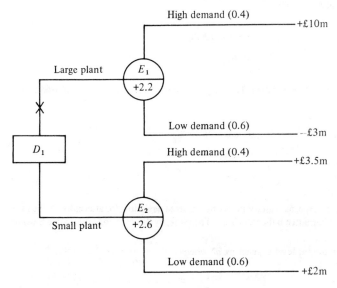

Figure 10-17

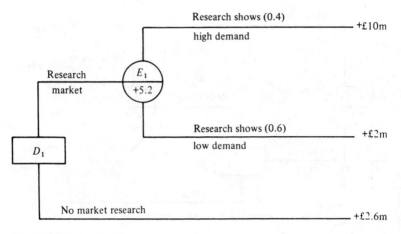

Figure 10-18

10-10 The effect of perfect market information would be to double expected value to £5.2m so that the value of accurate research to show what demand would be is £2.6m. The decision tree is shown in Fig. 10-18.

10-11 In the case of alternative A the expected value variance criterion gives:

$$u = EV - 0.2\sigma^2$$
$$= 20 - 0.2(8)^2$$
$$= 7.2$$

while in the case of alternative B:

$$u = 26 - 0.2(10)^2$$
$$= 6$$

so that alternative A would be preferred. The range of values of k for which A is preferred to B is such that:

$$20 - 64k > 26 - 100k$$
$$36k > t$$
$$\therefore \ k > \tfrac{1}{6}$$

If return is measured by expected value and risk by standard deviation, for alternative A the ratio EV/σ is 2.5, while for alternative B the ratio is 2.6. Therefore, by this criterion, alternative B would be selected.

10-12 (i) Break-even output level is given by q^* where

$$q^* = \frac{F}{p - b}$$

with the data given $F = £8000$, $p = £12$, $b = £7$ so

$$q^* = \frac{8000}{5} = 1600$$

This output therefore represents 50 per cent of plant capacity.

(ii) Break-even output level will not exceed 75 per cent capacity utilization, so long as price satisfies the relation:

$$\frac{8000}{p-7} \leqslant 2400$$

$$\therefore 2400(p-7) \geqslant 8000$$

$$2400p - \geqslant 24\,800$$

$$p \geqslant 10\tfrac{1}{3}$$

(iii) Maximun profit in the linear break-even model occurs at maximum plant capacity, i.e., 3200 units. Profit is given by:

$$\pi = pq - F - bq$$

$$= q(p-b) - F$$

$$= 3200(5) - 8000$$

$$= 8000$$

So the maximum weekly profit achievable is £8000.

10-13 For plant A, break-even output level is given by

$$q^* = \frac{20\,000}{25-15} = 2000 \text{ units}$$

while for plant B:

$$q^* = \frac{15\,000}{25-17} = 1875 \text{ units}$$

Profit from plant A at full capacity is:

$$3000(10) - 20\,000 = 10\,000$$

while for plant B maximum profit is:

$$3000(8) - 15\,000 = 9000$$

The output level so that plant A profit is no less than that of plant B is q where:

$$10q - 20000 \geqslant 8q - 15\,000$$

$$2q \geqslant 5000$$

$$q \geqslant 2500$$

The situation is shown in the profit-volume chart of Fig. 10-19.

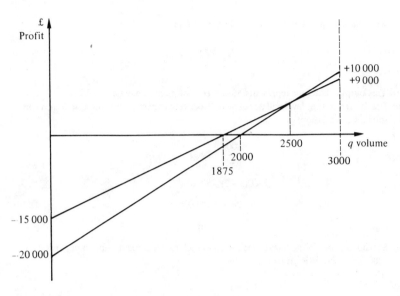

Figure 10-19

REFERENCES

Drury, J. C. (1988), *Management and Cost Accounting*, second edition, Van Nostrand Reinhold.
Taha, H. A. (1987), *Operations Research*, fourth edition, Collier Macmillan.
Wilkes, F. M. (1983), *Capital Budgeting Techniques*, second edition, Wiley.

FURTHER READING

Cook, T. M., and Russell, R. A. (1981), *Introduction to Management Science*, second edition, Prentice-Hall. Contains discussion of expected monetary value and shows relation of break-even analysis to LP.
Duckworth, W. E., Gear, A. E., and Lockett, A. G. (1977), *A Guide to Operational Reseach*, third edition, Chapman & Hall. Shows use of decision trees in project planning.
Livingstone, J. L. (1970), *Management Planning and Control*, McGraw-Hill. Contains large advanced section on cost/profit-volume analysis with links to discounted cash flow.
Marsland, N. W. (1971), *Quantitative Techniques for Business*, Polytech Publishers. (Contains simple introduction to break-even analysis).
Monks, J. G. (1982), *Operations Management, Theory and Problems*, second edition, McGraw-Hill. Contains discussion of expected values and decision trees and links break-even analysis with the contribution ratio.
Tinniswood, P. (1982), *Marketing Decisions*, Longman. Shows use of decision trees to evaluate market information.

ELEVEN

STATISTICAL REPLACEMENT METHODS

11-1 INTRODUCTION

Components fail, machinery malfunctions, staff resign unexpectedly—all common enough situations and all analysable by statistical replacement methods. The statistical methods can help management achieve an overall least cost policy of maintenance (where appropriate) and replacement. No equipment achieves permanent reliability but the way in which performance changes is significant. Where there is predictable *deterioration*—as with car tyres or printer ribbons—the time at which minimum serviceability will be reached can be forecast with reasonable accuracy. These situations of gradual deterioration give rise to one class of replacement problems. We have seen something of the way that these problems can be approached in Chapter Six, pages 141–144.

There is another class of problem, defined by situations where 100 per cent functioning is followed by sudden failure, which is not predictable at the level of the individual item. The threshold of minimal acceptance performance is crossed dramatically in a moment of total failure. A household item such as an electric light bulb is an example of this. Items which either work properly or not at all with no intermediate level of operation generally fall into this category. Thus they tend not to signal impending failure by a change in the character of their performance. These are the problems that will form the substance of the discussion in this chapter and to which statistical replacement methods apply. The two classes of problem are illustrated in Fig. 11-1.

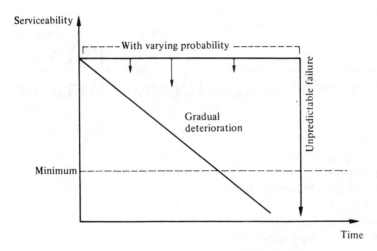

Figure 11-1

We shall examine those problems in which there is a large number of items of a certain type and where failures cannot be allowed to stand in a failed state for very long. This may be because the efficient functioning of the whole system can tolerate only a few down machines or because a prior decision has been taken to provide a high level of service. Speedy replacement may be virtually forced by competitive considerations—for instance, the replacement of faulty customer television sets by a rental company. We shall be dealing with problems in which failure is costly but not absolutely disastrous. Problems in which failure is fatal have to be dealt with by reducing failure probabilities to an absolute minimum and making provision to protect against the consequences when failure does occur. The method described will be set mainly in the context of mechanical failure but the approach is also useful in consideration of staffing problems.

11-2 FAILURE DATA

Statistical replacement methods require *failure data*. The probabilities of failure will be stable for large numbers of items and may be obtained from prior experience with the item or from sample testing. Having specified the level of service, the probability and cost data are used to select a least cost replacement policy. The level of service specified here will be close to 100 per cent although other assumptions are possible. Policies are distinguished according to how frequently (if ever) wholesale replacements of all items are made. For instance, how frequently should light bulbs in a building be replaced *in toto*, failed or not? The more often such *preventative* replacements are made the lest frequently will relatively costly individual replacements be necessary.

Average nos failing (n_t)	Months from installation (t)
0	0
15	1
45	2
60	3
30	4
$\Sigma n_t = n = 150$	

Figure 11-2

Consider an example. A firm's building contains 150 electric light bulbs. Failure data are as follows. In Fig. 11-2, the simplifying assumption is made that the bulbs fail at the *end* of the monthly intervals. Equivalently we can assume that any failures during a month are allowed to stand until the month's end, when replacement is made. This is the reason for the 'near' 100 per cent service level. It is a 100 per cent service in so far as *all* failures are attended to at the month's end.

From Fig. 11-2, the probabilities of failure of an individual light bulb at different times, f_t, are ascertained empirically as:

$$f_t = \frac{n_t}{\Sigma n_t}$$

The failure probabilities are shown in Fig. 11-3. Probabilities of survival can also be obtained. The survival probability is the probability that an individual bulb is still working at the end of the month t and that failure, therefore, occurs later on. Thus, the survival probability at time t is the sum of probabilities of later failure. With S_t as survival probability it follows that:

$$S_t = \sum_{h=t+1}^{4} f_h$$

Time	Probability of failure
0	$0.0 = f_0$
1	$0.1 = f_1$
2	$0.3 = f_2$
3	$0.4 = f_3$
4	$0.2 = f_4$
	$\Sigma f_t = 1.0$

Figure 11-3

Time	Survival probability
0	$1.0 = S_0$
1	$0.9 = S_1$
2	$0.6 = S_2$
3	$0.2 = S_3$
4	$0.0 = S_4$

Figure 11-4

Thus, for instance, $S_1 = f_2 + f_3 + f_4 = 0.3 + 0.4 + 0.2 = 0.9$. The survival probabilities for the bulbs are shown in Fig. 11-4. Alternatively, we can calculate survival probability at time t as one minus the chance that failure occurs *at or before* time t. Namely,

$$S_t = 1 - \sum_{h=0}^{t} f_h$$

So that for example $S_1 = 1 - (f_0 + f_1) = 1 - (0 + 0.1) = 0.9$. Having obtained the failure and survival probabilities for the item, the next stage of the method uses the probabilities to project the pattern of failures in future periods. This can be done in two equivalent ways.

11-3 FAILURE TREES

The *expected number of failures* at given times can be obtained from the data above. One way to do this is by the use of a *failure tree*. A failure tree is an example of a type of network that arises frequently in the analysis of problems that have many stages. As was seen in Chapter Ten, a tree is a network without any loops in it. For instance, Fig. 11-5(a) represents a tree while Fig. 11.5(b) does not.

The failure tree for the light bulb data can be begun as shown in Fig. 11-6. Starting with a completely fresh installation of 150 bulbs at $t = 0$ the number surviving at $t = 1$ is $150(0.9) = 135$. This number is shown in Fig. 11-6 on the *horizontal* line from $t = 0$. The number failing at $t = 1$ is expected to be $150(0.1) = 15$. This figure is entered on a *diagonal* line from $t = 0$. In each case the numbers are *expected*—what would happen on average—and are the

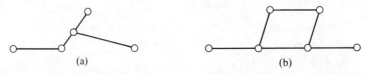

(a)   (b)

Figure 11-5

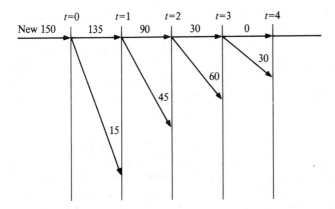

Figure 1-6

original numbers installed at $t=0$ multiplied by the survival and failure probabilities (for one month) respectively. Continuing with the history of the original 150 produces 90 surviving at $t=2$ ($=150(0.6)$) and 45 failing at $t=2$ ($=150(0.3)$). Obviously the total number both failing and surviving at $t=2$ must equal the number that were surviving at $t=1$. Thus $90+45=135$. The picture is continued in a similar fashion until $t=4$ at which time all 150 have failed.

Now consider the replacements that will have been necessary up to $t=4$. Consider the 60 that failed at $t=3$. With the near 100 per cent service level assumed, these must be replaced at $t=3$. Of these 60 the number still working after one month (i.e., at $t=4$) is expected to be $60(0.9)=54$ and the number that fail is, on average, $60(0.1)=6$. These values are inserted in Fig. 11-7. Now what

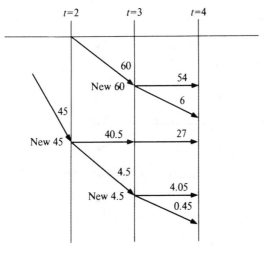

Figure 11-7

of the 45 that failed at $t=2$? Of these 45, there will be $45(0.9)=40.5$ surviving at $t=3$ and $45(0.6)=27$ surviving two months later at time $t=5$. But of this 45 there is an expected number $45(0.1)=4.5$ failures after one month at $t=3$. These 4.5 need replacing. Of these 4.5 replacements made at $t=3$ $4.05=4.5(0.9)$ will be working at $t=4$ and $0.45=4.5(0.1)$ will be failed at $t=4$. These decimal values are perfectly sensible as we are dealing with *averages* throughout. This complete history of the replacements needed at $t=2$ and $t=3$ is shown in Fig. 11-7.

Of course, the 15 failures at $t=1$ of the original 150 must be replaced and further branches will emanate from this point. The treatment is identical to that already described and the full picture is shown in Fig. 11-8. From the complete tree of Fig. 11-8 can be obtained the expected number of failures F_t (and therefore replacements necessary) at each point in time. Using the tree F_t

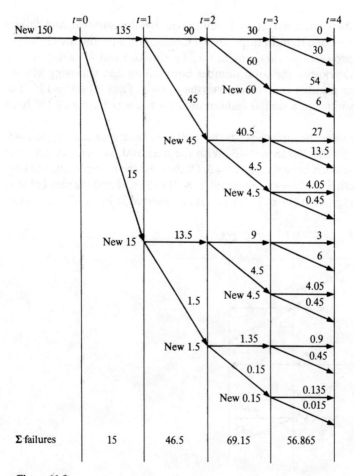

Figure 11-8

will be the sum of numbers on diagonal lines in month t. These values are shown at the bottom of each column in the figure. Of course the number surviving at time t, S_t, $= 150 - F_t$. If the tree was continued for long enough the expected number of failures in any month will approach the *mean number of failures* ($\bar{F}$), viz., $F_t \to \bar{F}$ as $t \to \infty$. This convergence is of an oscillatory nature and settles down quite quickly as will be illustrated later on. From $t = 9$ variations in F_t from period to period are within 1 per cent of $\bar{F}$. However, $\bar{F}$ may be calculated directly. If $\bar{x}$ is the *mean life* of a bulb then the mean number of failures is given by

$$\bar{F} = \frac{n}{\bar{x}}$$

For example, if the bulbs had a mean life of two months ($\bar{x} = 2$) then $\bar{F} = 150/2 = 75$. The mean rate of failures would be 75 per month. Sometimes it is clearer to see a relationship if the terms are rearranged. Thus $\bar{x} = n/\bar{F}$. So that if, on average, there were $\bar{F} = 50$ failures per month, this would correspond to a mean life of three months. In such a case

$$\bar{x} = \frac{150}{50} = 3$$

The mean life itself is found by the usual procedure for calculating the arithmetic mean of a discrete probability distribution, viz.

Life in months (x)	Probability (f_t)	xf_t
0	0	0
1	0.1	0.1
2	0.3	0.6
3	0.4	1.2
4	0.2	0.8
		$\bar{x} = \Sigma xf_t = 2.7$

Thus the mean number of failures per month is obtained as

$$\bar{F} = \frac{150}{2.7} = 55.\overline{55}$$

11-4 THE OPTIMAL REPLACEMENT POLICY

The information from the failure tree and the long run mean numbers of monthly failures are combined with cost data to evaluate the alternative intervals between *group replacements* (preventative maintenance) of all items. The interval with least cost per period time represents the optimal replacement policy. For a numerical example, suppose that it costs a firm £90 to replace all 150 light bulbs at the same time. To do an individual replacement costs £2. Failure data are as presented above. What replacement policy should be adopted to maintain to near 100 per cent operation of bulbs at minimum cost?

There are two kinds of policy open to the firm: (i) merely replace failures as they occur, or (ii) replace all bulbs at set intervals (failed or not) and in the meantime replace individual failures as they arise. Obviously type (i) is a special case of type (ii) in which the interval between group replacements is infinite. However, it is useful to evaluate this special case separately.

If policy type (i) is implemented then the monthly cost will in due course settle down to £111.$\overline{11}$ as an average 55.$\overline{55}$ will need to be replaced each month at a cost of £2 per replacement. In Fig. 11-9, I represents the decision variable being the interval between group replacements and the objective is to

I	Group cost	Individual costs in month				Total	Monthly average
		1	2	3	4		
1	90	—	—	—	—	90	90
2	90	30	—	—	—	120	60$\Leftarrow$
3	90	30	93	—	—	213	71
4	90	30	93	138.3	—	351.3	87.825
5	90	30	93	138.3	113.73	465.03	93.006

Figure 11-9

minimize average cost per month. Individual costs per month are the expected number of failures multiplied by the replacement cost of £2. It is here assumed that individual replacements are not needed in the month of group replacement. The group and individual costs are added and the total is divided by the number of months. The optimal policy is group replacement every two months ($I = 2$). The answer has been obtained by *enumeration* which means evaluation, directly or indirectly, of all alternatives. In this case, we have not explicitly evaluated the costs of policies with $I > 5$. In drawing the line as to where to stop the process, the decision maker must be satisfied that average costs will not dip below the minimum values so far obtained. This is a matter of judgement and it can be helpful to graph monthly average costs C_m as shown in Fig. 11-10. From Fig. 11-10, it is clear that, with the original data, it is safe to conclude that values of $I > 5$ will not produce a superior result to $I = 2$. The repeated use of the same interval between group replacements is known as a *stationary*

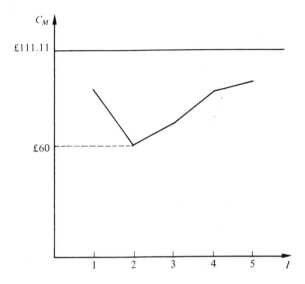

Figure 11-10

strategy and will be appropriate to all problems considered here. Further discussion of this concept can be found in Wagner (1972).

11-5 SENSITIVITY ANALYSIS

Sensitivity analysis can be carried out on any of the problem parameters. Of the data required, the failure and survival probabilities in many situations would be fairly well established. However, uncertainty may surround some elements of the cost data. The cost information needed relates to:

(i) the cost of each item;
(ii) other direct costs of making the individual and group replacements;
(iii) disruption costs.

The cost data are listed in order of increasing difficulty of estimation. Item (i) should, by and large, be a reliable figure that is fairly easy to obtain. Item (ii) would also usually be confidently established. Item (iii), however, can be very difficult to estimate and, where this is a significant element in costs, a sensitivity analysis should be conducted.

Consider first the cost of an individual replacement. This was £2 in the original light bulb example. Let this be £R in general. The costs per month of the alternative policies will now be as presented in Fig. 11-11.

With all other data at their original values, for what range of values of R will the two-month group replacement policy remain optimal? This is the range of values of R for which $45 + 7.5R$ is not greater than any of the other entries in Figure 11-11.

Policy	Cost per month (£)
1-month	90
2-month	$45 + 7.5R$
3-month	$30 + 20.5R$
4-month	$22.5 + 32.6625R$
5-month	$18 + 37.503R$
Individual	$55.55R$

Figure 11-11

First, *vis-à-vis* the one-month policy we must have

$$45 + 7.5R \leqslant 90$$

$$\therefore \ R \leqslant \frac{45}{7.5}$$

$$\therefore \ R \leqslant 6$$

Thus the one-month policy gives an *upper bound* on R. The other policies all have higher coefficients of R so these will seem relatively more attractive (the constant terms are lower) the lower R is. Each of these policies will set a *lower bound* on R. The *greatest* of these lower bounds (the GLB) determines the minimum level below which R must not fall for the two-month policy to be superior to three-, four-, or five-month and individual policies.

Vis-à-vis the three-month policy

$$45 + 7.5R \leqslant 30 + 20.5R$$

$$\therefore \ 13R \geqslant 15$$

$$R \geqslant 1.1538$$

in comparison to the four-month policy

$$45 + 7.5R \leqslant 22.5 + 36.6625R$$

$$\therefore \ 29.1625R \geqslant 22.5$$

$$R \geqslant 0.7715$$

in comparison to the five-month policy

$$45 + 7.5R \leqslant 18 + 37.503R$$

$$\therefore \ 30.003R \geqslant 27$$

$$R \geqslant 0.8999$$

and, finally, in comparison with the individual policy

$$45 + 7.5R \leqslant 55.\overline{55}R$$

$$\therefore \quad 48.0\overline{55}R \geqslant 45$$

$$R \geqslant 0.9364$$

Thus, the tolerance interval for R so that the two month policy remains optimal is:

$$1.1538 \leqslant R \leqslant 6$$

since the greatest of the lower bounds was 1.1538. Clearly with an original estimate of £2 there would have to be a considerable error in percentage terms to be outside of the permitted range. Of course, the *actual cost* of the two-month policy will change as R varies but it will remain the cheapest (*ceteris paribus*) so long as R remains within the above range.

A similar sensitivity analysis could be carried out against the group replacement cost. Call this G. In this case, with $R = 2$, the costs of the policies become:

Policy	Cost per month
1-month	G
2-month	$0.5G + 15$
3-month	$0.\overline{33}G + 41$
4-month	$0.25G + 65.325$
5-month	$0.2G + 75.006$
Individual	111.11

The reader may verify that the resultant range of values for G for which the two-month policy is optimal is

$$30 \leqslant G \leqslant 156$$

so that here again the parameter is centrally located in the permitted range.

But what about *joint* variation of both R and G? The original range for R applied only to the value of 90 for G, but what if G is *not* 90, and what becomes of the range for G if R is not 2? We can determine a permitted region or *area* for both G and R in the following way. First set out the policy costs in terms of both G and R. Thus we have:

Policy	Cost per month
1-month	G
2-month	$0.5G + 7.5R$
3-month	$0.\overline{33}G + 20.5R$
4-month	$0.25G + 32.6625R$
5-month	$0.2G + 37.503R$
Individual	$55.\overline{55}R$

Now for the two-month policy to be superior to the one-month policy

$$0.5G + 7.5R \leqslant G$$
$$\therefore \ G \geqslant 15R$$

From the three-month case we obtain

$$0.5G + 7.5R \leqslant 0.\overline{33}G + 20.5R$$
$$0.1\overline{66}G \geqslant 13R$$
$$G \leqslant 78R$$

From comparison with the four-month case

$$0.5G + 7.5R \leqslant 0.25G + 32.6625R$$
$$\therefore \ 0.25G \leqslant 25.1625R$$
$$G \leqslant 100.65R$$

From the five-month case

$$0.5G + 7.5R \leqslant 0.2G + 37.503R$$
$$0.3G \leqslant 30.003R$$
$$G \leqslant 100.01R$$

Finally from the individual case

$$0.5G + 7.5R \leqslant 55.55R$$
$$\therefore \ G \leqslant 96.1\overline{1}R$$

So that the original policy is optimal provided

$$15R \leqslant G \leqslant 78R$$

Notice that setting $R = 2$ gives the range for G alone and putting $G = 90$ gives the range for R alone.

As a diagram with, for clarity, the G scale compressed we have the situation shown in Fig. 11-12. The original tolerance intervals for G and R in the single parameter sensitivity analysis are shown as broken lines in Fig. 11-12. It is evident that the single parameter results show only a fraction of the tolerable relative variation in the values of G and R.

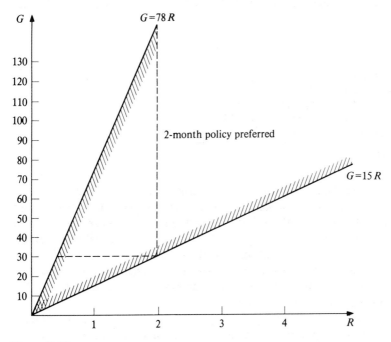

Figure 11-12

11-6 EXPECTED FAILURES: TABULAR METHOD

The failure tree is a most useful analytical tool, particularly in problems where the optimal interval between preventative replacements is likely to be short and in those cases where it is desirable to keep track of groups of particular components. But, as we have seen, they can involve very large numbers of branches as the number of time periods becomes large.

In such cases a tabular approach can be used. It is easy enough to demonstrate that where L is the maximum number of periods of life that any item can have ($L=4$ in the current example) the number of failures in any month m can be written as

$$
F_m = \begin{cases} nf_m + \sum_{t=1}^{m-1} f_t F_{m-t} & \text{for } m \leqslant L \\ \sum_{t=1}^{L} f_t F_{m-t} & \text{for } m > L \end{cases}
$$

where it will be recalled that the f_t are the failure probabilities, the F_t are the actual numbers falling and n is the total number of items. The formula is simpler to use than might appear at first glance. The results for the original light bulb example are presented in Fig. 11-13. As an exercise in the use of the

$F_1 = nf_1$	$= 15$
$F_2 = nf_2 + f_1 F_1$	$= 46.5$
$F_3 = nf_3 + f_1 F_2 + f_2 F_1$	$= 69.15$
$F_4 = nf_4 + f_1 F_3 + f_2 F_2 + f_3 F_1$	$= 56.415$
$F_5 = \quad f_1 F_4 + f_2 F_3 + f_3 F_2 + f_4 F_1$	$= 47.986\ 5$
$F_6 = \quad f_1 F_5 + f_2 F_4 + f_3 F_3 + f_4 F_2$	$= 58.683\ 15$
$F_7 = \quad f_1 F_6 + f_2 F_5 + f_3 F_4 + f_4 F_3$	$= 56.660\ 265$

Figure 11-13

tabular method the reader may wish to verify that (to two decimal places) $F_8 = 53.75$, $F_9 = 55.44$, $F_{10} = 56.07$. In section 11-3, we saw that the expected number of failures in months following a group replacement settled down to the mean number of failures in an oscillatory fashion. The tabular method allows the generation of sufficient data on the F_m to confirm this phenomenon. By this process the effect is even more apparent, as seen in Fig. 11-14. The damped fluctuations also make it clear that monthly costs would not alter course and dip below the two month optimal value.

The problem of estimating the expected number of failures in future periods is easily computerized. An instance of such a programme is found in Cohen (1985).

11-7 COMPONENT DESIGN APPLICATION

Statistical replacement methods can be of value where the problem is to choose between alternative ways of carrying out the same task—for example, where there are competing designs for a component. The least cost replacement cycle is determined for each alternative and the type giving rise to the lowest costs per period is preferred. Consider an example, a firm needs 200 components to fulfil a particular function. Its research department have produced two alternative designs for the components, the Gremlin and the Spanna. For the

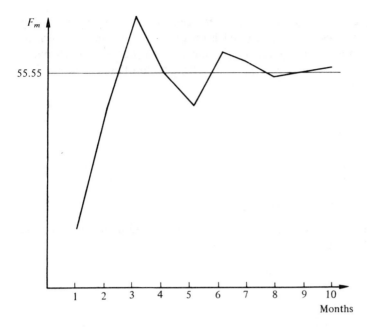

F_m

55.55

1 2 3 4 5 6 7 8 9 10

Months

Figure 11-14

Gremlin the numbers failing at the end of 1, 2, and 3 weeks from a fresh installation of 200 are estimated to be:

Week	Nos failing
1	40
2	60
3	100

The cost of an individual Gremlin replacement would be £2. Replacement of all 200 at one go would cost £175.

For the Spanna the failure data are:

Week	Nos failing
1	20
2	120
3	60

The cost of an individual Spanna replacement would be £2.50 and group replacement would cost £190. The board of directors have chosen the Gremlin on the grounds that: (a) individual replacement is cheaper; (b) group replacement is cheaper; and (c) mean life is longer. The question to be decided is whether or not these arguments are sound. Consider each component individually—the Gremlin to begin with. The Gremlin failure and survival probabilities are:

t	f_t	s_t
0	0	1
1	0.2	0.8
2	0.3	0.5
3	0.5	0

and the Gremlin failure tree is shown in Fig. 11-15. The Gremlin mean life and mean number of failures are found as follows:

f_1	Life (t)	$t \cdot f_t$
0	0	0
0.2	1	0.2
0.3	2	0.6
0.5	3	1.5
		2.3 = mean life

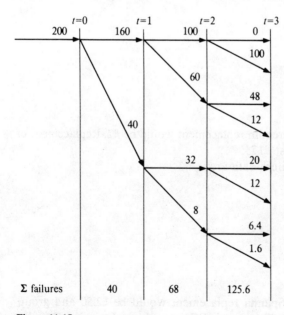

Figure 11-15

$$\text{mean number of failures} = \frac{200}{2.3} = 86.96$$

So that with an individual failure costing £2 and group replacement costing £175 the policies can now be costed:

I	Group cost	Costs in week			Total	Weekly average
		1	2	3		
1	175				175	175
2	175	80			255	127.5
3	175	80	136		391	130.33
4	175	80	136	251.2	642.2	160.55
∞						173.92

Thus a two-weekly policy would be best for the Gremlin design producing an average weekly cost figure of £127.5. Note that the individual replacements only policy corresponds to an infinite interval between group replacements. Incidentally, a five-week interval would produce a weekly average cost of £154.65.

Now consider the Spanna design in a similar fashion. Summarizing, the mean life is 2.2 weeks and the mean number of failures per week is 90.90. By use of the failure tree or Table 8-8 we find that:

$$F_1 = 20, \; F_2 = 122, \; F_3 = 84.2$$

so that with group cost at £190 and individual replacements at £2.5 the table of costs is:

I	Group cost	Costs in week			Total	Weekly average
		1	2	3		
1	190				190	190
2	190	50			240	120
3	190	50	305		545	181.66
4	190	50	305	210.5	755.5	188.875
∞						227.27

So that again a two-month policy would prove to be optimal, but the cost is only £120. The reason is that the bulk of the Spanna failures occur in the second month and are thus caught by the group replacement at month two.

Thus the directors were in error and the Spanna design should be selected despite some contrary but superficial indications.

11-8 DISCOUNTING IN STATISTICAL REPLACEMENT

So far, we have considered replacement problems in which the time periods involved are comparatively short. Where there are lengthy periods of time involved—years rather than weeks or months—it is important to take interest into account. This can easily be done. If we return to Fig. 11-9 and for the purposes of illustration suppose that the time periods are *years* rather than months then the *annual equivalent annuity* method described in Chapter Six can be brought in to the statistical replacement procedure. Figure 11-16 shows

I	Group cost $(t=0)$	Individual costs at year				Present value	AE factor (15%)	Annual equivalent annuity
		1	2	3	4			
1	90	—	—	—	—	90	1.15	103.50
2	90	30	—	—	—	116.0880	0.6151	71.41
3	90	30	93	—	—	186.4053	0.4380	81.65
4	90	30	93	138.3	—	277.3376	0.3503	97.15
5	90	30	93	138.3	113.73	342.3684	0.2983	102.13
Individual								111.11

Figure 11-16

the revised calculations using an interest rate of 15 per cent. The AE column in Fig. 11-16 gives the annual equivalent annuity factors drawn from Table 5. As regards these factors it should be noted that in this method the first of the notional annuity payments occurs *after one year*. So that, for example, in the case of the one-year policy, an *annuity due* of £90 has the same present value as an *immediate annuity* of £103.5 when the interest rate is 15 per cent. The optimal decision will therefore be to carry out preventative replacements on a two-year cycle. The equipment involved could be the company's fleet of vehicles. A sensitivity analysis could be carried out on the interest rate as well as on the other components of cost.

11-9 PERSONNEL LEAVING RATES

Statistical replacement methods can be of value in certain personnel and staffing problems. While there is rarely any question of 'preventative maintenance', the policy choices would be between various strategies designed to affect the 'failure' probabilities which in this context represent the chance of an employee leaving at any given point. There are costs associated with recruitment and re-filling casual vacancies. The idea is to take action to affect the leaving probabilities in order to lower recruitment costs. Consider an example.

The personnel division of a large firm is concerned that staff turnover is too high. Recruitment costs are well above the industrial average. The personnel manager's investigations reveal that the high leaving rates may be due to some aspects of working conditions. After presenting a strategy to the board, the personnel manager is given approval to carry out a pilot study involving clerical staff. The typing pool would be re-organized into sections removing the open plan layout and extending flexitime working. As a result it is estimated that the probabilities of clerical staff leaving after one two, three and four years with the firm improve from the situation shown in Fig. 11-17(a) to that shown in Fig. 11-17(b). The cost of recruiting a member of staff is £100 and the one-off costs of the office re-organization are £5000. Fifty staff are involved in all and the firm's cost of capital is 13 per cent. Would the re-organization be worthwhile in financial terms over (a) a five year horizon and (b) in the very long term?

Year end (t)	Leaving probability (f_t)	Year end	Leaving probability
1	0.7	1	0.1
2	0.1	2	0.3
3	0.1	3	0.4
4	0.1	4	0.2

(a)   (b)

Figure 11-17

Consider first the comparative assessment over a five year period. With the original probabilities, the expected number of staff leaving in each of the first five years would be:

$$
\begin{aligned}
F_1 &= 0.7(50) &&= 35 \\
F_2 &= 0.1(50) + 0.7(35) &&= 29.5 \\
F_3 &= 0.1(50) + 0.7(29.5) + 0.1(35) &&= 29.15 \\
F_4 &= 0.1(50) + 0.7(29.15) + 0.1(29.5) + 0.1(35) &&= 31.855 \\
F_5 &= 0.7(31.855) + 0.1(29.15) + 0.1(29.5) + 0.1(35) &&= 31.6635
\end{aligned}
$$

while under the new arrangements the results would be:

$$
\begin{aligned}
F_1 &= 0.1(50) &&= 5 \\
F_2 &= 0.3(50) + 0.1(5) &&= 15.5 \\
F_3 &= 0.4(50) + 0.1(15.5) + 0.3(5) &&= 23.05 \\
F_4 &= 0.2(50) + 0.1(23.05) + 0.3(15.5) + 0.4(5) &&= 18.955 \\
F_5 &= 0.1(18.955) + 0.3(23.05) + 0.4(15.5) + 0.2(5) &&= 16.0105
\end{aligned}
$$

On the assumption that each process above is begun at $t = 0$, the cash saving in any year is the reduced number of recruitments necessary multiplied by the cost per employee recruited. Thus at $t = 1$ the saving is:

$$(35 - 5)100 = £3000$$

while at $t = 5$ the estimated saving is:

$$(31.6635 - 16.0105)100 = £1565.30$$

The cash savings for each year are weighted by the 13 per cent discount factors from Table 2 (page 486) and the net present value is calculated. The results are:

Time	$t = 0$	$t = 1$	$t = 2$	$t = 3$	$t = 4$	$t = 5$
Cash flow	−5000	3000	1400	610	1290	1565.3
Discount factor	1	0.8850	0.7813	0.6931	0.6133	0.5428
Present value	−5000	2655	1096.34	422.79	791.16	849.64

The sum of the present values of the cash flows is £849.64 so that over a five year horizon the improvements would be worthwhile. We have somewhat simplified the calculations to illustrate the general principle. A more refined analysis could have been carried out separating out 'old' and 'new' staff. The 'new' staff would have the new probabilities while amended probabilities would be determined for existing staff already in employment for various lengths of time.

In the very long run the reduced numbers to be recruited would settle down to the difference between the mean number of departures resulting from the two probability distributions. In the original circumstances we have:

t	ft	tft	
1	0.7	0.7	
2	0.1	0.2	mean number of departures
3	0.1	0.3	$= \dfrac{50}{1.6} = 31.25$ per year
4	0.1	0.4	

mean stay $= 1.6$ years

So that an average 31.25 staff would leave each year. With the new arrangements the results are:

t	ft	tft	
1	0.1	0.1	mean number of departures
2	0.3	0.6	$=\dfrac{50}{2.7}=18.52$
3	0.4	1.2	
4	0.2	0.8	

mean stay $= 2.7$ years

So, in this case, the average number of people to be recruited is just 18.52 per year—a difference of 12.73 per annum which would produce an annual saving of £1273. If these savings were continued in perpetuity the result would be a gross present value of:

$$\frac{1273}{0.13}=£9792.31$$

The net present value will, therefore, be £4792.31 and the revised arrangements are definitely worthwhile in the longer term.

EXERCISES

11-1 Revision exercise
   (i) Distinguish the two main types of replacement problem.
   (ii) How should problems where failure is fatal be approached?
   (iii) Explain what is meant by a failure tree and how it is constructed.
   (iv) How is the mean number of failures calculated?
   (v) Could an optimal policy be arrived at where the interval between preventative replacements exceeded the maximum life of a component?
   (vi) On what parameters is sensitivity analysis likely to be warranted?
   (vii) Under what circumstances is the tabular method of calculating the expected numbers of failures likely to be preferred to the construction of a failure tree?
   (viii) State some areas of application of statistical replacement methods.
   (ix) How can the time value of money be taken into account in statistical replacement problems?

11-2 The failure statistics for a certain type of light bulb are:

End of month	1	2	3	4	5	6
Probability of failure	0.05	0.10	0.25	0.25	0.2	0.15

There are 200 bulbs in use, the cost of replacing an individual failed bulb is £1.00 and the cost of a group replacement of all bulbs averages £0.4 per bulb. It has been decided to replace failed bulbs at the end of the month of failure and to replace all bulbs periodically.

(i) Find the expected number of failures one, two, three, four, and five months after a fresh installation. (*Hint:* the algebraic method is preferable here.)
(ii) At what intervals should group replacement occur? (Individual failures need not be attended to separately in the month of group replacement.)

11-3 Repco Ltd has a large number of machines which incorporate a particular component which is liable to sudden failure. Repco's present policy is to replace each component individually upon failure. Records have been kept of the working lives before failure of 800 of the components and the following data were obtained:

Number of components	Length of life (months)
120	1
360	2
240	3
80	4
800	

Repco is now considering the possibility of periodic replacement of all components, failed or not. Each individual failure costs £10 to replace, but in a replacement of all components the cost per unit replaced is £6.25.

Individual failures in months prior to the group replacement would still have to be attended to, with the exception of those which occur in the month of the group replacement itself.

(i) What is the best interval between group replacements?
(ii) Conduct a sensitivity analysis on the cost of an individual replacement.
(iii) Conduct a joint sensitivity analysis on the individual and group replacement costs.
(iv) Suppose that capital expenditure of £20 000 was necessary to change over to the group replacement policy. With an interest rate of 20 per cent, and a practically infinite horizon, what figure may be placed on the benefit of the changeover of the optimal policy?

11-4 A new department store plans to employ 250 sales staff. Experience suggests that 60 per cent of the staff will leave after one year and only 10 per cent will still be employed after two years, but these 10 per cent are expected to stay for a further two years before leaving. At the end of each year all vacancies that have arisen are filled by employing new staff, the 'leaving rates' for whom may be assumed to be the same as for the original 250.

(i) How many sales staff will be expected to leave at the end of three and four years?
(ii) What is the average number of resignations per year?
(iii) It is thought that the poor state of canteen facilities causes some employees to leave earlier than they would otherwise have done. If £400 per year was spent on improving canteen facilities the percentage of employees leaving at the end of the first year would be reduced to 40. However, the extra 20 per cent who do stay will leave at the end of the second year. The cost of recruiting a new sales employee is £20. Is it worth improving the canteen facilities?

11-5 Coltel Ltd have just begun to hire out a total of 200 coloured television sets. Market research has shown that out of a hundred hirings the pattern of the length of hire is as follows:

Length of hire (years)	1	2	3	4
Number of hirings	20	40	30	10

Required:

(a) Determine the number of new rentals required each year for the next four years to maintain Coltel's total rentals at 200 (round to nearest whole number in your calculations).

(b) What is the average length of hire period?

(c) What is the average number of new rentals required each year?

(d) Coltel Ltd, in an attempt to reduce their administrative overheads, are launching an advertising campaign aimed at their existing customers to encourage them to rent for longer periods. They would regard their campaign as successful if the following pattern of hiring was achieved in the long-run:

Length of hire (years)	1	2	3	4	5
Number of hirings	10	30	35	15	10

If the administrative cost of arranging a hire is £20, what is the maximum amount Coltel Ltd should spend on their advertising campaign each year?

(Chartered Association of Certified Accountants)

Solution guides

11-2 (i) $F_1 = 10$; $F_2 = 20.5$; $F_3 = 52.025$; $F_4 = 57.151\,25$; $F_5 = 55.685$.

(ii) Mean life $= 3.9$ months. Mean no. of failures $= 200/3.9 = 51.2821 =$ cost of individual policy (∞ interval between group replacements). Group replacement intervals: costs 1 month £80 per month; 2 months £45 per month; 3 months £36.83 per month; 4 months £40.63 per month; 5 months £43.94 per month; 6 months £45.89 per month. Thus the 3-month interval is optimal.

11-3 The failure tree is shown in Fig. 11-18. The mean life is 2.35 months, found as follows:

Life	f_t	$f_t \times$ life
0	0	0
1	0.15	0.15
2	0.45	0.90
3	0.30	0.90
4	0.10	0.40
		2.35

So that the mean no. of failures is $800 \div 2.35 = 340.426$ per month. Thus attending to individual failures only would cost £3404.26 per month. For the finite intervals between group replacements

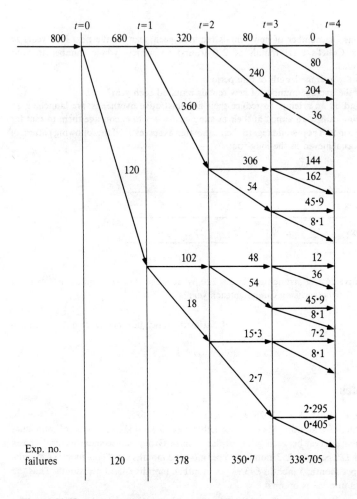

Figure 11-18

the workings are:

Interval	Group cost	Individual costs in month				Total	Monthly average
		1	2	3	4		
1	5000					5 000	5000
2	5000	1200				6 200	3100
3	5000	1200	3780			9 980	3326.66
4	5000	1200	3780	3507		13 487	3371.75
5	5000	1200	3780	3507	3387.05	16 874.05	3374.81

From which it is concluded that the best interval between group replacements is two months.

(ii) If the individual replacement cost is £R then we have:

Interval	Monthly average cost
1	5000
2	$2500 + 60R$
3	$1666.\overline{66} + 166R$
4	$1250 + 212.175R$
5	$1000 + 237.481R$
∞	$340.426R$

So that

$$2500 + 60R \leqslant 5000 \qquad \rightarrow R \leqslant 41.\overline{66}$$

$$2500 + 60R \leqslant 1666.\overline{66} + 166R \rightarrow R \geqslant 7.86$$

$$2500 + 60R \leqslant 1250 + 212.175R \rightarrow R \geqslant 8.21$$

$$2500 + 60R \leqslant 1000 + 237.481R \rightarrow R \geqslant 8.45$$

$$2500 + 60R \leqslant 340.426R \qquad \rightarrow R \geqslant 8.92$$

The tolerance interval for R will be the range between the GLB and the LUB. Thus, the two month policy will remain optimal as long as R is in the range:

$$8.92 \leqslant R \leqslant 41.\overline{66}.$$

(iii) With the group replacement cost as G, the two-month policy costs $0.5G + 60R$. So in comparison with the other intervals:

$$0.5G + 60R \leqslant G \qquad \rightarrow G \geqslant 120R$$

$$0.5G + 60R \leqslant 0.\overline{33}G + 166R \qquad \rightarrow G \leqslant 636R$$

$$0.5G + 60R \leqslant 0.25G + 212.175R \rightarrow G \leqslant 608.70R$$

$$0.5G + 60R \leqslant 0.2G + 237.481R \rightarrow G \leqslant 591.60R$$

$$0.5G + 60R \leqslant 340.426R \qquad \rightarrow G \leqslant 560.85R$$

$$\therefore \ 120R \leqslant G \leqslant 560.85R$$

(iv) The monthly saving is $5000 - 3100 = 1900$ which is 22 800 per annum in perpetuity. The net present value of the changeover is then

$$\frac{22\,800}{0.2} - 20\,000 = 94\,000$$

11-4 (i) 144 after three years, 161 after four years (160.9).

(ii) The mean length of stay is 1.6 years as worked out below:

t	f_t	tf_t
0	0	0
1	0.6	0.6
2	0.3	0.6
3	0.0	0
4	0.1	0.4
		1.6

Thus the mean number of resignations per year is $250 \div 1.6 = 156.25$.

(iii) With the improved facilities the mean stay becomes 1.8 years giving an average leaving rate of 138.89 per year. The annual saving in recruitment costs is then £20(156.25 − 138.89) = £347.20 which, being less than the extra expenditure of £400 p.a., means that the improvements are not worth while.

11-5 (*a*) The failure tree (rounded workings) is shown in Fig. 11-19.

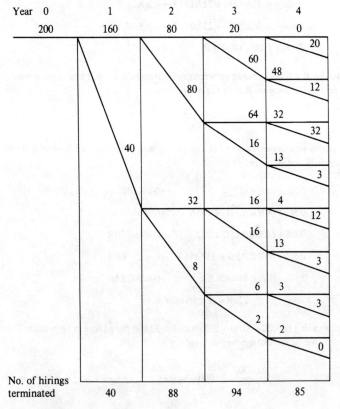

Year   0   1   2   3   4
        200   160   80   20   0

No. of hirings terminated   40   88   94   85

Figure 11-19

(b) 2.3 years.

(c) To maintain the total, the number of new rentals must equal the average number of hirings terminated $= 200 \div 2.3 = 87$.

(d) With the new probabilities the expected length of hire becomes 2.85 years, therefore, average number of new renters per year $= 200 \div 2.85 = 70$.

The saving in administrative costs is $(87 - 70)20 = 340$ per year. This is the upper limit on costs for the advertising campaign.

REFERENCES

Wagner, H. M. (1972), *Principles of Operational Research*, Prentice Hall.

FURTHER READING

Cohen, S. S. (1985), *Operational Research*, Edward Arnold. Links replacement discussion to reliability and maintenance.

Harper, W. M. (1975), *Operational Research*, Macdonald & Evans. Includes discussion of failure trees and considers depreciation.

Littlechild, S. C. (1977), *Operational Research for Managers*, Philip Allan. Shows use of simulation methods in replacement problems.

TWELVE

FORECASTING METHODS

12-1 INTRODUCTION

All operational research methods require data inputs and to the extent that the data are future values of variables forecasting methods are called for. Capital budgeting is the most obvious example but many other areas of the firm's activities will require forecast data. However, the requirements and the situations are many and varied and a *range* of forecasting techniques is needed—no one method being best for all situations.

The production manager, for example, will want to know about future demand for products (and potential products), the consequent materials requirements and prices. In stock control, the main requirement is for comparatively short-term forecasting of demand for those items kept in stock. Equipment replacement or repair decisions require longer term forecasts of operating and maintenance costs, resale values and new equipment prices. The marketing manager will require product demand forecasts and estimates of market share (*relative demand*) along with predictions of prices and perhaps even indications of general trends in design. Information of this kind is essential to effective sales promotion campaigns.

For investment decision making and financial management, the main requirement will be for cash flow forecasts. In obtaining these it is highly desirable to predict individually the values of the components of cost and the contributions to revenue. Capital outlays may, in larger projects, extend over a number of years and forecasts of these charges are essential. In financial management generally it is valuable to have advance information about requirements for working capital and the actual income from accounts receivable.

As we saw in Chapter Eleven, forecasts of staff turnover are valuable in controlling recruitment costs. Estimates of future staff requirements in various categories are needed to design training and recruitment programmes and early retirement packages.

The company's overall policy making and strategic review calls not only for estimates of the timing of major future activities but also needs more general information about competitors' intentions, the market as a whole and national and international policy trends.

These requirements are so various, ranging from detailed weekly forecasts of individual items to general economic analysis that they cannot be met by a single technique or even a single class of methods. There are three main classes of forecasting and predictive methods:

(a) *Quantitative techniques* (e.g., moving averages, exponential smoothing, regression).
(b) *Qualitative techniques* (e.g., technological forecasting).
(c) *Subjective methods* (e.g., analysts' expectations in portfolio analysis).

In this section we shall be concentrating on a few of the quantitative methods which tend to work better for the *short* and *medium* terms. It is often convenient to partition the future into four slices:

(i) The *very short term*: sometimes referred to as the *immediate term*. Here is meant a period of days or a few weeks. The appropriate length depends on the context varying from *hours* (stock market) through *days* at the retail level or *weeks* at the wholesale level.
(ii) The *short term*: perhaps 1 to 6 months again depending generally on the distance of remove from final demand.
(iii) The *medium term*: a 'few' months to a 'few' years depending on context. Perhaps from as little as three months in retailing to five years (investment in government securities).
(iv) The *long term*: more than a 'few' years.

Here it will be the moving averages and exponential smoothing that apply mainly to (i) and (ii) and regression that applies mainly to (iii) although extrapolations can be made some way into (iv).

There is also the situation of *demand dependent* items forecasting. As we saw in Chapter Eight on inventory control, when a complex product is composed of fixed numbers of numerous component parts—for instance, a particular make of car—*given* the level of demand for the finished product there will be absolutely precise consequent requirements for the components. The given levels of sales of the complete product are exploded to determine component requirements. The method of *material requirements planning*, or MRP, goes on to aggregate and project these requirements over time. MRP is especially useful in production-to-order companies, Ordnance factories and specialized machine tools providing examples.

Before considering the first of the methods, one fact should be borne in mind. As with other statistical and OR methods, to justify themselves (taking costs into account) forecasting methods need not produce pinpoint accuracy. Nothing can do that. *They have only to improve on what would otherwise have been done.* That this is generally the case has been amply demonstrated by business experience.

12-2 SIMPLE LINEAR REGRESSION

The name *regression* relates to an early use of the method in a study of the psychological process of the same name. 'Simple' means only that *one* independent variable is involved rather than many. The method of *least squares* has its origins in eighteenth-century studies of errors of observation and was formulated by Gauss in 1798.

In simple linear regression, given two random variables X and Y, an equation of the form

$$Y = a + bX \tag{12-1}$$

is fitted to the data. In equation (12-1) a and b are constants that have to be determined to produce the best fit, X is called the *independent variable* and Y is said to be *dependent*. There should generally be some grounds for supposing that changes in X *actually cause* changes in Y. For instance X may be income and Y expenditure, or X may be sales promotion expenditure and Y might be total sales revenue. If neither variable actually brings about a change in the other then we could equally well write

$$X = c + dY$$

and unless there is perfect correlation between X and Y there will be inconsistent estimates of Y from X and X from Y.

Figure 12-1 (a *scatter diagram*) shows a possible case in which Y tends to increase as X increases ($\therefore b > 0$) and where a, the intercept term, is negative. The actual pairs of values of X and Y in the sample are related by

$$Y_i = a + bX_i + e_i \tag{12-2}$$

where the e_i are errors and where a and b are chosen so that the sum of the

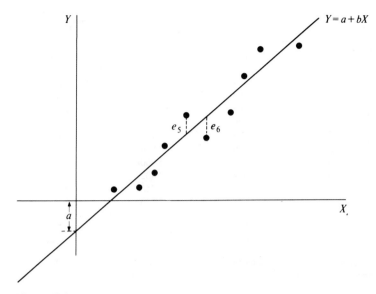

Figure 12-1

squared errors, Σe_i^2, is as small as possible. In the figure, e_5 would be positive and e_6 would be negative and they would almost cancel—hence the squaring. Under certain conditions, the *least squares coefficients* a and b are the *best* (least variance) *linear*, *unbiased* estimators of the true parameters that would be obtained from a study of the entire population of X and Y values.

Formulae for a and b, obtained by use of calculus methods, come in a variety of guises. The expressions that will be used here are:

$$a = \bar{Y} - b\bar{X} \qquad \qquad (12\text{-}3)$$

$$b = \frac{N\Sigma XY - (\Sigma X)(\Sigma Y)}{N\Sigma X^2 - (\Sigma X)^2} \qquad (12\text{-}4)$$

where in Eq. (12-3) $\bar{X}$ and $\bar{Y}$ are the arithmetic means of X and Y. Although Eq. (12-4) looks complicated at first glance nothing other than simple arithmetic is required to ascertain b. The example shown in Fig. 12-2 illustrates this.

The columns headed X and Y in Fig. 12-2 are sample data consisting of 15 pairs of values of X and Y. The first step is to calculate ΣX and ΣY and hence $\bar{X}$ and $\bar{Y}$. Thus:

$$\bar{X} = \frac{\Sigma X}{N} = \frac{300}{15} = 20; \quad \bar{Y} = \frac{\Sigma Y}{N} = \frac{876}{15} = 58.4$$

The third column in Fig. 12-2 squares every entry in the X column and the sum

X	Y	X^2	XY	Y^2
10	33	100	330	1 089
12	37	144	444	1 369
15	45	225	675	2 025
13	41	169	533	1 681
17	51	289	867	2 601
18	53	324	954	2 809
17	54	289	918	2 916
16	50	256	800	2 500
21	60	441	1 260	3 600
22	66	484	1 452	4 356
25	70	625	1 750	4 900
25	69	625	1 725	4 761
28	77	784	2 156	5 929
30	82	900	2 460	6 724
31	88	961	2 728	7 744
$\Sigma X = 300$	$\Sigma Y = 876$	$\Sigma X^2 = 6\,616$	$\Sigma XY = 19\,052$	$\Sigma Y^2 = 55\,004$

Figure 12-2

of the squared X values is 6616. In the XY column each X value is multiplied by its corresponding Y value. The sum if 19 052. For the moment we do not require the Y^2 column, but this will be needed later on. Thus, substituting in Eq. (12-4) gives:

$$b = \frac{15(19\,052) - (300)(876)}{15(6616) - (300)(300)} = \frac{22\,980}{9240} = 2.487$$

and substitution of $b = 2.487$, $\bar{X} = 20$ and $\bar{Y} = 58.4$ into Eq. (12-3) gives

$$a = 58.4 - 2.487(20) = 8.66$$

so that the regression equation of Y upon X obtained from the sample is

$$Y = 8.66 + 2.487X$$

We shall need to know how good a *fit* we have. The formulae will always give values for a and b regardless of whether or not there is any real relationship between X and Y. The reader might like to plot the scatter and put in the regression line. This graphical work will suggest that the fit is very good—all the points are 'close' to the line—but what is needed is a numerical measure of how good the fit is. This is provided by the coefficient of linear correlation.

12-3 THE CORRELATION COEFFICIENT

The coefficient of linear correlation, r, is given by

$$r = \frac{N\Sigma XY - (\Sigma X)(\Sigma Y)}{\sqrt{(N\Sigma X^2 - (\Sigma X)^2)(N\Sigma Y^2 - (\Sigma Y)^2)}}$$

and it can be shown that

$$-1 \leqslant r \leqslant +1$$

If $r \simeq 0$ there is no linear correlation between the variables; if r *is* significantly positive this means that there is linear correlation and the regression line slopes up. If r is significantly negative the regression line slopes down. Thus in Fig. 12-3(a) there is good positive linear correlation. Figure 12-3(b) exhibits good negative linear correlation. In Fig. 12-3(c) there is clearly no relation so $r \simeq 0$. In Fig. 12-3(d) there is strong *curvilinear* relationship but the coefficient of linear correlation would still be zero or thereabouts. Thus zero correlation should not be interpreted as *necessarily* implying no relationship of any kind.

In our example, bringing in the Y^2 column and substituting in the formula for r gives:

$$r = \frac{22\,980}{\sqrt{(9240)(57\,684)}} = 0.995$$

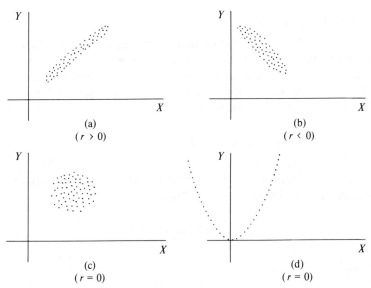

(a)
$(r > 0)$

(b)
$(r < 0)$

(c)
$(r = 0)$

(d)
$(r = 0)$

Figure 12-3

which is a very high value, suggesting a very strong linear relation between X and Y. We would thus have good justification for use of the estimated regression equation for predictive purposes. In the testing of economic models (which usually involve *multiple regression*) it is not uncommon to have correlation coefficients well over 0.9. This will be so when the model has been properly formulated and all important variables included.

The *square* of the correlation coefficient is called the *coefficient of determination* and gives the proportion of the variation in Y that is explained by variation in X. In our case, variation in X accounts for 99 per cent of the variation in Y. When r drops below about 0.7 then X is accounting for less than half the variation in Y and we should have cause to be dissatisfied with the performance of the model if a comprehensive explanation of variability is sought. It should be pointed out, however, that r^2 values can sometimes be 'manipulated' by changes of variable and that low values *can* be satisfactory if one factor among several is being studied.

Generally, a test of significance (using the 't' distribution) should be conducted on r. Whether a value of r is 'significant' depends not only upon the value itself but also on the number of observations in the sample. Hypotheses concerning the values of the regression coefficients can be similarly tested. Here, we shall simplify matters very much and say that if there is a reasonable number of observations (say 10 or more) and a good value of r (say 0.7 or more) then the correlation is significant.

12-4 FORECASTING WITH REGRESSION

(i) Point estimates

There are two kinds of forecasts that we shall be concerned with. The first use *interpolation*. This involves predicting a value for *Y when the X value is within the range of X values in the sample*. The procedure is very simple. Insert the value of X into the regression equation (call this special value X^* and the resulting forecast Y^*) to determine the predicted value of Y. Thus if $X^* = 20$

$$Y^* = 8.66 + 2.487(20) = 58.4$$

(which confirms the fact that the regression line should pass through the *centroid* of the data, $\bar{X}$, $\bar{Y}$). Similarly if $X^* = 14$

$$Y^* = 8.66 + 2.487(14) = 43.478$$

and if $X^* = 27$

$$Y^* = 8.66 + 2.487(27) = 75.809$$

Recall that the forecast values of Y have been marked with a star to distinguish them from actual observations.

Next is *extrapolation*. Here the X^* values are outside of the sample range. Thus if $X^* = 32$

$$Y^* = 8.66 + 2.487(32) = 88.244$$

if $X^* = 8$

$$Y^* = 8.66 + 2.487(8) = 28.556$$

if $X^* = 35$

$$Y^* = 8.66 + 2.487(35) = 96.705$$

and if $X^* = 40$

$$Y^* = 8.66 + 2.487(40) = 108.14$$

The cases of interpolation and extrapolation are distinguished because there is generally more confidence in the model structure remaining valid if X^* stays within the range of the sample experience. The further that X^* goes outside of the range then the less sure we are that the model structure will still apply. This is shown in Fig. 12-4 where in fact although the X, Y relationship is exponential, linear predictions are satisfactory within or near to the sample range of values.

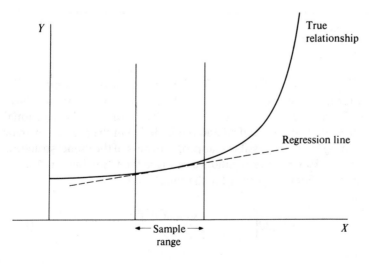

Figure 12-4

12-5 FORECASTING WITH REGRESSION

(ii) Confidence intervals

The questions naturally arise as to what confidence we may have in the predictions—and can this be quantified? Our predictions are point estimates (which should be rounded off) but we know that a reasonable margin of error should be allowed. It would be nice to be able to give a *bracketed prediction* with a stated degree of confidence. Unfortunately, this is no easy matter. To accomplish this we need to know the *prediction error variance*. This could then be used to give 95 per cent confidence intervals for the forecasts made. The 95 per cent confidence band-width increases with movement away from the point $(\bar{X}, \bar{Y})$ as shown in Fig. 12-5. In Fig. 12-5 the region of 95 per cent confidence is

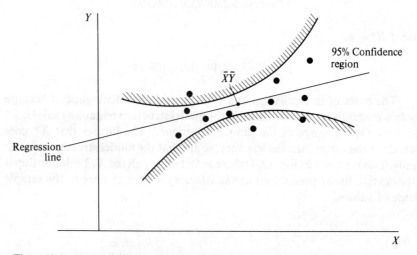

Figure 12-5

unshaded and for X values a 'long way' from the mean it becomes very wide. It is narrowest for interpolative forecasts near the mean, in which we may have greatest confidence. When extrapolation is involved there are the additional possible sources of error (unspecified and not included in the prediction error variance) resulting from the possible inappropriateness of the model structure. Given that the model structure is valid we can give the following formula for the 95 per cent confidence interval for the prediction

$$Y^* \pm t\hat{\sigma}\left[1 + \frac{1}{n} + \frac{(X^* - \bar{X})^2}{\Sigma(X - \bar{X})^2}\right]^{1/2} \tag{12-6}$$

in which t is the appropriate value of the 't' statistic and where $\hat{\sigma}^2$, the sample based estimate of the variance of the error term, is given by

$$\hat{\sigma}^2 = \frac{\Sigma(Y_i - Y^*)^2}{n-2}$$

The value of t for the 95 per cent confidence interval depends on the number of *degrees of freedom* (d). This is the number in the sample less two. Thus there were 13 degrees of freedom in the example above. Values of t (for the 95 per cent range) for selected d are shown in Fig. 12-6.

$d = 10$	11	12	13	14	15	16	17	
$t = 2.228$	2.201	2.179	2.160	2.145	2.131	2.120	2.110	
$d = 18$	19	20	21	22	23	24	25	
$t = 2.101$	2.093	2.086	2.080	2.074	2.069	2.064	2.060	
$d = 26$	27	28	29	30	40	60	120	∞
$t = 2.056$	2.052	2.048	2.045	2.042	2.021	2.000	1.980	1.960

Figure 12-6

Now consider the use of the formula (12-6) in the numerical example previously given. First compute $\Sigma(X - \bar{X})^2$. We have the results as shown in Fig. 12-7. Now determine $\hat{\sigma}^2$. For this we need the 'forecast' values Y^* given by the regression equation for the original sample values of X. Thus when $X = 10$,

X	$X - \bar{X}$	$(X - \bar{X})^2$
10	-10	100
12	-8	64
15	-5	25
13	-7	49
17	-3	9
18	-2	4
17	-3	9
16	-4	16
21	$+1$	1
22	$+2$	4
25	$+5$	25
25	$+5$	25
28	$+8$	64
30	$+10$	100
31	$+11$	121
	$\Sigma(X - \bar{X})^2 = 616$	

Figure 12-7

X	Y	Y^*	$Y - Y^*$	$(Y - Y^*)^2$
10	33	33.530	-0.530	0.281
12	37	38.504	-1.504	2.262
15	45	45.965	-0.965	0.931
13	41	40.991	0.009	0.000
17	51	50.939	0.061	0.004
18	53	53.426	-0.426	0.181
17	54	50.939	3.061	9.370
16	50	48.452	1.548	2.396
21	60	60.887	-0.887	0.787
22	66	63.374	2.626	6.896
25	70	70.835	-0.835	0.697
25	69	70.835	-1.835	3.367
28	77	78.296	-1.296	1.680
30	82	83.270	-1.270	1.613
31	88	85.757	2.243	5.031
				$35.496 = \Sigma(Y - Y^*)^2$

Figure 12-8

$Y^* = 8.66 + 2.487(10) = 33.530$. The other Y^* entries in the workings of Fig. 12-8 were similarly obtained. From Fig. 12-8 it is evident that:

$$\hat{\sigma}^2 = \frac{\Sigma(Y - Y^*)^2}{n-2} = \frac{35.496}{13} = 2.730$$

So $\hat{\sigma} = 1.652$. Now consider a 95 per cent confidence interval for Y if $X^* = 32$. In using Eq. (12-6) we note that the appropriate t value is that for $15 - 2 = 13$ degrees of freedom and is thus 2.160. Note also that the point estimate, $Y^* = 88.244$. The range will then be:

$$88.244 \pm (2.160)(1.652)\left[1 + \frac{1}{15} + \frac{(32-20)^2}{616}\right]^{1/2}$$

$$= 88.244 \pm (2.160)(1.652)(1.140)$$

$$= 84.176 \text{ to } 92.312$$

which had better be rounded off to

$$84.2 \text{ to } 92.3$$

because of rounding errors in the fifth figure and so as not to give a false impression of accuracy.

To get the 95 per cent confidence interval for $X^* = 35$ we have

$$95.705 \pm (2.160)(1.652)\left[1 + \frac{1}{15} + \frac{(35-20)^2}{616}\right]^{1/2}$$

which gives

$$91.4 \text{ to } 100$$

and, throwing caution to the winds, the reader may verify that for $X^* = 40$ the range is 103.5 to 112.8.

12-6 PROFITS FORECASTING EXAMPLE

Quite often an economic variable (such as company profits) is recorded against time as the X variable. In the example below the first observation is for 1977 which is set as $X = 1$, 1978 becomes $X = 2$ and so on. Suppose it is required to forecast profits in 1990 and 1991 and to establish 95 per cent confidence intervals for these predictions. With the Y variable as profits (in £millions) the data and workings are shown in Fig. 12-9. So

$$b = \frac{13(2087.3) - (91)(266.5)}{13(819) - 8281} = 1.219$$

whence

$$a = 20.5 - 1.219(7) = 11.967$$

Year	X	Y	X^2	XY	Y^2
1977	1	13.2	1	13.2	174.24
1978	2	14.2	4	28.4	201.64
1979	3	16.0	9	48.0	256.00
1980	4	17.1	16	68.4	292.41
1981	5	17.6	25	88.0	309.76
1982	6	18.9	36	113.4	357.21
1983	7	21.0	49	147.0	441.00
1984	8	21.6	64	172.8	466.56
1985	9	23.0	81	207.0	529.00
1986	10	24.0	100	240.0	576.00
1987	11	25.5	121	280.5	650.25
1988	12	26.6	144	319.2	707.56
1989	13	27.8	169	361.4	772.84
	$\Sigma X = 91$	$\Sigma Y = 266.5$	819	2087.3	5734.47
	$\therefore \ \bar{X} = 7$	$\bar{Y} = 20.5$			

Figure 12-9

So that the regression equation is

$$Y = 11.967 + 1.219X$$

Checking for goodness of fit, the correlation coefficient is

$$r = \frac{13(2087.3) - (91)(266.5)}{\sqrt{(13(819) - 8281)(13(5734.47) - 71\,022.25)}} = 0.998$$

which is excellent. So the point estimates will be

For 1990 $(X = 14)$: $Y^* = 11.967 + 1.219(14) = 29.033 \simeq 29.0$

For 1991 $(X = 15)$: $Y^* = 11.967 + 1.219(15) = 30.252 \simeq 30.3$

Now for the confidence intervals further work is required as shown in Fig. 12-10. From the data of Fig. 12-10 we see that

$$\hat{\sigma} = \sqrt{\frac{0.916\,502}{13 - 2}} = 0.289$$

With $n = 13$ there are 11 degrees of freedom so that the correct t value equals 2.201 and the confidence interval for the 1990 prediction $(X = 14)$ is

$$29.033 \pm (2.201)(0.289)\left[1 + \frac{1}{13} + \frac{(14 - 7)^2}{182} \right]^{1/2}$$

$X - \bar{X}$	$(X - \bar{X})^2$	Y^*	$Y - Y^*$	$(Y - Y^*)^2$
-6	36	13.186	0.014	0.000 196
-5	25	14.405	-0.205	0.042 025
-4	16	15.624	0.376	0.141 376
-3	9	16.843	0.257	0.066 049
-2	4	18.062	-0.462	0.213 444
-1	1	19.281	-0.381	0.145 161
0	0	20.500	0.500	0.250 000
1	1	21.719	-0.119	0.014 161
2	4	22.938	0.062	0.003 844
3	9	24.157	-0.157	0.024 649
4	16	25.376	0.124	0.015 376
5	25	26.595	0.005	0.000 025
6	36	27.814	-0.014	0.000 196
	182			0.916502

Figure 12-10

which results in

$$28.3 \text{ to } 29.8$$

and for 1991 the range is

$$30.252 \pm (2.201)(0.289)\left[1 + \frac{1}{13} + \frac{(15-7)^2}{182}\right]^{1/2}$$

which results in

$$29.5 \text{ to } 31.0$$

This latter range appears no wider than the 1990 range, but this is caused by rounding.

12-7 TIME SERIES ANALYSIS

A succession of observations of a variable or variables over time—a time series—can be decomposed into its constituent parts in a number of ways. Economic time series will always contain 'errors', there will almost always be a trend (but not necessarily linear), there is frequently seasonal or monthly variation, and there may be longer-term cyclical factors. One of the most frequently used devices to estimate linear trend is regression analysis, and this is the most useful way as far as forecasting purposes are concerned. There is another way of identifying trends in *time series* data along with other components of the time series. There are two types of model, the *additive* and the *multiplicative*. The original data (Y) may be decomposed into *trend* (T), *seasonal variation* (S), *cyclical variation* (C) and *residual variation* (R). The models are:

Additive	Multiplicative
$Y = T + S + C + R$	$Y = TSCR$

Each of the ingredients of the models T, S, C, R, are themselves series. Only in very long series is it worth trying to identify the cyclical ingredient and we shall consider only T, S, and R in the work to follow. There are various ways in which a trend series can be produced. One of the simplest is by *moving averages*, which we shall illustrate in the context of an additive model.

An n period moving average of a series of observations, $Y_1, Y_2, Y_3, Y_4, \ldots,$ is the series of arithmetic means:

$$\frac{Y_1 + Y_2 + Y_3 + \cdots + Y_n}{n}, \ \frac{Y_2 + Y_3 + Y_4 + \cdots + Y_{n+1}}{n}, \ \frac{Y_3 + Y_4 + Y_5 + \cdots + Y_{n+2}}{n}$$

		Y	Sum 4	Sum 2	Trend (T)	$Y-T$ $(=S+R)$	Deseasonalized
1987	Q_1	92					100.09
	Q_2	105					108.03
	Q_3	116	436	895	111.875	+4.125	110.21
	Q_4	123	459	940	117.5	+5.5	117.65
1988	Q_1	115	481	990	123.75	−8.75	123.09
	Q_2	127	509	1043	130.375	−3.375	130.03
	Q_3	144	534	1094	136.75	+7.25	138.21
	Q_4	148	560	1144	143	+5	142.65
1989	Q_1	141	584	1189	148.625	−7.625	149.09
	Q_2	151	605	1231	153.875	−2.875	154.03
	Q_3	165	626				159.21
	Q_4	169					163.65

Figure 12-11

Replacing the original series by the moving average series has the effect of eliminating irregularities and revealing the underlying trend in the data. The larger the value of n, the less significant is the role of an individual observation. This is a mixed blessing. The average with large n is less affected by extreme observations but is by the same token slower to reflect change and will 'lag behind' more. Frequently there is an obvious value of n to take. With quarterly data, $n=4$ is used; with monthly data, $n=12$. Consider a numerical example. Figure 12-11 gives quarterly sales data for a product.

A four-period moving average is indicated. First, a four-period moving *total* is shown in the column headed 'Sum 4'. Thus $436 = 92 + 105 + 116 + 123$. The next term $459 = 105 + 116 + 123 + 115$ and is most easily calculated as $436 - 92 + 115$. However, it will be noted that the Sum 4 term falls *between* quarters. The next column 'Sum 2' forms a *two*-period moving total of the Sum 4 elements. This has the effect of 'centering' the total so that 895 is located alongside Q_3 for 1987. There is no need to do this second summing when n is an odd number. The Sum 2 entries are now divided by 8 to give the moving average version of trend.

The model that we are employing here is $Y = T + S + R$ so that $Y - T = S + R$. Thus the $Y - T$ column contains seasonal and residual effects. If the residuals are well behaved they can be eliminated by averaging. The entries in the $Y - T$ column are grouped under quarters and averaged thus:

	Q_1	Q_2	Q_3	Q_4	
			+4.125	+5.5	
	−8.75	−3.375	+7.25	+5	
	−7.625	−2.875			
Average:	−8.19	−3.13	+5.69	+5.25	[$\Sigma = -0.38$]
Adjusted average	−8.09	−3.03	+5.79	+5.35	

The sum of the averages should ideally be zero. In fact it comes to -0.38. Each average is adjusted by adding 0.1 ($\simeq 0.38 \div 4$) to bring the total nearer to zero. These adjusted averages represent the *seasonal fluctuations* (S). If these are subtracted from the original data a *deseasonalized* series is produced. Official statistics are often given in this form. This is shown in the last column of workings.

If there is very little trend in the data, the moving average can be used to forecast one period ahead. The forecast for period $t+1$, $\hat{y}_{t+1}$ would then be

$$\hat{y}_{t+1} = \frac{1}{n}(y_t + y_{t-1} + y_{t-2} + \cdots + y_{t-n+1})$$

In our example—ignoring the presence of trend and seasonal factors—the moving average forecast for Q_1 of 1990 using the formula above would be $626/4 = 156.5$. The forecast can be improved by taking the seasonal fluctuations into account and/or making some 'freehand' allowance for trend. An illustration of this process is provided in the answer to question 12-5 on page 373. However, the use of moving average as a forecasting device is best limited to the most simple cases.

The moving average version of trend is not, however, the most convenient for forecasting purposes. Trend calculated by least squares regression is more useful. We shall now use this in an illustration of the multiplicative model $Y = TSR$. There would frequently be occasion to use constant *compound* growth in the multiplicative model, but here we shall stick to linear trend T given by $T = a + bX$ where a and b are the least squares regression coefficients calculated in the usual manner. Workings are shown in Fig. 12-12. For practice, an alternative version of the slope formula is employed. It is

		X	Y	X^2	XY	Trend(T)	$100\left(\dfrac{Y}{T}\right)$	Deseasonalized
1987	Q_1	1	92	1	92	97.63	94.23	97.84
	Q_2	2	105	4	210	104.06	100.90	106.46
	Q_3	3	116	9	348	110.49	104.99	111.31
	Q_4	4	123	16	492	116.92	105.20	119.28
1988	Q_1	5	115	25	575	123.35	93.23	122.30
	Q_2	6	127	36	762	129.78	97.86	128.76
	Q_3	7	144	49	1 008	136.21	105.72	138.18
	Q_4	8	148	64	1 184	142.64	103.76	143.52
1989	Q_1	9	141	81	1 269	149.07	94.59	149.95
	Q_2	10	151	100	1 510	155.50	97.11	153.10
	Q_3	11	165	121	1 815	161.93	101.90	158.33
	Q_4	12	169	144	2 028	168.36	100.38	163.89
		78	1596	650	11 293			

Figure 12-12

stated below. In this model the seasonal residual mix SR is given by the original series *divided* by the trend value. For convenience $100(Y \div T)$ is shown, the entries in this column are then grouped by quarter and averaged as before. The sum of the averages should be 400 and the adjustment mechanism is to multiply each unadjusted figure by 400/399.95. Relevant workings for Fig. 12-12 are:

$$\bar{X} = 6.5, \quad \bar{Y} = 133$$

$$b = \frac{n\Sigma XY - \Sigma X \Sigma Y}{n\Sigma X^2 - (\Sigma X)^2}$$

$$\therefore \ b = \frac{12(11\,293) - (78)(1596)}{12(650) - (6084)} = \frac{11\,028}{1716} = 6.43$$

$$\therefore \ a = 133 - 6.43(6.5) = 91.2$$

$$\therefore \ \text{Trend} = 91.2 + 6.43X$$

The workings for the quarters are:

	Q_1	Q_2	Q_3	Q_4	
	94.23	100.90	104.99	105.20	
	93.23	97.86	105.72	103.76	
	94.59	97.11	101.90	100.38	
Unadjusted:	94.02	98.62	104.20	103.11	$\Sigma = 399.95$
Adjusted:	94.03	98.63	104.21	103.12	

So the *seasonal factors* are 0.9403 for the first quarter, 0.9863 for the second, 1.0421 for the third, and 1.0312 for the fourth quarter. Deseasonalized data in this model are found by *dividing* the original data by the seasonal factors. Thus the first entry in the deseasonalized column, $97.84 = 92 \div 0.9403$. The second entry $106.46 = 105 \div 0.9863$, etc.

The reader should compare the trend and deseasonalized results produced by the two approaches. By and large the correspondence is good. In general it cannot be said that one method is *always* superior to the other. That model is better which most faithfully reflects the nature of the underlying economic mechanism generating the data, but this is sometimes unknown. However, if there is a significant trend in the data it is more likely that seasonal effects will be *proportional* to trend rather than additive—this suggests the multiplicative model.

Furthermore, as can be seen from the example, the moving average method 'loses' data—only eight trend values can be obtained. Finally, estimating trend by regression (rather than moving average) is more convenient for forecasting purposes.

To use the model for forecasting, the trend component is first determined and then multiplied by the appropriate seasonal factor. To illustrate, suppose forecasts are required for the four quarters of 1990. First determine the trend values for these times. For the first quarter (which would correspond to $X = 13$) we should have

$$1990 \ Q_1 \ \text{trend} = a + b(13)$$

$$= 91.2 + 6.43(13)$$

$$= 174.79$$

and for Q_2:

$$1990 \ Q_2 \ \text{trend} = 91.2 + 6.43(14)$$

$$= 181.22$$

Obviously, all that is being done is the addition of a further 6.43 each quarter. Thus the 1990 Q_3 trend = 187.65 and for the final quarter the trend value is 194.08. Each of these values must now be multiplied by the appropriate seasonal factor. The full results are:

		X	Trend	S factor	Forecast $(= TS)$
1990	Q_1	13	174.79	0.9403	164.36
	Q_2	14	181.22	0.9863	178.74
	Q_3	15	187.65	1.0421	195.55
	Q_4	16	194.08	1.0312	200.14

12-8 EXPONENTIAL SMOOTHING

Exponential smoothing methods are widely used for short-term forecasting. The technique was brought to the fore in the late nineteen-fifties. The method irons out irregularities in the data (hence *smoothing*) and can be expressed as a model in which coefficients of successive terms diminish exponentially— hence *exponential* smoothing.

The exponential smoothing model can be presented in a number of ways. One is to write

$$\hat{y}_{t+1} = \alpha y_t + (1 - \alpha)\hat{y}_t \tag{12-7}$$

in which t refers to the current period, $\hat{y}_{t+1}$ is the forecast for the next period, y_t is the *actual value* of the variable in the current period and $\hat{y}_t$ was the previous forecast (generated in the same way). α is the exponential *smoothing constant*,

$0 \leqslant \alpha \leqslant 1$. The value of α has to be decided upon by some means, but is typically in the range 0.05 to 0.3. A smaller value of α is indicated if it is known that the time series contains a good deal of random variability—it being undesirable to give undue emphasis to a current value and over-react to an individual deviation from forecast. In contrast, if it is known that the time series contains relatively little 'noise', a larger value of α would give more responsive adjustment of the forecast to genuine changes.

The relationship (12-7) can be spelt out to fully reveal the *recursive* character of the device. The forecast for period t would have been

$$\hat{y}_t = \alpha y_{t-1} + (1-\alpha)\hat{y}_{t-1} \tag{12-8}$$

Substituting for y_t from (12-8) into (12-7) gives

$$\hat{y}_{t+1} = \alpha y_t + \alpha(1-\alpha)y_{t-1} + (1-\alpha)^2 \hat{y}_{t-1} \tag{12-9}$$

but by the same process:

$$\hat{y}_{t-1} = \alpha y_{t-2} + (1-\alpha)\hat{y}_{t-2} \tag{12-10}$$

and repeated substitution produces the result:

$$\hat{y}_{t+1} = \alpha y_t + \alpha(1-\alpha)y_{t-1} + \alpha(1-\alpha)^2 y_{t-2} + \cdots + \alpha(1-\alpha)^n y_{t-y(t-n)} + \cdots \tag{12-11}$$

which reveals the *autoregressive* scheme in which it is seen that the forecast value for the next period is a *weighted* average of current and past values of the variable. Since $(1-\alpha) < 1$ the weights decline exponentially. The meaning of this is that the older the observation *the less emphasis it receives in framing the forecast*. This should be contrasted with the moving average case in which *equal* weight is given to all observations included in the average. Note that the weights in Eq. (12-11) form a geometric progression with first term α and constant difference $(1-\alpha)$. The sum to infinity (S_∞) of the weights is therefore:

$$S_\infty = \frac{\alpha}{1-(1-\alpha)} = 1$$

as must be the case with a true average.

By way of illustrating the declining influence of data of increasing age, if $\alpha = 0.2$ the first six coefficients $(\alpha, \alpha(1-\alpha)$, etc.) in Eq. (12-11) would be:

$$0.2, \ 0.16, \ 0.128, \ 0.1024, \ 0.08192, \ 0.065536$$

The bigger the value of α the less important are the older data. For instance with $\alpha = 0.4$ the first six coefficients are:

$$0.4, \ 0.24, \ 0.144, \ 0.0864, \ 0.05184, \ 0.031104$$

in which it is seen that (in comparison with $\alpha = 0.2$) more weight is given to the first three terms and less to all subsequent ones, with the sixth term being halved in importance. In the extremes, if $\alpha = 1$ only the current value of the variable is of any importance—the forecast for the next period being this period's value. At the other extreme as α approaches zero the past periods have almost equal weights. As $\alpha \to 0$ the forecast tends towards the arithmetic mean of a large number of periods, i.e., it approaches a very long period moving average value.

For actual usage of exponential smoothing it is convenient to rearrange the terms in Eq. (12-7) as:

$$\hat{y}_{t+1} = \hat{y}_t + \alpha(y_t - \hat{y}_t) \tag{12-12}$$

which reads: 'The new forecast is equal to the old forecast plus a proportion, α, of the difference between the current value and the old forecast of that value'. The term $y_t - \hat{y}_t$ is called the *current forecasting error*. Consider an example. A series of fifteen monthly observations of a variable are shown in the first column of Fig. 12-13.

The first observation is 148 and the forecast of this figure (boxed) was 146. This is a given datum. We can now proceed to forecast the second entry in the 'actual observation' column. The forecasting error is $+2$ and so, using $\alpha = 0.3$,

Actual observation (y)	Forecast $(\hat{y})$	Forecasting error $(y - \hat{y})$	$\alpha = 0.3$ correction	Next forecast
148	146	+2.00	+0.60	146.60
147	146.60	+0.40	+0.12	146.72
149	146.72	+2.28	+0.68	147.40
146	147.40	−1.40	−0.42	146.98
144	146.98	−2.98	−0.89	146.09
145	146.09	−1.09	−0.33	145.76
145	145.76	−0.76	−0.23	145.53
147	145.53	+1.47	+0.44	145.97
146	145.97	+0.03	+0.01	145.98
143	145.98	−2.98	−0.89	145.09
145	145.09	−0.09	−0.03	145.06
146	145.06	+0.94	+0.28	145.34
147	145.34	+1.66	+0.50	145.84
148	145.84	+2.16	+0.65	146.49
146	146.49	−0.49	−0.15	146.34

Figure 12-13

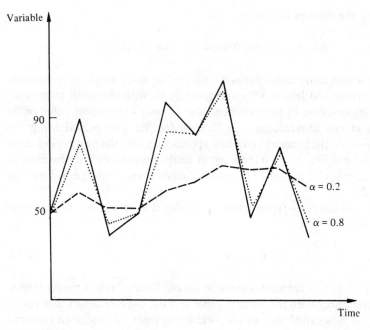

Figure 12-14

the correction is $+0.6$ giving a forecast of 146.6. This becomes the next entry in the Forecast column and corresponds to an actual observation of 147 and so on. The list of next forecasts is the exponentially smoothed series. As a numerical exercise, the reader should try $\alpha = 0.1$ and $\alpha = 0.5$ and compare the results with Fig. 12-13. For a diagrammatic illustration of the effect of different sized smoothing constants, consider Fig. 12-14. The solid line represents the original series, the broken line represents the smoothed series with $\alpha = 0.2$ and the dotted line represents the 'smoothed' series with $\alpha = 0.8$ (a value well beyond anything that would be used in practice or justified by the model). The figure illustrates the substantial difference between the low and the (very) high values of α. As further practice, the reader should reproduce these results. The series used was 50, 90, 35, 45, 95, 80, 105, 45, 80, 30, with an initial forecast of 50.

In any forecasting situation, it is important to audit the forecast results. There are two respects in which the situation can change. The first is that while demand remains trendless the degree of variability of the data may increase, i.e., the variable may become more volatile. This volatility can be measured by standard deviation or *mean absolute deviation* (MAD) of the forecasting errors. In *adaptive forecasting* the sensitivity of the forecast adjusts to reflect changes in data volatility. In the present model this would correspond to changes in the value of α. The world 'adaptive' is here used to refer to in-built responsiveness in the forecasting technique itself—the *automatic* revaluing of parameters as conditions are perceived to change. The continual adjustment of parameters to reduce forecast errors is called *adaptive filtering*.

Then there may be a change in the level of demand. For instance there may be a sudden and unforeseen 'ramp' in demand. This situation can be detected (in a probabilistic sense) by a *tracking signal* (a good discussion of which is found in Littlechild (1977) Chapter 10). Exponential smoothing yields unbiased forecasts of 'stationary' series but (as with all moving averages) lags behind (i.e., becomes biased) after structural changes take place. The method can be extended to cope with the presence of trend (e.g., *Holt's* method). A famous generalization was provided by Box and Jenkins in 1962; the *Box–Jenkins* approach now being widely used.

12-9 CONCLUSIONS

A sufficient justification for the use of forecasting methods is that better results are obtained *with* statistical forecasting techniques than without them. There is a further and even more compelling reason to forecast—it is unavoidable. As Smallbone (1968) put it:

> nearly every decision rests upon some kind of forecast. The choice is not between making or not making an extrapolation into the future; it is between making the projection in overt and sometimes quantitative terms and proceeding by feel and faith. Even inaction implies some picture of the future (Kuznets)

With the range of techniques available and the software packages on offer the selection of technique to use in a particular situation can be difficult, but the firm is unlikely to be in an entirely unique situation and industrial experience can greatly narrow the range. One factor that should be borne in mind is the degree of detail that is required. Wheelwright and Makridakis (1985) cite the illustration that: 'The corporate planning department would see little value in having a forecast by individual items in the company's product line; similarly, the production foreman would find little value in having a general sales estimate of total corporate sales when he is trying to schedule his weekly production.' There is also the problem that the introduction of new methods and changes in decision-making procedures in an organization will usually meet with resistance. As a rule it is best to introduce first those forecasting methods that are most closely related to existing procedures.

We have presented here the simple t versions of a few procedures. Techniques in actual usage can be more complicated. In the case of regression, for instance, the effects of several factors can be taken into account simultaneously in multiple linear regression by fitting an equation of the form:

$$Y = a_0 + a_1 X_1 + a_2 X_2 + \cdots + a_n X_n \qquad (12\text{-}13)$$

An example of the use of this form would be with four of the X's in (12-13) as *seasonal dummies.* In other words, seasonal analysis can be conducted by regression methods alone if multiple regression is employed.

Less commonly, non-linear regression may be used. Sometimes, however, non-linear relationships can be estimated by use of linear regression methods. If the true relationship is of the form

$$Y = aX^b \qquad (12\text{-}14)$$

(as, for instance, in the case of growth at a compound rate) then by taking logarithms we can fit:

$$\text{Log } Y = \log a + b \log X \qquad (12\text{-}15)$$

so that the parameters of the non-linear relationship (12-14) *a* and *b* are estimated from (12-15) which is linear in the logarithms.

There is also the question of data, its collection and quality. While the normal accounting processes will produce a good deal of data, and sales records will normally be kept, the collection of much new data can be time-consuming and costly and the importance of the decision and its likely repetition need to be borne in mind. Computer people have a famous acronym—GIGO—'garbage in, garbage out'. The quality of forecasts is dependent upon the quality of data as well as the forecasting techniques.

There are numerous software packages available for forecasting with multivariate regression. Some calculators have simple linear regression programmes. At the other extreme of complexity, large scale econometric models may involve hundreds of simultaneous equations and variables. These models are used in forecasting economic aggregates and of course require mainframe computing capability. At the commercial level, computerized inventory management systems will operate with associated forecasting packages using exponential smoothing.

Forecasting methods are highly valuable OR tools and while absolute precision is rare there are many companies that are able regularly to forecast their sales to within 2 per cent of the actual values. With this standard in mind, Morrell's (1972) statement of the objective of forecasting as being 'to minimize uncertainty and identify and evaluate risk' is clearly achievable.

EXERCISES

12-1 Revision exercise
  (i) In what areas of management activity are forecasts needed? Give examples of the kind of information that is likely to be required in each area.
  (ii) What are the three main classes of forecasting methods?
  (iii) Explain what is meant by *very short-term, short-term, medium-term* and *long-term.* What quantitative forecasting techniques are likely to be most useful in each case?
  (iv) Briefly explain what is meant by material requirements planning.

(v) On what grounds can the use of forecasting methods be justified?

(vi) Explain what is meant by simple linear regression and its usefulness in forecasting.

(vii) Explain the meaning of positive, negative and zero values for the coefficient of linear correlation. Does a value of $r \simeq 0$ mean that no relationship exists between the variables?

(viii) Distinguish between interpolation and extrapolation and between point estimates and bracketed predictions.

(ix) What are the four principal systematic components of economic time series?

(x) What is the method of moving averages? How is a deseasonalized series produced?

(xi) How may trend in series best be estimated for forecasting purposes?

(xii) Explain what is meant by exponential smoothing. Under what circumstances does exponential smoothing become similar to a very long period moving average?

(xiii) Briefly explain what is meant by multiple linear regression. How can seasonal effects be estimated in such a model?

(xiv) Give an example of a non-linear relationship that can be estimated by the use of linear regression methods.

12-2 Given the following time series data:

X	Y
106	155
90	110
92	130
100	145
112	160

(i) Find the least squares regression equation of Y upon X.

(ii) Use the equation to predict the value of Y for $X = 120$.

(iii) Find the value of the coefficient of linear correlation. What does this value measure?

(iv) Find the value of the coefficient of determination. What does this value measure?

12-3 The data below show road accident and traffic figures for a period of twelve months.

Month	Traffic index	Casualties (thousands)
Nov.	129	33
Dec.	126	33
Jan.	124	29
Feb.	121	25
Mar.	138	31
Apr.	153	32
May	160	34
June	169	35
July	179	36
Aug.	185	36
Sept.	161	34
Oct.	155	34

(i) Find the least squares regression line and the coefficients of correlation and determination.

(ii) Find 95 per cent confidence intervals for casualties for the following values of the traffic index: 150, 190, 220.

12-4 For the data of question 12-2 find the 95 per cent confidence interval for the prediction of Y when $X = 120$. (For three degrees of freedom the appropriate value of the t statistic is 3.182.)

12-5 Given the following quarterly time series data:

		Y
1987	Q_1	269
	Q_2	280
	Q_3	256
	Q_4	241
1988	Q_1	277
	Q_2	280
	Q_3	258
	Q_4	247
1989	Q_1	281
	Q_2	284
	Q_3	260
	Q_4	253

(i) Produce a deseasonalized series using the additive model with moving averages.

(ii) Produce a forecast for the first quarter of 1990 based solely upon the four-period moving average (ignoring any trend and seasonal effects).

(iii) Devise a means of making some allowance for trend and seasonal effects and produce another forecast value. (*Hint:* First look at the way the Trend (T) data have been changing and try to extend this series.)

12-6 For the following quarterly time series data:

		Y
1988	Q_1	82
	Q_2	79
	Q_3	90
	Q_4	96
1989	Q_1	87
	Q_2	103
	Q_3	110
	Q_4	117
1990	Q_1	116
	Q_2	120

(i) Produce a deseasonalized series using a regression estimated trend in a multiplicative model.

(ii) Produce forecasts for the third and fourth quarters of 1990 and the first two quarters of 1991.

12-7 For the following monthly production data produce an exponentially smoothed series using a value of 0.4 for the smoothing constant. Also, give a forecast for June of 1990. The forecast value for June 1989 was 300.

Year	Month	Actual production
1989	June	304
	July	302
	Aug.	306
	Sept.	300
	Oct.	296
	Nov.	298
	Dec.	298
1990	Jan.	302
	Feb.	300
	Mar.	296
	Apr.	298
	May	300

12-8 The following data were collected from the Industrial Products Manufacturing Company Limited.

Month	Total overhead (y)	Direct labour hours (DLH) (x)	Plant hours (PH)
Jan.	15 000	736	184
Feb.	14 500	800	160
Mar.	15 750	1 008	168
Apr.	15 250	880	176
May	16 250	1 056	176
June	15 000	840	168
	$\Sigma y = 91\,750$	$\Sigma x = 5\,320$	
	$\bar{y} = 15\,291.7$	$\bar{x} = 886.7$	

(a) compute a least squares equation based on direct labour hours;
(b) compute the coefficient of determination (r^2) for (a);
(c) compare and discuss the relationship of your solution in (a) to the equation of:

$$\text{Total overhead} = 5758 + 4.7\,\text{DLH} + 31\,\text{PH}$$

(where DLH = direct labour hours, PH = plant hours), obtained by a regression using DLH and PH as variables and coefficient of determination $R^2 = 0.9873$;
(d) estimate the total overhead for a month with 1000 DLH and 168 PH, using the equation in (c).

(The Chartered Institute of Management Accountants)

12-9 The results of the Mercia division of Offa Ltd over the last five years are summarized as follows:

Year	1	2	3	4	5
			£'000		
Sales	70	93	119	118	152
Costs: Materials	20	28	42	37	48
Labour	27	36	39	48	54
Overheads	24	24	28	33	32
	71	88	109	118	134
Net profit	(1)	5	10	0	18
Sales units	2100	2800	3400	3100	4000

The Mercia Division manufactures a single product. Stocks have been negligible at all relevant times. Price changes have been rare in Offa's business. During the last five years, the only changes in the prices of resources used have been an increase in the price of materials of 25 per cent three years ago (at the end of year 2), and an increase in wage rates of $33\frac{1}{3}$ per cent two years ago (at the end of year 3); overhead costs have not been affected by price changes. Plans for the coming year (year 6) are now being prepared. No further increases in the prices of resources are expected. The sales manager has provided the following estimates of the sales price–volume relationship for the coming year:

Volume	Price
4500	£37
4000	£40
3400	£42

(a) estimate the optimal selling price from amongst the three possible prices £37, £40, or £42 using linear regression analysis to estimate the cost–volume relationship; and

(b) discuss the advantages and limitations of linear regression analysis for the estimation of cost–volume relationships.

(Institute of Chartered Accountants in England and Wales)

Solution guides

12-2 (i) The workings are:

X	Y	$X-\bar{X}$	$Y-\bar{Y}$	$(X-\bar{X})(Y-\bar{Y})$	$(X-\bar{X})^2$	$(Y-\bar{Y})^2$
106	155	+6	+15	+90	36	225
90	110	−10	−30	+300	100	900
92	130	−8	−10	+80	64	100
100	145	0	+5	0	0	25
112	160	+12	+20	+240	144	400
500	700			+710	344	1650

$$\bar{X}=\frac{\Sigma X}{n}=\frac{500}{5}=100; \quad \bar{Y}=\frac{\Sigma Y}{n}=\frac{700}{5}=140$$

The required equation is $Y=a+bX$

$$b=\frac{(X-\bar{X})(Y-\bar{Y})}{(X-\bar{X})^2}=\frac{710}{344}=2.064$$

$$a=\bar{Y}-b\bar{X}=140-2.064(100)=-66.4$$

∴ equation is $\qquad Y=-66.4+2.064X$

(ii) For $X=120$ the prediction for Y is 181.28.

(iii) $r=\dfrac{(X-\bar{X})(Y-\bar{Y})}{\sqrt{(X-\bar{X})^2(Y-\bar{Y})^2}}=\dfrac{710}{\sqrt{(344)(1650)}}=0.9424$

This value measures the degree of *linear* relationship between the variables. It is a measure of the goodness of fit of the regression line.

(iv) The coefficient of determination is the square of the correlation coefficient. This value gives the proportion of variation in Y that is accounted for by variation in X. In the present case $r^2=0.8881$.

12-3 (i) The workings are:

X	Y	$X-\bar{X}$	$Y-\bar{Y}$	$(X-\bar{X})(Y-\bar{Y})$	$(X-\bar{X})^2$	$(Y-\bar{Y})^2$
129	33	−21	0.33	−6.93	441	0.11
126	33	−24	0.33	−7.92	576	0.11
124	29	−26	−3.67	95.42	676	13.47
121	25	−29	−7.67	222.43	841	58.83
138	31	−12	−1.67	20.04	144	2.79
153	32	3	−0.67	−2.01	9	0.45
160	34	10	1.33	13.30	100	1.77
169	35	19	2.33	44.27	361	5.43
179	36	29	3.33	96.57	841	11.09
185	36	35	3.33	116.55	1225	11.09
161	34	11	1.33	14.63	121	1.77
155	34	5	1.33	6.65	25	1.77
1800	392			613	5360	108.68

$$\bar{X}=\frac{\Sigma X}{n}=\frac{1800}{12}=150; \quad \bar{Y}=\frac{\Sigma Y}{n}=\frac{392}{12}=32.67$$

In $Y=a+bX$, $b=\dfrac{613}{5360}=0.114$

$$a=32.67-0.114(150)=15.57$$

∴ regression equation is

$$Y=15.57+0.114X$$

The correlation coefficient is $r = \dfrac{613}{\sqrt{(5360)(108.68)}} = 0.803$

$$\therefore \ r^2 = 0.645$$

(ii) First we need to find the sample based estimate of the variance of the error term, $\hat{\sigma}^2$. With Y^* representing the regression equation values of Y for the sample X values we have

$$\hat{\sigma}^2 = \frac{\Sigma(Y_i - Y^*)^2}{n-2}$$

where $n-2$ is the number of degrees of freedom, i.e., 10. The workings for $\hat{\sigma}$ are

X	Y	Y*	Y − Y*	(Y − Y*)²
129	33	30.28	2.72	7.40
126	33	29.93	3.07	9.42
124	29	29.71	−0.71	0.50
121	25	29.36	−4.36	19.01
138	31	31.30	−0.30	0.09
153	32	33.01	−1.01	1.02
160	34	33.81	0.19	0.04
169	35	34.84	0.16	0.03
179	36	35.98	0.02	0.00
185	36	36.66	−0.66	0.44
161	34	33.92	0.08	0.01
155	34	33.24	0.76	0.58
				38.54

So that $\hat{\sigma} = \sqrt{\dfrac{38.54}{12-2}} = 1.963$

Now with 10 degrees of freedom, Fig. 12-6 gives the relevant t value of 2.228. So using formula (6) we obtain

$$\text{for } X^* = 150, \ Y^* = 32.67; \ \text{range} = 32.67 \pm 2.228(1.963)\sqrt{1 + \frac{1}{12}}$$

(since in this case $X^* = \bar{X}$).

Thus the 95 per cent confidence interval is

$$32.67 \pm 4.55$$

For $X^* = 190, \ Y^* = 37.23$;

$$\text{range} = 37.23 \pm 2.228(1.963)\sqrt{1 + \frac{1}{12} + \frac{(190-150)^2}{5360}}$$

$$\therefore \ \text{range} = 37.23 \pm 5.14$$

For $X^* = 220$, $Y^* = 40.65$;

$$\text{range} = 40.65 \pm 2.228(1.963)\sqrt{1 + \frac{1}{12} + \frac{(220 - 150)^2}{5360}}$$

$$\therefore \text{ range} = 40.65 \pm 6.18$$

12-4 The workings for $\hat{\sigma}$ are:

X	Y	Y^*	$Y - Y^*$	$(Y - Y^*)^2$
106	155	152.38	2.62	6.86
90	110	119.36	−9.36	87.61
92	130	123.49	6.51	42.38
100	145	140.00	5.00	25.00
112	160	164.77	−4.77	22.75
				184.60

So that $\hat{\sigma} = \sqrt{\dfrac{184.6}{3}} = 7.84$

The 95 per cent confidence interval will then be

$$181.28 \pm 3.182(7.84)\sqrt{1 + \frac{1}{5} + \frac{(120 - 100)^2}{344}} = 181.28 \pm 38.35$$

(Note: the width of the interval is very large. This is partly due to the very small number of observations which fact results in a high t value. For instance, if there had been 60 observations with prediction errors on the same scale as above, the $\hat{\sigma}$ value would have come down to about 6.2 and the t value would be about 2. The square root term would also be reduced (examine its components to see why) resulting in a range of about 181.28 ± 13.09 which is only one-third as wide.)

12-5 (i) The de-seasonalized data are shown in the last column of workings below. Trend data are sum 2 data divided by eight. The de-seasonalized data are the original Y values minus the quarterly averages.

Quarter	Y	Sum 4	Sum 2	Trend (T)	$Y - T$	De-seasonalized
1987 Q_1	269					255.75
Q_2	280	1046				264.75
Q_3	256	1054	2100	262.50	−6.50	263.25
Q_4	241	1054	2108	263.50	−22.50	262.25
1988 Q_1	277	1056	2110	263.75	+13.25	263.75
Q_2	280	1062	2118	264.75	+15.25	264.75
Q_3	258	1066	2128	266.00	−8.00	265.25
Q_4	247	1070	2136	267.00	−20.00	268.25
1989 Q_1	281	1072	2142	267.75	+13.25	267.75
Q_2	284	1078	2150	268.75	+15.25	268.75
Q_3	260					267.25
Q_4	253					274.25

The averaging for the quarters is as follows:

	Q_1	Q_2	Q_3	Q_4	
	+13.25	+15.25	−6.50	−22.50	
	+13.25	+15.25	−8.00	−20.00	
Average	+13.25	+15.25	−7.25	−21.25	[Σ=0]

for which no adjustments are necessary.

(ii) The crudest moving average-based forecast for the first quarter of 1990 would be simply $1078 \div 4 = 269.5$. A somewhat more subtle approach would be to make some 'allowance' for trend and seasonal variation. Using the Trend column (T) the sum of the first four entries is 1054.5 which divided by four gives 263.625. This is the average value of 'trend' in the first half of the trend data. In the second half the average value is 267.375. The difference between these two figures is 3.75. Over a one-year period the average value of trend has risen by 3.75. This is itself an average rate of 0.9375 per quarter. We are going to estimate the 1990 Q_1 figure by first estimating what the trend figure would be corresponding to that year and then adding the seasonal factor. Thus if we suppose the trend figure to increase on average by 0.9375 per quarter, the trend figure opposite 1990 Q_1 will be $268.75 + 3(0.9375) = 271.5625$. Adding the seasonal factor for this quarter of 13.25 gives the estimate of $284.8125 \simeq 285$. Thus our estimate would be 285. This is a plausible result if the data is examined carefully.

12-6 (i)

Quarter	X	Y	X^2	XY	$(\hat{Y})$	$100\left(\dfrac{Y}{T}\right)$	De-seasonalized
1988 Q_1	1	82	1	82	78.36	104.65	84.39
Q_2	2	79	4	158	83.17	94.99	80.99
Q_3	3	90	9	270	87.98	102.30	88.32
Q_4	4	96	16	384	92.79	103.46	92.85
1989 Q_1	5	87	25	435	97.60	89.14	89.53
Q_2	6	103	36	618	102.41	100.58	105.60
Q_3	7	110	49	770	107.22	102.59	107.95
Q_4	8	117	64	936	112.03	104.44	113.16
1990 Q_1	9	116	81	1044	116.84	99.28	119.38
Q_2	10	120	100	1200	121.65	98.64	123.03
	55	1000	385	5897			

$$\bar{X} = 5.5; \quad \bar{Y} = 100$$

$$b = \frac{n\Sigma XY - \Sigma X\Sigma Y}{n\Sigma X^2 - (\Sigma X)^2} = \frac{58\,970 - 55\,000}{3850 - 3025} = \frac{3970}{825} = 4.81$$

So that

$$a = 100 - (4.81)5.5 = 73.55.$$

The regression equation is then

$$Y = 73.55 + 4.81X$$

For the quarterly averaging:

	Q_1	Q_2	Q_3	Q_4	
	104.65	94.99	102.30	103.46	
	89.14	100.58	102.59	104.44	
	99.28	98.64			
Unadjusted	97.69	98.07	102.45	103.95	$\Sigma = 402.16$
Adjusted	97.17	97.54	101.90	103.39	

(ii) The forecast is the trend value (using the regression equation with the higher X values) multiplied by the seasonal index. The final column gives the rounded values.

	X	Trend	Seasonal factor	Forecast	Rounded
1990 Q_3	11	126.46	0.9717	122.88	123
Q_4	12	131.27	0.9754	128.04	128
1991 Q_1	13	136.08	1.0190	138.67	139
Q_2	14	140.89	1.0339	145.67	146

12-7 The 'next forecast' column in the table below is the exponentially smoothed series. The last entry, 298.94 (rounded in the forecast column) is the forecast of June of 1990.

Month	Actual production	Forecast	Forecasting error	$X = 0.4$ correction	Next forecast
June	304	300	+4.00	+1.60	301.60
July	302	301.60	+0.40	+0.16	301.76
Aug.	306	301.76	+4.24	+1.70	303.46
Sept.	300	303.46	−3.46	−1.38	302.08
Oct.	296	302.08	−6.08	−2.43	299.65
Nov.	298	299.65	−1.65	−0.66	298.99
Dec.	298	298.99	−0.99	−0.40	298.59
Jan.	302	298.59	+3.41	+1.36	299.95
Feb.	300	299.95	+0.05	+0.02	299.97
Mar.	296	299.97	−3.97	−1.59	298.38
Apr.	298	298.38	−0.38	−0.15	298.23
May	300	298.23	+1.77	+0.71	298.94
June	299				

12-8 (a) We are required to estimate the regression equation of total overhead (y) against direct labour hours (x). The formula for slope

$$b = \frac{n\Sigma XY - \Sigma X\Sigma Y}{n\Sigma X^2 - (\Sigma X)^2}$$

will be used. Total overhead data will be expressed in units of one thousand. The workings are:

Month	Total overhead Y	DLH X	XY	X^2	Y^2
Jan.	15.00	736	11 040	541 696	225.0
Feb.	14.50	800	11 600	640 000	210.25
Mar.	15.75	1 008	15 876	1 016 064	248.0625
Apr.	15.25	880	13 420	774 400	232.5625
May	16.25	1 056	17 160	1 115 136	264.0625
June	15.00	840	12 600	705 600	225.0
	91.75	5 320	81 696	4 792 896	1404.9375

$$\bar{Y} = 15.2917; \quad \bar{X} = 886.7$$

$$b = \frac{6 \times 81\,696 - 91.75 \times 5320}{6 \times 4\,792\,896 - (5320)^2}$$

$$= \frac{2066}{454\,976} = 0.00454$$

Intercept $a = \bar{Y} - b\bar{X}$

$$= 15.2917 - 0.004\,54 \times 886.7$$

$$= 11.266$$

So: $\quad y = 11.266 + 0.004\,54X$

Since total overhead is measured in thousands of pounds the relationship is

$$\text{Total overhead} = 11\,266 + 4.54 \times \text{DLH}$$

(b) The coefficient of determination, r^2, can be expressed as

$$r^2 = \frac{(N\Sigma XY - \Sigma X\Sigma Y)^2}{[n\Sigma X^2 - (\Sigma X)^2][n\Sigma Y^2 - (\Sigma Y)^2]}$$

$$= \frac{(2066)^2}{454\,976 \times [6 \times 1404.9375 - (91.75)^2]}$$

$$= 0.8114$$

(c) In the multiple regression equation, the appearance of plant hours has more than halved the intercept term while the DLH coefficient is hardly changed. The inclusion of PH has explained much that was originally lumped into the intercept term. The fact that the DLH regression coefficient is virtually unchanged suggests that PH and DLH are unrelated. As an exercise the reader may verify that the correlation between PH and DLH is only -0.08. The coefficient of determination gives the proportion of the variation in the dependent variable (overhead) that is explained by changes in the independent variable(s). With DLH alone in the equation, 81.14 per cent of the variation in overhead was accounted for. With both DLH and PH in, the proportion of explained variation rises to 98.73 per cent.

The question might arise as to which of DLH and PH has the more important effect on overhead. The size of regression coefficients is nothing to go by as these can be scaled up or down depending on the units of measure of the independent variables. The high explained variation with DLH alone in the regression equation (81 per cent) might lead us to expect that this is the more important influence. This can be confirmed using *beta weights*. The beta (β) weight for DLH is the ratio of the standard deviations of DLH and overhead multiplied by the DLH regression coefficient. Thus:

$$\beta(\text{DLH}) = \frac{123.5}{620.82} \times 4.7 = 0.932$$

while for PH:

$$\beta(\text{PH}) = \frac{8.39}{620.82} \times 31 = 0.419$$

where 8.39 is the standard deviation of plant hours. So DLH are seen to be the more important factor.

(d) Inserting the values given into the equation:

$$\text{Total overhead} = 5758 + 4.7(1000) + 31(168) = 15\,666$$

12-9 (a) For a cost–volume relationship to be useful, the costs involved should be directly comparable. Substantial changes in prices of resources can make a nonsense of the relationship which is intended—as the name implies—to relate cost to output level alone. In this example, it is most convenient to work in year (5) prices (as whole numbers result). To deal with the materials price change we inflate the materials cost figures in year (1) and (2) by 25 per cent. Similarly the labour costs in the first three years are increased by $33\frac{1}{3}$ per cent to bring them into year (5) terms. So, in terms of year (5) values (in units of £1000) we have:

	Year:	1	2	3	4	5
Costs:	Materials	25	35	42	37	48
	Labour	36	48	52	48	54
	Overheads	24	24	28	33	32
Total		85	107	122	118	134

With the revised data, the regression workings are shown below. Sales data are in units of one hundred.

Year	Sales X	Total cost Y	$(X - \bar{X})$	$(Y - \bar{Y})$	$(X - \bar{X})^2$	$(X - \bar{X})(Y - \bar{Y})$
1	21	85	−9.8	−28.2	96.04	276.36
2	28	107	−2.8	−6.2	7.84	17.36
3	34	122	3.2	8.8	10.24	28.16
4	31	118	0.2	4.8	0.04	0.96
5	40	134	9.2	20.8	84.64	191.36
Totals	154	566			198.80	514.20

$$\bar{X} = \frac{\Sigma X}{n} = \frac{154}{5} = 30.8 \quad \text{and} \quad \bar{Y} = \frac{\Sigma Y}{n} = \frac{566}{5} = 113.2$$

$$b = \frac{\Sigma(X - \bar{X})(Y - \bar{Y})}{\Sigma(X - \bar{X})^2} = \frac{514.20}{198.80} = 2.5865$$

$$a = \bar{Y} - b\bar{X} = 113.2 - 2.5865(30.8) = 33.535$$

So the full regression equation is:

$$Y = 33.535 - 2.587X$$

The interpretation of this equation is that total fixed cost is £33 535 and unit variable cost is £25.87. Now, using the regression equation to forecast costs for the possible volumes, and where revenue is price times volume, the greatest excess of revenue over costs is seen to result from a price of £40.

Volume	Cost (C)	Price	Revenue (R)	$R - C$
4500	149 950	37	166 500	16 550
4000	137 015	40	160 000	22 985
3400	121 493	42	142 800	21 307

(b) The main advantage of linear regression analysis is that in comparison to other methods of fitting straight lines it produces the *best, linear, unbiased* estimates. There are plenty of software packages if these are needed and many calculators have regression programmes for the smaller scale work. Regression is a well-worked-through method and properties and dangers are well understood. There are a number of limitations (some of which apply to other methods too). Usually, rather more than five observations would be desirable (as we saw in Q12-4) so that we may be dealing with a long period of time over which many important factors (specifically the firm's technology) may have changed. The line may be a poor fit, and predictions based on poorly fitting lines can be very misleading. The fit may be good only close to the range of outputs sampled. The relationship between cost and output may not be linear: there may be economies (or diseconomies beyond a certain point) of scale.

REFERENCES

Littlechild, S. C. (1977), *Operational Research for Managers*, Philip Allan.
Morrell, J. (1972), *Management Decisions and the Role of Forecasting*, Penguin.
Smallbone, D. W. (1968), *An Introduction to Marketing*, Granada Publishing.
Wheelwright, S. C., and Makridakis, S. (1985), *Forecasting Methods for Management*, fourth edition, Wiley.

FURTHER READING

Bennett, D., Lewis, C., and Oakley, M. (1988), *Operations Management*, Philip Allan. Contains further material on short-term forecasting methods and material requirements planning.
Cohen, S. S. (1985), *Operational Research*, Edward Arnold. Includes wide discussion of exponential smoothing and moving averages.
Lewis, C. D. (1982), *Industrial and Business Forecasting Methods*, Butterworth. A comprehensive review of business forecasting.
Makridakis, S., and Wheelwright, S. C. (1987), *The Handbook of Forecasting*, Wiley. A comprehensive guide to the full range of forecasting methods.

THIRTEEN

SIMULATION

13-1 INTRODUCTION

Some operational research problems may depend on random variables and complex interactions in such a way that analytical results are unobtainable. For example, most traffic flow problems fall into this category. Practical considerations and cost may rule out real world experimentation. In such cases, *simulation* is likely to be the technique of choice. In simulation (also known as *Monte-Carlo methods* or *simulated .sampling*) data drawn from appropriate probability distributions are fed into a computer-based mathematical model of the system under study. From the resulting output of the model, the relevant system parameters are estimated. In a queueing application, estimates of expected queue length or system process time would result. In a capital budgeting application, the empirical distribution of NPV would be generated from which mean and variance of NPV may be calculated and risk profiles drawn up.

In this chapter we shall illustrate the principles involved in simulation and something of the range of problems to which it can be addressed via hand-worked examples—although a computer program is presented in section 13-3. In general, Monte-Carlo simulation is indicated whenever the uncertainties arise in such a way as to make possible their characterization by probability distributions. Computers are ideally suited to Monte-Carlo simulation exercises as repeated calculation of the same model is required.

Once the performance of the original system has been measured, changes can be considered. Structural changes in the model can be made and the values of parameters re-set. The modified model is then run and the effects of the changes on the system parameters is seen. Substantial improvements in the performance of the system can be effected in this way. It may take a number of runs to identify those parameters that most influence system performance and even the construction of the model itself can reveal unnoticed aspects of the system. The number of independently variable factors in the model should not be large as the task of finding near-optimal values increases exponentially.

Simulation is a widely used technique both inside and outside OR. It is likely to prove valuable in any complex logistical exercise and where new and unusual situations have to be confronted. It is also valuable in studying dynamic processes over shortened time-scales. As with any OR technique, simulation should not be relied on exclusively when other approaches may have a significant contribution to make.

We shall illustrate the principles involved in simulation with a number of examples drawn from a range of areas of operational research. Naturally, the examples will be much less complicated than practical problems but should show something of the range of the methodology and its value.

13-2 EXPECTED VALUE OF PROFITS

Here we shall show how simulation methods can assist in finding the expected value of profits from trading by a small business or sole trader. The variability of profit will be estimated too, and the profit consequences of structural changes evaluated. Suppose that the situation is as follows. A trader receives supplies of a product from a wholesaler each working day. The quantity supplied by the wholesaler is a random variable as is the subsequent (same day) retail demand for the commodity. The probability distribution for the amount supplied to the trader by the wholesaler is known from previous experience to be as follows:

Supply from wholesaler (units)	Probability
1	0.08
2	0.17
3	0.20
4	0.25
5	0.17
6	0.13

Independently of the above supply data, customers' demand also follows a discrete probability distribution which records reveal to be:

Retail customers' demand (units)	Probability
1	0.07
2	0.14
3	0.22
4	0.30
5	0.18
6	0.09

The tradesman buys from the wholesaler at £10 per unit and sells to his retail customers at £20 per unit. Unsold units on any day can be stored in any required numbers and can be sold at the full price at any time in the future. However, if the tradesman is unable to satisfy retail customers' demand there is an estimated cost of £5 per unit of unsatisfied demand. The working year is 289 days.

The objective is to simulate ten days' demand as a basis for annual profits. While the problem is small enough to calculate expected values directly, this will not be so in general.

The first step of the simulation exercise is to allocate blocks of two digit numbers $(00, 01, 02, \ldots, 98, 99)$ to each outcome on the side of wholesaler supply and customer demand. The size of each block of two digit numbers must be in proportion to the probabilities for the variable concerned. A series of random numbers is then obtained and the occurrence of a particular digit pair within the range allocated to a supply or demand level will cause that supply or demand figure to be included in the calculations for that run of the simulation.

On the supply side, since the probability of a supply of one unit is 0.08 (or 8 in percentage terms), 8 per cent of the digit pairs 00 to 99 would be allocated to correspond to this event. In principle, *any* eight pairs of digits could be selected. For convenience, let 00–07, inclusive, signal one unit of supply. From the table 381, the chance of a supply of two units is 0.17 so 17 per cent of the two digit numbers will be reserved to correspond to this outcome. Again, these could be any 17 numbers except the ones already used. For convenience, let these be 08–24, inclusive. The next 20 per cent of the numbers will correspond to a supply of three units, and so on. The allocation of digits on the supply side is then:

Supply	Probability	Digits
1	0.08	00–07
2	0.17	08–24
3	0.20	25–44
4	0.25	45–69
5	0.17	70–86
6	0.13	87–99

and on the demand side the same process results in:

Demand	Probability	Digits
1	0.07	00–06
2	0.14	07–20
3	0.22	21–42
4	0.30	43–72
5	0.18	73–90
6	0.09	91–99

The next stage of the procedure is to generate the necessary random digits. This can be done by use of a computer, some calculators, or by random entry into a book of random number tables. Here we shall use the digits:

$$07837188929284372828913418482163207520618$$

The digits are now considered in alternate pairs for supply and demand. The digits could have been used from right to left, or in some other way. Once supply and demand levels are triggered, the associated costs and revenues are worked out and a single value of profit emerges. The exercise is then repeated.

Day	Random no.	Supply	Cost	Random no.	Demand	Sales	Revenue	Sh. loss	Σ store	Π
1	07	1	10	83	5	1	20	20	—	−10
2	71	5	50	88	5	5	100	—	—	50
3	92	6	60	92	6	6	120	—	—	60
4	84	5	50	37	3	3	60	—	2	10
5	28	3	30	28	3	3	60	—	2	30
6	91	6	60	34	3	3	60	—	5	—
7	18	2	20	48	4	4	80	—	3	60
8	21	2	20	63	4	4	80	—	1	60
9	20	2	20	75	5	3	60	10	—	30
10	26	3	30	18	2	2	40	—	1	10

Total Π = £300

Figure 13-1

A convenient layout for the workings is shown in Fig. 13-1. In Fig. 13-1 the first drawing, 07, is in the group assigned to one unit supplied. Cost will therefore be £10. The next pair of digits is 83 corresponding to demand of 5 but sales can only be one unit (as nothing is in store initially). Thus revenue is £20, but with the notional shortage loss of £5 per unit of unsatisfied demand the total shortage loss on the day is £20. There is nothing to put in store and the net 'profit', Π, on the day is Revenue − Cost − Shortage Loss =

$20-10-20=-£10$. The next pair of digits is 71 which gives a second-day supply figure of 5 units. And so on. On day 4 we have the first items going into store—which builds up to be drawn upon on days 7, 8, and 9. The total profit on the 10 days' business is £300, giving an estimated daily profit figure of £30. With a working year of 289 days the *point estimate* of annual profit is therefore $£289 \times 30 = £8670$.

It should be noted that the supply and demand levels used do *not* represent forecasts and that far more than 10 'runs' would be used in practice. If a sufficiently large number of runs is used, any difference in results due to the particular random digits used or the way in which they were drawn on, would approach zero.

Now consider the value of the storage facilities to the trader. To estimate their worth using the same data, simply recalculate the profit (Π) column if store facilities had *not* been available. The Sales, Revenue, Shortage Loss, and Profit columns would then have been as shown in Fig. 13-2. From Fig. 13-2, it is evident that only on days 7, 8, and 9 is any impact felt, but here the effects are quite considerable. The result is that estimated daily profit drops to £17.50. The difference between this, and the earlier figure of £30 with storage—£12.50— represents the daily value of the facilities. In other words if there had been a proposal to rent storage facilities for £10 per day, this would have been acceptable since the firm would have been left a £2.50 net improvement. In general, storage would also have the effect of reducing *variability* of income—a fact which may also command a price.

Return now to the question of annual profits. So far, we have used the simulation to give a point estimate. We can also use the data generated to produce a confidence interval for annual profit. To do this, we shall need the variance of annual profit. On the assumption of independence between days, the annual variance will be the sum of the daily variances. This will be 289 times the variance estimated for the values of π in Fig. 13-1 which represents

Day	Sales	Revenue	Sh. loss	Π
1	1	20	20	-10
2	5	100	—	50
3	6	120	—	60
4	3	60	—	10
5	3	60	—	30
6	3	60	—	—
7	2	40	10	10
8	2	40	10	10
9	2	40	15	5
10	2	40	—	10
			Total $\Pi =$	175

Figure 13-2

Π	Π − Π̄	(Π − Π̄)²
−10	−40	1600
50	20	400
60	30	900
10	−20	400
30	0	0
0	−30	900
60	30	900
60	30	900
30	0	0
10	−20	400
		6400 = Σ(Π − Π̄)²

Figure 13-3

a sample of $n = 10$ days. Daily variance will be:

$$\frac{\Sigma(\pi - \bar{\pi})^2}{n-1} = \frac{\Sigma(\pi - 30)^2}{9}$$

Workings for the sum of squares are shown in Fig. 13-3. Thus estimated daily variance is $\frac{6400}{9}$ and annual variance is therefore estimated as:

$$\frac{289(6400)}{9}$$

and annual standard deviation is therefore

$$sd = \sqrt{\frac{289(6400)}{9}} = 453.\overline{33}$$

Now the sum of a large number of days profit will be approximately normally distributed so that a 95 per cent confidence interval for annual profit would be given by:

$$\text{mean value} \pm 1.96 \text{ (standard deviation)}$$

$$= 8670 \pm 1.96(453.\overline{33})$$

that is:

$$7781 \quad \text{to} \quad 9559$$

Table 6 (page 494) can be used to find other ranges and probability figures for annual profit. For example the 99 per cent confidence interval will be:

$$8670 \pm 2.58(\overline{453.33})$$

that is:

$$7500 \text{ to } 9840$$

The probability that profit exceeds a particular minimum value can be calculated by finding the number of standard deviations that value is away from the mean. For example, the specific value of profit of £8000 is 1.48 standard deviations below the mean, viz:

$$\frac{8670 - 8000}{453.33} = 1.48$$

Table 6 (page 494) shows that 93.06 per cent of the area under a normal curve will be in excess of a value 1.48 standard deviations below the mean. Therefore, the probability that profit exceeds £8000 is 0.9306. On the other hand, however, there is little chance of a five figure profit being made. £10 000 is 2.93 standard deviations above the mean and as Table 6 shows 99.83 per cent of the area under the curve is below this value. Therefore, the probability of a five figure profit is $1 - 0.9983 = 0.0017$ which is less than two chances in a thousand.

When looking at the value of a structural change such as storage facilities, the point was made that variability is undesirable and that steps taken to reduce variability of profit as well as increase the mean would have a value. The maximum potential gain could be estimated by comparing the profit estimate from the simulation with the profit that could be achieved if demand and supply were constant at their mean values of 3.65 in each case. A steady profit of 36.50 could be achieved which would represent a £1878.5 increase on the average value with random supply and demand or £5491 more than the situation without the storage facilities which may be the more relevant comparison. Random variability always has its cost and the simulation methodology allows estimates of this to be made.

13-3 INVESTMENT APPRAISAL EXERCISE

Suppose that it is known with certainty that the outlay on a project would be £50 000, the discount rate is 10 per cent and the project would run for four years. Risk is attached only to the returns in each year. Suppose that these are given by the probability distribution below (the same for each year, independence between years):

Probability (p)	Return (R)
0.10	9 000
0.25	12 000
0.35	18 000
0.25	24 000
0.05	36 000

Now, the mean or 'expected' return in each year is $\Sigma pR = 18\,000$. *If* there was no variability and this mean return occurred each year then the net present value would be

$$-50\,000 + \frac{18\,000}{(1.1)} + \frac{18\,000}{(1.1)^2} + \frac{18\,000}{(1.1)^3} + \frac{18\,000}{(1.1)^4}$$

However, the returns are *not* assured, and we shall use simulation to estimate the mean and variance of present value. As in the expected profits example, the first step in the simulation exercise is to allocate blocks of *two-digit numbers* to each value of return. To correspond to the 9000 we shall select 00 to 09 inclusive. Now the 12 000 return has probability 0.25 of arising so that 25 per cent of the 2-digit numbers are assigned to this eventuality. Again these 25 could be any of the remaining 90 numbers but we shall employ 10 to 34 inclusive. The procedure is applied in a similar fashion to the remaining returns with the results shown below:

Return	Nos allocated
9 000	00–09
12 000	10–34
18 000	35–69
24 000	70–94
36 000	95–99

The randomly generated digits are:

035857935381938823229670906149467

The first number 03 falls in the range 00–09 so that the first return is 9000. The second return is then given by the next pair of digits in the string. This is 58 and being in the range 35–69 signifies a return of 18 000 in year 2. In similar fashion the third and fourth year returns are 18 000 and 24 000 as pointed to by the numbers 57 and 93. This completes the 'drawings' for Run no. 1, the cash flow being:

$t=0$	$t=1$	$t=2$	$t=3$	$t=4$
− 50 000	9000	18 000	18 000	24 000

It is important to note that this cash flow pattern *is in no sense a prediction* of what would happen if the project was accepted. It is merely a simulated sample of possible futures drawn according to the appropriate probabilities. Discounting the Run no. 1 cash flow at 10 per cent gives an NPV of + 2974. Now Run no. 2 is started. The first return here (recall that the outlay is always 50 000 in this example) is 18 000 as given by the next pair of digits in the string, 53. Working along the line of digits the reader may verify that the results of the

	Run number			
	1	2	3	4
$t=0$	− 50 000	− 50 000	− 50 000	− 50 000
$t=1$	9 000	18 000	12 000	9 000
$t=2$	18 000	24 000	12 000	12 000
$t=3$	18 000	24 000	36 000	24 000
$t=4$	24 000	24 000	24 000	18 000
NPV	+ 2 974	+ 20 622	+ 14 266	− 1 575

Figure 13-4

second and subsequently third and fourth runs are as shown in Fig. 13-4. Now four runs would be quite insufficient in a practical case. For safety a much larger number would be required, but for convenience we shall restrict ourselves to four runs here. The important row of Fig. 13-4 is the last one—an array of numbers being four observations of NPV. From these numbers we obtain the simulation estimate of expected net present value (ENPV*) as the *arithmetic mean of the NPV output* thus:

NPV
2 974
+ 20 622
+ 14 266
− 1 575
+ 36 287

$$\therefore \text{ENPV*} = \frac{36\,287}{4} = 9072$$

Next we can obtain an estimate of the standard deviation of NPV from the data generated; using the expression for standard deviation of an array of numbers (using $N - 1$ as extra-sample inferences are to be drawn) we obtain

$$\sigma^*_{NPV} = \sqrt{\frac{\Sigma(NPV - ENPV^*)^2}{N - 1}}$$

where N is the number of observations, i.e., the number of runs of the simulation. Using rounded numbers the workings are:

NPV	NPV–ENPV*	(NPV–ENPV*)²
2 974	− 6 098	37 185 604
20 622	+ 11 550	133 402 500
14 266	+ 5 194	26 977 636
− 1 575	− 10 647	113 358 609
		310 924 349

thus:

$$\sigma^*_{NPV} = \sqrt{\frac{310\,924\,349}{3}} = 10\,180$$

It then follows that the simulation estimated *coefficient of variation, c**, will be:

$$c^* = \frac{10\,180}{9072} = 1.12$$

As we have seen, the coefficient of variation is often a useful statistic in investment appraisal. It can be viewed either as an index of risk, in which account has been taken of the scale of the investment; or as a criterion of acceptability in a single-project framework. In the latter role the coefficient of variation states units of standard deviation per unit of mean or, interpreted in the usual fashion, units of risk per unit of return. Thus the lower c is the better.

In practice, in an investment context the whole approach can be much more ambitious than described here but the procedure would in principle be the same. For instance, suppose that a half dozen factors had been singled out as important and subject to risk. These might be selling price(s), unit cost(s), sales volume(s), initial outlay, project life, and discount rate. For each of these factors a probability distribution has to be specified (perhaps normal, beta, or gamma) and simultaneous drawings are taken from these distributions to give sample values of the parameters. Then NPV is calculated using this data and the exercise is repeated many times over. The distribution of yield may thus be obtained as well as that of NPV, and *risk profiles* can be produced. At the end of the exercise a decision is still to be taken in the light of the evidence produced.

There are a considerable number of computer programs available for simulation exercises in the area of investment appraisal and financial management generally. A number of illustrative programs and a description of information technology and computer-based financial management are contained in Wilkes and Brayshaw (1986). At the micro-computer level, the output of a simulation exercise (for example, generating the probability distribution of NPV) can be displayed in the form of a histogram. From this can be read the percentage of times that a 'hurdle' level is exceeded by the criterion variable. Dynamic output of the histograms is possible showing the results of the simulation as they arise while the program is running. The following programme by J. Morris produces dynamic histogram output for the net present value example of this section.

```
REM Dynamic NPV histograms.
DIM cash (5),prob(5)
FOR i = 1 to 5
   READ cash(i),prob(i)
NEXT i
DATA  9000,0·1
DATA 12000,0·25
DATA 18000,0·35
DATA 24000,0·25
DATA 36000,0·05
REM now set up cumulative probability vector
DIM cump(5)
cump(1) = prob(1)
FOR i = 2 to 5
   cump(i) = cump(i − 1) + prob(i)
NEXT i
REM now the remaining data items
READ initialoutlay
DATA 50000
READ discountrate
DATA 0·1
REM now declare memory for cash flow
DIM cashflow(4)

REM first find the smallest possible npv outcome with smallest cashflow values.
FOR i = 1 to 4
   cashflow(i) = cash(1)
NEXT i

REM the user function FNnpv computes npvfor various values of the cashflow
REM vector.
snpv = FNnpv
REM now for the largest npv
FOR i = 1 to 4
   cashflow(i) = cash(5)
```

```
NEXT i
gnpv = FNnpv

REM now before spinning the Monte-Carlo wheel switch on graphics mode on the
REM BBC micro
natural = 1
color = red
GCOL natural, color
fill = 85
REM and let us say 40 bars will be distinguished
DIM CategoryCount(40)
REM Here starts the major Monte-Carlo loop
trial = 0
REPEAT
  trial = trial + 1
  REM sample each year's cashflow
    uniformrn = RND(1)
    i = 0
    REPEAT i = i + 1
    UNTIL uniformrn < cump(i)
    cashflow(year) = cash(i)
  NEXT year
  REM now calculate npv using above sampled cashflow vector
  npv = FNnpv
  REM now to find where to plot the above npv observation on our histogram.
  REM first find which bar.
  barno = INT((npv − snpv)/(gnpv − snpv)*40)
  REM now find the graphics coordinate at which the observation symbol is to
  REM be plotted.
  x0 = 20*barno + 200
  y0 = 20*CategoryCount(barno) + 100
  REM now to draw 20 by 20 square at x0, y0 we need to paint two triangles
  REM on the BBC screen
  REM here is the lower diagonal's triangle
  MOVE x0, y0
  MOVE x0, y0 + 20
  PLOT fill, x0 + 20,y0
  REM and here is the upper diagonal's
  PLOT fill,x0 + 20, y0 − 20
    REM now update the category count
    CategoryCount(barno) = categorycount(barno) + 1
    REM now check the simulation exit condition
  UNTIL (trials = 100) OR (CategoryCount(barno) = 45)
END
DEF FNnpv
  cdcf = 0
  f = 1
  discf = 1/(1 + discountrate)
  FOR i = 1 to 4
    cdcf = cdcf + f*cashflow(i)
    f = f*discf
  NEXT
= cdcf − initialoutlay
FNEND
```

13-4 SIMULATION WITH NORMALLY DISTRIBUTED VARIABLES

In sections 13-2 and 13-3, we conducted exercises in simulation where the random variables followed discrete probability distributions. It is possible to conduct similar exercises where the variables follow continuous distributions. The following example illustrates this.

In a week's trading, a firm will manufacture and sell 100 units of a certain product. Selling price is *normally distributed* about a mean of £80, with a standard deviation of £10. The only sources of cost are unit variable cost and overhead. Unit variable cost (which is independent of price and overhead) is normally distributed with a mean value of £60 and a standard deviation of £4. Overhead (which is independent of price) is normally distributed with a mean of £1000 and a standard deviation of £300. Figure 13-5 allocates random digits to the numbers of standard deviations that a normally distributed variable is away from its mean. The company would like *point* and *bracketed* estimates of profitability. Profit is the difference between revenue and costs (fixed plus variable) so with sales of 100 units, revenue will be 100 × price and variable costs are unit variable costs × 100. The first pair of digits 27 applied to price corresponds to a value of p which is 0.6 standard deviations below the

Normal distribution: allocation of random digits

Random number	No. of standard deviations from mean	Random number	No. of standard deviations from mean	Random number	No. of standard deviations from mean
00	−2.5	22–24	−0.7	79–81	0.8
01	−2.3	25–27	−0.6	82–83	0.9
02	−2.0	28–31	−0.5	84–85	1.0
03	−1.9	32–34	−0.4	86–87	1.1
04	−1.8	35–38	−0.3	88–89	1.2
05	−1.7	39–42	−0.2	90–91	1.3
06	−1.6	43–46	−0.1	92	1.4
07	−1.5	47–53	0.0	93	1.5
08	−1.4	54–57	0.1	94	1.6
09–10	−1.3	58–61	0.2	95	1.7
11–12	−1.2	62–65	0.3	96	1.8
13–14	−1.1	66–68	0.4	97	1.9
15–16	−1.0	69–72	0.5	98	2.0
17–18	−0.9	73–75	0.6	99	2.3
19–21	−0.8	76–78	0.7		

Random digits

2798964728107740839652429098528866899431503
74008078518473949

Figure 13-5

mean. So the actual value of price indicated is

$$p = 80 - 0.6(10) = 74$$

This will give a revenue of £7400. Let the next two digits signal a value for unit variable cost (v). Thus the value will be 2.0 standard deviations above the mean, as signalled by the number 98. Thus:

$$v = 60 + 2(4) = 68$$

and total variable costs will be £6800. Finally, the first value of fixed costs (F) will be 1.8 standard above its mean as indicated by the digits 96. Thus

$$F = 1000 + 1.8(300) = 1540$$

The remainder of the results, obtained in a similar fashion, are as shown in Fig. 13-6. Thus the estimated mean weekly profit ($\bar{\Pi}$) will be:

$$\bar{\Pi} = \frac{10\,000}{10} = 1.000$$

Simulation estimated weekly variance is given by:

$$\sigma^2 = \frac{\Sigma(\Pi - \bar{\Pi})^2}{n - 1}$$

Mean profit: normal distribution example

		Costs		
Digit pairs	Revenue	Variable	Fixed	Profit ( )
27/98/96	7 400	6 800	1 540	−940
47/28/10	8 000	5 800	610	+1 590
74/40/83	8 700	5 920	1 270	+1 510
96/56/24	9 800	6 040	790	+2 970
29/09/85	7 500	5 480	1 300	+720
28/86/89	7 500	6 440	1 360	−300
94/31/50	9 600	5 800	1 000	+2 800
37/40/08	7 700	5 920	580	+1 200
07/85/18	6 500	6 400	730	−630
47/39/49	8 000	5 920	1 000	+1 080
				= 10 000

Figure 13-6

Variance calculations

$\pi - \bar{\pi}$	$(\pi - \bar{\pi})^2$
− 1940	3 763 600
+ 590	348 100
+ 510	260 100
+ 1970	3 880 900
− 280	78 400
− 1300	1 690 000
+ 1800	3 240 000
+ 200	40 000
− 1630	2 656 900
+ 80	6 400
	15 964 400

Figure 13-7

The workings for this are shown in Fig. 13-7. Thus weekly standard deviation will be:

$$\sigma = \sqrt{\frac{15\,964\,400}{9}} = 1322$$

and the simulation estimated 95 per cent *confidence interval* for weekly profit is therefore:

$$\bar{\Pi} \pm 1.96\sigma$$

that is:

$$-1611 \quad \text{to} \quad +3611$$

13-5 QUEUEING THEORY EXPERIMENT

Queueing theory is an area in which there is much scope for the successful use of simulation methods. We shall illustrate the approach in this context through a numerical exercise.

In what is known to be a simple queueing situation, the following inter-arrival times are observed:

Arrival no.	1	2	3	4	5	6	7	8	9	10
	38	3	41	20	57	10	46	99	87	221

The time units are seconds. The numbers are drawings from a negative exponential distribution with a mean of 60 seconds. Thus while the *average* time between arrivals is 60 seconds, the first 'person' arrives 38 seconds after observations begin, the second person arrives just 3 seconds later still, and so on.

1. Arrival no.	1	2	3	4	5	6	7	8	9	10	Σ
2. Inter-arrival time	38	3	41	20	57	10	46	99	87	221	
3. Arrival time	38	41	82	102	159	169	215	314	401	622	
4. Service time	136	17	23	4	70	55	36	17	12	62	
5. 'Into' time	38	174	191	214	218	288	343	379	401	622	
6. 'From' time	174	191	214	218	288	343	379	396	413	684 =	Total time
7. Queueing time	0	133	109	112	59	119	128	65	0	0	725
8. s.p. idle time	38	0	0	0	0	0	0	0	5	209	
9. System time	136	150	132	116	129	174	164	82	12	62	1157

Figure 13-8

In Fig. 13-8 the fourth row gives drawings from an exponential service distribution with a mean service time of 40 seconds. The first person, however, takes 136 seconds to be served, the next arrival takes 17 seconds to be served, and so on. The remaining data are calculated in the following fashion. Arrival time of row (3) is the sum of the inter-arrival times up to and including the arrival in question. It is the time of arrival into the system (and the queue if there is one). If the whole process is started at $t = 0$, then person 4 arrives after 102 seconds ($= 38 + 3 + 41 + 20$). The 'into' time of arrival n is the time that person n reaches the service point. This time will be either:

(a) the previous person's 'into' time plus service time (i.e., the 'from' time of person $n-1$); or
(b) the arrival time of person n

whichever is the greater. This is (a) for all persons up to and including no. 8, who leaves the system at $t = 396$; but person 9 does not arrive until $t = 401$, thus 401 is person 9's into time. The queueing time will be the into time less the arrival time. Row 8 gives the service point (s.p.) idle time, being the difference, if any, between the into time of person n and the from time of $n-1$. Row 9 gives the system process time for each individual and is queueing time plus service time.

Now from all of this we can produce estimates of the important system parameters:

1. *Average queueing time.* Total queueing time for all ten people is 725 seconds

so that the average time spent queueing was $725/10 = 725$ *seconds*. This is the simulation estimate. In fact we know that the true average is

$$\frac{\lambda}{\mu(\mu-\lambda)} = \frac{60}{90(90-60)} \times 3600 = 80 \text{ seconds}$$

so that with only 10 observations the simulated sample estimate is remarkably close to the true value. In carrying out this comparative exercise here, it should be borne in mind that, in practice, simulation is used when the situation does not fit well with the assumptions of any analytical model.

2. *Average system process time* (ASPT). This is the total of the system times (1157) divided by 10; giving 115.7. The true value is

$$\frac{1}{\mu-\lambda} \times 3600 = 120 \text{ seconds}$$

so once again the simulation result is close.

3. *Avarage queue length.* This is obtained as

$$\frac{\text{total queueing time}}{\text{total time of problem}} = \frac{725}{684} = 1.06$$

On average (all times considered) there is a queue length of 1.06 persons. The ratio above is not obvious, but consider a much smaller example when total queueing time $= 30$ seconds and problem time (when the last person observed leaves the system) is 15 seconds. For total queueing time to be 30 seconds then in each of the 15 seconds of real time there must be an average of two persons in the queue. The true average queue length is

$$\frac{\lambda^2}{\mu(\mu-\lambda)} = 1.\overline{33}$$

4. *Average queue when there is a queue.* This statistic is rather more difficult to extract from the exercise. We need to prepare a separate table breaking down the total problem time into intervals when there were particular queue lengths. This is done in Fig. 13-9.

While there is only one person in the system there is no queue. The second person arrives after 41 seconds and the first person is still being served. The first person is still in service at $t = 82$ when the third customer arrives (row (3) of Fig. 13-8). Thus the length of queue has now risen to 2. When the fourth person arrives at $t = 102$ the first person is still in the system. And so the queue length builds up (as shown in the X column of Fig. 13-9) until $t = 174$ when the first person leaves. The break points in the

Time	No. in queue (X)	Seconds (S)	XS
0–41	0	41	0
41–82	1	41	41
82–102	2	20	40
102–159	3	57	171
159–169	4	10	40
169–174	5	5	25
174–191	4	17	68
191–214	3	23	69
214–215	2	1	2
215–218	3	3	9
218–288	2	70	140
288–314	1	26	26
314–343	2	29	58
343–379	1	36	36
379–401	0	22	0
401–684	0	283	0
		$\Sigma S = 684$	$\Sigma XS = 725$

Figure 13-9

time column are moments when a person leaves or enters the system, thus affecting queue length. The average queue length is the weighted average of the numbers in the queue, the weights being the durations for which the particular lengths existed, viz.,

$$\text{average queue length (all times)} = \frac{\Sigma XS}{\Sigma S} = \frac{725}{684} = 1.06$$

which confirms the result previously obtained. To find the average queue length only where there is a queue, instead of taking the total $\Sigma S = 684$, add up only those times when there *is* a queue. Thus

$$\text{average queue length (when queue exists)} = \frac{\Sigma XS}{\Sigma S(\text{for } X > 0)}$$

$$= \frac{725}{338} = 2.14$$

whereas the true average is

$$\frac{\mu}{\mu - \lambda} = 3$$

5. *Average number in the system.* The simulated sampling estimate of this parameter is given by the ratio

$$\frac{\Sigma \text{ system process time}}{\text{total problem time}} = \frac{1157}{684} = 1.69$$

and the correct value is

$$\frac{\lambda}{\mu - \lambda} = 2$$

6. *System state probabilites.* Figure 13-10 in similar fashion to Fig. 13-9 shows the numbers in the system over the length of the experiment. From the data in this form we can easily estimate the probability of having one person in the system (P_1) or the system being empty (P_0) or in general containing n people (P_n). The numbers in the system are called states and the P_n are *state probabilities*. Thus to find the simulation estimate of P_0 we use Fig. 13-10 to add the lengths of time for which the system is empty and divide by the total time.

Time	No. in system	Sec.
0–38	0	28
38–41	1	3
41–82	2	41
82–102	3	20
102–159	4	57
159–169	5	10
169–174	6	5
174–191	5	17
191–214	4	23
214–215	3	1
215–218	4	3
218–288	3	70
288–314	2	26
314–343	3	29
343–379	2	36
379–396	1	17
396–401	0	5
401–413	1	12
413–622	0	209
622–684	1	62

Figure 13-10

From Fig. 13-10 the

$$\text{simulation estimate of } P_0 = \frac{38 + 5 + 209}{684} = 0.37$$

whereas in truth

$$P_0 = 1 - \frac{\lambda}{\mu} = 0.33$$

As a further example,

$$\text{estimate of } P_2 = \frac{41 + 26 + 36}{684} = 0.15$$

$$\text{true value} = \left(1 - \frac{\lambda}{\mu}\right)\left(\frac{\lambda}{\mu}\right)^2 = 0.15$$

As a further example of the use of Fig. 13-10 we can estimate

$$P(n \geqslant 5) = \frac{10 + 5 + 17}{684} = 0.05$$

whereas

$$P(n \geqslant 5) = \left(\frac{\lambda}{\mu}\right)^5 = 0.13$$

Figure 13-10 can also be used to confirm the average number in system result of (5) above.

7. *Service point idle time.* The proportion of total time that the service point is idle is, from the eighth row of Fig. 13-8

$$\frac{38 + 5 + 209}{684} = 0.37$$

so that the service point operative would have 37 per cent of their time available for interruptable tasks. Of course, the proportion of service point idle time is P_0 and since $P_0 = 1 - \rho$ the implied estimate of ρ is 0.63.

On the whole the results of the simulation were in very good accord with the true values (which in general will be unknown). This with only 10 'runs'. Many more observations would be taken in a practical case and the results would, accordingly, be even more dependable. Further runs would require more data and we now examine how the drawings were taken. Consider the inter-arrival times. A given average time of one minute between arrivals means $\lambda = 60$ per hour. Inter-arrival time T follows the distribution.

$$f(T) = \lambda e^{-\lambda T}$$

The probability that up to T minutes elapses between arrivals is given by:

$$\int_0^T f(T)dT = \int_0^T \lambda e^{-\lambda T}dT = [-e^{-\lambda T}]_0^T = 1 - e^{-\lambda T} = F(T)$$

This is the *cumulative probability function*. It is this function which is most convenient for generating the simulation data. The appearance of $F(T)$ is shown in Fig. 13.11. To generate the sample data, random points in the 0–1 interval on the vertical axis are selected and, going through the function $F(T)$, sample values of T are read off the horizontal axis.

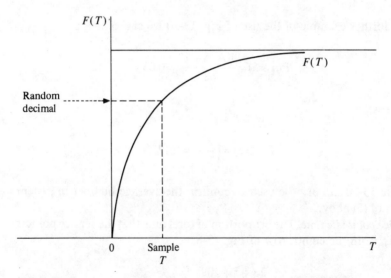

Figure 13-11

It is not necessary to use the graph to generate the data. Supppose that a table of random numbers (entered at an arbitrary point) yields the following string of digits:

$$47105149127961315253980876497 5$$

Use these in triplets (for sufficient accuracy) to generate random values of $F(T)$. These will be the random decimals shown in Fig. 13-12.

Random decimal $(=F(T))$	T (min)	T (sec)
0.471	0.637	38
0.051	0.052	3
0.491	0.675	41
0.279	0.327	20
0.613	0.949	57
0.152	0.165	10
0.539	0.774	46
0.808	1.650	99
0.764	1.444	87
0.975	3.689	221

Figure 13-12

The first random number is 0.471 so that we must now solve for T where:

$$0.471 = 1 - e^{-T}$$

Use of a calculator or natural logarithms gives $T = 0.637$, i.e. 38 seconds (rounded). This is the first inter-arrival time. Proceeding, the next triplet of random digits gives 0.051 and solving:

$$0.051 = 1 - e^{-T}$$

gives $T = 0.052$ minutes or 3 seconds. The full workings are shown in Fig. 13-12.

The service time data were generated in a similar fashion setting $\mu = 1.5$ (per minute) and solving for service time, S, from:

$$F(S) = 1 - e^{-\mu S}$$

and using the following digits in triplets to generate values of $F(S)$:

$$96735343708982674659235386 1789$$

In the case of the first triplet .967 is the value of $F(S)$ so that:

$$1 - e^{-1.55} = 0.967$$

From which the value of S emerges as $2.2\overline{66}$ minutes or the 136 seconds as shown in Fig. 13-8, row 4.

In practice, for many queueing problems computer simulation is often the first choice of method. A good example is provided by queueing situations involving variable routes through multiple service points with fluctuating arrival rates. The flexibility of computer simulation in such circumstances is a valuable asset and the visual display of the output is helpful too. We now turn to consider an example from within an area where waiting line problems can only be addressed by simulation methods.

13-6 TRAFFIC MANAGEMENT PROBLEM

Simulation methods are successfully used in traffic management problems of great complexity. Here, in the context of a small scale example, we aim to convey the essence of the approach.

The installation of traffic lights at a T-junction is under consideration. Two lanes of traffic are possible on each side of the roads. The possibility of vehicles crossing in front of each other is ruled out as too dangerous. This condition is to be stringently observed and the use of separate but adjacent lanes by traffic that otherwise may have crossed is also ruled out. Simulation is to be used to find the best timings for the lights.

Firstly, the various routes through the junction must be identified. Flow along each route must be allowed in at least one of the light settings. Each setting will allow flow along a combination of routes. The form of the junction is as illustrated in Fig. 13-13, with the three approaches to the junction being

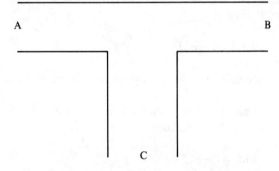

Figure 13-13

labelled. The possible routes are permutations of the letters ABC. Thus with the first letter representing the 'origin' and the second the 'destination' the routes are: AB, AC, BA, BC, CA, CB. We must now sort out which combinations of these routes are allowable and which are not. The crossing-over prohibition obviously rules out the combining of BA and CB as shown in Fig. 13-14(a). But also ruled out by the 'adjacency' ban are such combinations as AB and CB of Fig. 13-14(b). Figure 13-15 shows, for each route, the other routes that are allowed or prohibited by the regulations. A means of sorting out what combinations of routes are allowed is shown in Fig. 13-16. In the figure, each route is represented by a point. Any two points in the diagram are joined by a line if and only if they can operate simultaneously. Thus for AB we

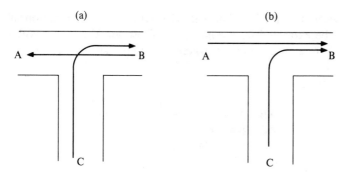

Figure 13-14

Route	Prohibited	Allowed
AB	CB	AC, BA, BC, CA
AC	BA, BC, CB	AB, CA
BA	AC, CB, CA	AB, BC
BC	AC	BA, AB, CB, CA
CA	BA	BC, AC, AB, CB
CB	AB, AC, BA	BC, CA

Figure 13-15

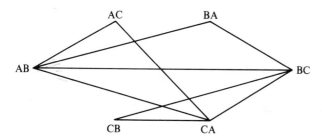

Figure 13-16

look at the 'allowed' list in Fig. 13-15 and join AB up with AC, BA, BC, and CA. Then AC will be joined up with AB (already done) and CA. Thus Fig. 13-16 is an alternative representation of Fig. 13-15 but it presents the information in a more convenient way. The point is this: *a combination of routes* (say AB, BA, and BC) *can be operated simultaneously if and only if the corresponding points are ALL directly connected to each other.*

Thus the combination AB, BA, and BC is permitted since each point is connected directly with a single straight line to every other point in the combination. But AB, AC, and BA is *not* permitted because of the absence of a direct link between AC and BA. Four triangles (with route combinations at the vertices) can be extracted from Fig. 13-16. These are the four possible combinations of three routes along which the light settings can allow simultaneous flow.

These combinations are:

AB	AB	AB	BC
AC	BA	BC	CB
CA	BC	CA	CA
(1)	(2)	(3)	(4)

Notice that CB appears only in (4) and that BA and AC appear only in (2) and (1) respectively. These three groups also include all the remaining routes. Thus arrangement (3) is not necessary. Finally, note that no quadrilaterals can be extracted from Fig. 13-16. Thus no combination of four routes is possible. There are also smaller arrangements that include only two routes or even one, but each of these will be already included in (1), (2) or (4) and must represent inferior situations with the unnecessary closing of one or more routes. The light settings appropriate to the arrangements (1), (2), and (4) are shown in Fig. 13-17, in which G represents green (go) and red (stop) is indicated by R.

		Arrangement	
Route	(1)	(2)	(4)
AB	G	G	R
AC	G	R	R
BA	R	G	R
BC	R	G	G
CA	G	R	G
CB	R	R	G

Figure 13-17

Looking across the rows there must be at least one G in each row for feasibility. Two questions now arise: (a) for how many seconds should each arrangement be shown and (b) can arrangement (3) be discarded altogether? To take the second question first—in fact we cannot say *a priori* that it is always going to be optimal to have only the minimum number of arrangements that include all routes at least once, especially so when connections with other sets of lights have to be considered. So, strictly speaking, we should include (3) in the simulation exercise *including some runs in which* (3) *is shown for zero seconds* (i.e., is excluded). However, in the simple, isolated system under study here, it is safe to assume that the fewer the arrangements the better. One way to begin the simulation would be to allow each arrangement an equal length of time, say, 90 seconds. This would have the effect of giving routes AB, BC, and CA twice as much time as for the remaining three. This may be desirable if they are the busiest routes, but it is the main task of the simulation exercise to obtain the 'best' timings. We put the world 'best' in quotes for two reasons: (a) given a criterion (such as expected queueing time overall) there is no guarantee of reaching the global optimum by simulation and (b) there may be other possible criteria against which the system performance can be assessed (e.g., queue length or a priority system for certain routes). However, it is usual to try to minimize expected waiting time overall. This is the obvious statistic and the system performance will be judged according to this criterion.

The simulation would then *vary* the lengths of the settings and ascertain the effects on total waiting time. For instance, to begin with we might try (1) for 40 seconds, (2) for 110 seconds, and (4) for 50 seconds; these numbers being 'reasonable' values based on inspection of traffic flow rates. A number of runs would then be conducted with these timings, with average waiting time as the end product. Then the timings would be changed—in a direction which seems promising or by some systematic automated procedure—some runs conducted, and again average waiting time ascertained. Then there would be more changes of timings and more sets of random drawings. The arrangement which provided the least overall waiting time would then be preferred.

The above initial values of timings might have resulted from the following flow data:

Route	Average number of vehicles per minute
AB	17
AC	8
BA	30
BC	7
CA	13
CB	10

BA being the busiest route and being represented only in (2) suggests that (2) must be given considerably longer time than (1) or (4). As a guide Fig. 13-18 gives the total time (per 200 seconds) that each route is open (column (6)) and the percentage of time in column (7). The figures suggest that increasing the proportion of time given to (2) might next be attempted. The simulation could also investigate the desirability of quick changes for the same proportionate times: viz., 20 s for (1), 55 s for (2), and 25 s for (3).

Clearly, the flow data is vital if the simulation is to be a good proxy for the real situation. One problem in gathering this data is that rates of flow will vary with time of day. Perhaps the data given above are for the early evening

| 1 | 2 | 3 | 4 | 5 | 6 | 7 |
| | Average | | | | | |
Route	flow	(1) time	(2) time	(4) time	Total	%
AB	17	40	110		150	75
AC	8	40			40	20
BA	30		110		110	55
BC	7		110	50	160	80
CA	13	40		50	90	45
CB	10			50	50	25

Figure 13-18

rush-hour with BA being the out-of-city route. A different pattern would be arrived at if 8 a.m. to 9 a.m. flow data were used. Clearly, if the settings can be varied according to time of day then perhaps four sets of timings could be provided (morning rush, day-time/evening, evening rush, night-time). At any rate the data would need to be compiled over a period of weeks (as 'there will be day-to-day as well as within-day variations) to ensure valid results. Further, we have not considered the varying *nature* of traffic flows. If one route is much used by heavy commercial vehicles (taking longer to manoeuvre and causing obstruction) then the results may be questionable. If resources allow, it would be wise to monitor the system for a while after the simulation results have been implemented. Finally, recall that we have been considering the junction as an isolated system. Changes or unexpected events elsewhere may, in practice, significantly affect results.

13-7 CONCLUSIONS

Considered as a distinct technique, simulation is the most widely-used operational research method today. Of course, it is a way of approaching a queueing, stock control, scheduling, or other problem, that cannot be tackled by analytical means. In this chapter, we have sought to show something of the principles and scope of the method through manual examples. Practical problems are dealt with by using computers and often a specially written programme will be needed. This may be produced using one of the specialized simulation languages now available. Cook and Russell (1981) set out a nine step procedure for practical simulation studies, as follows.

The first step is to *formulate the problem*—making clear and specific the objectives of the organization, questions to be addressed and consequences deduced. The second and third steps are *data collection* and *data analysis* where observations are compiled to identify the correct probability distributions to be used in the simulation. The next step is *model formulation* where a mathematical model of reasonable scale is constructed to capture the essentials of the system. The fifth step is *program generation*, the writing of the computer program of the simulation possibly involving a special purpose language. Next comes *model validation* where the initial results are checked against reality. If they are unreasonable, the model is subject to *'fine tuning'* until confidence is gained in the output. The eighth stage identified by Cook and Russell is *experimental design* where the structural alternatives and parameter variations to be investigated are set out. Finally, comes the *analysis of results* stage—interpreting the results and drawing the conclusions as to action required to implement them.

At the other end of the spectrum of simulation exercises is *deterministic simulation*. This is simply the projection of the consequences if a specific course of action is undertaken. For example, the balance sheets implied by an investment or takeover decision could be worked out. Alternatively, various states of the world or *scenarios* can be hypothesized and, for example, the present value of an investment opportunity worked out in each case. This method is illustrated in Wilkes (1983) where the cash flow consequences of different particular assumptions concerning inflation rates are projected.

With extensive computer software now available, computer simulation is used in an increasingly wide variety of problems in practice. Simulation allows information to be displayed and presented in ways which lead to increased acceptance at senior management level. A survey by Cook and Russell found that only 11 per cent of 500 top US companies surveyed did *not* use computer simulation as an aid to decision making.

Simulation has many obvious advantages—it is highly flexible and adaptable, powerful, widely used and of proven value. Its disadvantages are few and, apart from the fact that formal optimization is not usually possible in the method, the disadvantages relate to misuse. The method should not, outside of the classroom, be used on problems where analytical results can be obtained or where data problems are intractable. (A judgemental approach may then be needed.) The cost of the method when appropriately used in small in relation to potential benefit and the use of simulation will continue to increase in the coming years.

EXERCISES

13-1 Revision exercise
  (i) Why is simulation likely to prove useful in an operational research context?
  (ii) Broadly, how does a simulation exercise proceed?
  (iii) Explain how data may be generated for a simulation exercise by use of the cumulative probability function.
  (iv) How can structural changes in a system be evaluated in a simulation study?
  (v) Outline the steps involved in a computer simulation exercise in practice.
  (vi) What is meant by deterministic simulation?
  (vii) What are the advantages of the simulation approach? Are there any disadvantages?
  (viii) For what reasons are computers especially suited to, and of particular value in, Monte-Carlo simulation exercises?

13-2 Pisces Ltd trade in a perishable commodity. Each day Pisces receive supplies of the good for a wholesaler but the quantity supplied is a random variable as is subsequent retail customer demand for the commodity. Both supply and demand are expressed in batches of 50 units and over the past working year (300 days) Pisces have kept records of supplies and demands. The results are given in the table:

Wholesaler supplies	No. of days occurring	Customers' demand	No. of days occurring
50	60	50	60
100	90	100	60
150	90	150	150
200	60	200	30

Pisces Ltd buys the commodity at £6 per unit and sells at £10 a unit. At present unsold units at the end of the day are worthless and there are no storage facilities. Pisces estimate that each unit of unsatisfied demand on any day costs them £2. Using the following random numbers:

$$848033479615$$

(i) Simulate six days' trading and estimate annual profit.
(ii) Re-run the exercise to estimate the value of storage facilities.
(iii) Briefly, what other information could be gleaned from the exercise and what qualifications should be made in respect of the results?

13-3 An investment requires an outlay of £12 000 and runs for three years. The discount rate is 10 per cent. Returns are independent between years and in each of the years are given by:

Probability	Return (£)
0.06	1500
0.17	2000
0.22	4500
0.29	6000
0.16	7500
0.10	9400

Given the following digits:

$$870569058194271421877495315804$$

conduct a simulation exercise (five runs) to estimate ENPV. Use the information obtained to estimate the coefficient of variation.

13-4 Coltel Ltd is considering the introduction of a new product and has compiled the following information:

Variable	Expected value	Standard deviation
Sales quantity	5 000	400
Selling price per unit(£)	300	5
Fixed costs (£)	580 000	10 000
Variable costs per unit (£)	175	7.5

(For simplicity assume that all the random variables are independent and that the probability distributions are normal.)

    (a) Calculate, using break-even analysis and expected values, the break-even volume and the expected profit for the period.

    (b) Explain how you would carry out a simulation to arrive at an approximate distribution of profits. Illustrate your answer by using (Fig. 13-5) and the following random numbers 20, 96, 68, 59 to obtain one simulated figure for profit.

    (c) What is the value to Coltel Ltd of having carried out a simulation rather than simply estimating profit using expected values?

(Chartered Association of Certified Accountants)

13-5 For several years our local council's policy on housing has given widespread cause for concern. The main body of criticism has been levelled at the priority scheme operated by our council. This involves an allegedly crude classification of applicants as 'urgent' or 'non-urgent'. Urgent cases move directly to the head of the housing list provided no other urgent case is already there. The destitute fall into this category but similar accelerated treatment of other needy groups, e.g., the disabled, is being pressed.

    Applications for housing are received at the rate of two per week. The following table details the rates at which houses are found for those reaching the head of the list:

Case type	Percentage of applicants	Time in days to find acceptable accommodation
Urgent	10	2
Non-urgent (a)	80	5
(b)*	10	7

*Applicants with 'special requirements', e.g. disabled applicants.
(Assume a 5-day working week.)

    (a) Describe how you would carry out a simulation of the present policy clearly stating each logical step. Point out all the assumptions you make.

    (b) What further simulation would you want to carry out in order to advise the local council about extending its priority scheme?

    (c) How would you carry out the simulations to minimize the effect of chance creating differences between the existing scheme and any proposed new scheme?

(Chartered Association of Certified Accountants)

13-6 The Popage Company Ltd has a contract to supply 1 000 000 cans of spinach a year for three years to a major supermarket company. This is a new venture for the company and they need to purchase three new machines A, B, and C for the canning operation. The market situation is fluid however and the company cannot assume that the contract will be renewed after three years or that some other similar business will replace it. They are therefore reluctant to spend a substantial amount on the machines and the management has narrowed the possible choices of equipment to two manufacturers.

The less expensive equipment is built by Company X at a total cost of £60 000 and has an expected life of three years. All three types of machines are needed, and they all have to be purchased from the same company. The operating characteristics are as follows:

Company X

Machine	A	B	C
Daily output when operating	4500	4500	4500
Probability of breaking down on any particular day	0.04	0.04	0.04
If broken down, probability of downtime duration			
1 day	0.40	0.40	0.35
2 days	0.35	0.30	0.40
3 days	0.25	0.30	0.25

The more expensive equipment is built by Company Y at a total cost of £120 000 and also has a life expectancy of three years. The operating characteristics which are more favourable, are as follows:

Company Y

Machine type	A	B	C
Daily output when operating	4500	4500	4500
Probability of breaking down on any particular day	0.035	0.035	0.035
If broken down, probability of downtime duration			
1 day	0.50	0.50	0.40
2 days	0.35	0.35	0.40
3 days	0.15	0.15	0.20

At the end of the three years the scrap value of the equipment from either company is estimated to be zero.

The contract requires 1 000 000 cans of spinach a year to be produced. The yearly total can however vary slightly from that figure but if 3 000 000 cans are not delivered in three years, a substantial penalty will be imposed. The number of working days in the year for the company is 300. You may assume that the three types of machine A, B, and C are all necessary for producing a can of spinach. Breakdown on any machine will stop all production for the duration of the breakdown.

Explain how you would carry out a simulation to evaluate the performance of each company's equipment in order to advise the management of Popage Company Ltd which, if either, should be purchased.

(Chartered Association of Certified Accountants)

13-7 During the course of any one week the sales revenue, variable costs and overheads for a firm are all independently normally distributed. Data are:

	Mean	Standard deviation
Sales revenue	11 000	1 000
Variable costs	7 000	500
Overheads	2 000	400

Using Fig. 13-5 and the random digits given below, conduct eleven runs of a simulation to produce:

(a) a point estimate of profitability;

(b) a 95 per cent confidence interval for weekly profit.

Digits: 9 9 3 8 0 7 5 8 3 9 2 1 8 5 5 1 9 4

0 7 6 7 3 5 3 0 0 0 9 6 3 9 9 5 9 0

0 5 4 2 6 1 4 8 5 1 1 9 4 3 9 6 2 9

5 8 4 0 5 0 6 1 3 8 8 4

Solution guides

13-2 In carrying out the allocation of random numbers, note that only single-digit numbers are required in this problem. They will be allocated as follows:

Supply	Prob.	Nos allocated	Demand	Prob.	Nos allocated
50	0.2	0,1	50	0.2	0,1
100	0.3	2,3,4	100	0.2	2,3
150	0.3	5,6,7	150	0.5	4,5,6,7,8
200	0.2	8,9	200	0.1	9

The six runs of the simulation produce the following results:

Day	No.	Supply	Cost	No.	Demand	Sales	Revenue	Sh. loss	Profit
1	8	200	1200	4	150	150	1500	—	300
2	8	200	1200	0	50	50	500	—	−700
3	3	100	600	3	100	100	1000	—	400
4	4	100	600	7	150	100	1000	100	300
5	9	200	1200	6	150	150	1500	—	300
6	1	50	300	5	150	50	500	200	0
									600

It therefore follows that:

(i) Estimated annual profit $= 600(50) = £30\,000$.

(ii) The first six columns above remain unchanged. We now have:

Sales	Revenue	Sh. loss	Σstore	Profit
150	1500	—	50	300
50	500	—	200	−700
100	1000	—	200	400
150	1500	—	150	900
150	1500	—	200	300
150	1500	—	100	1200
				2400

Thus the storage facilities would increase weekly profit in the simulation exercise by £1800. This is no less than £90 000 per annum!

(iii) A confidence interval for annual profit could be obtained which would be more useful than a single-figure estimate. The simulation could be re-worked for changes other than the installation of storage, for instance, a sale-or-return arrangement with the supplier. Part of the value of simulation is in its ability to evaluate structural changes. Of course, six runs is not enough to give a basis from which firm conclusions can be drawn. Otherwise, the usual caveats about the use of the procedure apply.

13-3 The allocation of two-digit numbers is as follows:

Probability	Return	Nos allocated
0.06	1500	00–05
0.17	2000	06–22
0.22	4500	23–44
0.29	6000	45–73
0.16	7500	74–89
0.10	9400	90–99

Now using the digits given, in pairs from left to right to generate return data for the first run, we obtain the results

Random no.	Return
87	7500
05	1500
69	6000

Thus the NPV will be given by

$$-12\,000 + \frac{7500}{(1.1)} + \frac{1500}{(1.21)} + \frac{6000}{(1.331)} = 565.74$$

The data for the full five runs are given in the table below.

	Cash flow (returns)			NPV
Run no. 1	7500	1500	6000	565.74
2	1500	7500	9400	2624.34
3	4500	2000	2000	−4753.57
4	7500	7500	9400	8078.89
5	4500	6000	1500	−1823.44
			$\Sigma =$	4691.96

The five run total of £4691.96 gives an average per run of £938.39. This the simulation estimate of ENPV.

Having obtained the estimate on ENPV we can go on the estimate the variance and hence standard deviation and coefficient of variation. The variance will be

$$\frac{\Sigma(NPV - ENPV)^2}{4}$$

The workings are:

NPV	(NPV—ENPV)	(NPV—ENPV)^2
565.74	− 372.65	138 868
2 624.34	1 685.95	2 842 427
−4 753.57	− 5 691.96	32 398 409
8 078.89	7 140.50	50 986 740
−1 823.44	− 2 761.83	7 627 705
		93 994 149

Thus variance is

$$\sigma^2 = \frac{93\,994\,149}{4} = 23\,498\,537$$

so that the coefficient of variation, c, is given by

$$c = \frac{\sqrt{23\,498\,537}}{938.39} = 5.17$$

13-4 (a) Recall that the break-even volume is the level of output at which costs are just covered. This means that revenue equals costs. Revenue is selling price (p) times volume (v). Total costs are unit variable costs (c) times volume (v) plus fixed costs (F), i.e., break-even means that $pv = cv + F$. Another way of expressing this is

$$v = \frac{F}{p - c}$$

So is expected value terms in the present case

$$v = \frac{580\,000}{300 - 175} = 4640$$

The expected profit, Π, is given by

$$\Pi = v(p - c) - F$$
$$= 5000(300 - 175) - 580\,000 = £45\,000$$

(b) The procedure in any one run of the simulation would be that for each component of the profit equation a random number is selected; Fig. 13-5 is then used to identify the number of standard deviations the variable is away from its mean value. Since the standard deviations are known, this procedure identifies a particular value of the variable. For instance, using the numbers given in the question:

Variable	Expected value	Standard deviation	Random number	Deviation from mean	Value of variable
v	5 000	400	20	-0.8	4 680
p	300	5	96	$+1.8$	309
F	580 000	10 000	68	$+0.4$	584 000
c	175	7.5	59	$+0.2$	176.5

Taking the variables in the order given in the question, the first random number 20, means that v is 0.8 standard deviations below its mean value, $\therefore v = 5000 - 0.8(400) = 4680$. The second random number 96 means that p is 1.8 of its standard deviations above its mean, i.e., $p = 300 + 1.8(5) = 309$. Thus profit in the first run of the simulation is

$$\Pi = 4680(309 - 176.5) - 584\,000 = +36\,100$$

This procedure would be repeated many times—ideally over a hundred—though 30 or so runs would give fairly reliable results. The mean and variance of this simulated sample of profit values can then be determined.

(c) Once the parameters (mean and variance) of the profit distribution have been obtained from the simulation, confidence intervals can be ascertained, and the probability of making a profit can be found. In practice a more complicated model might be used as it is unlikely that sales volume and price vary independently.

13-5 (a) Before setting up a simulation exercise it is often useful to carry out a preliminary analysis with what data is to hand. This may give some useful clues as to the features of the system. First, the mean 'service time' seems to be 4.9 days ($= 2(0.1) + 5(0.8) + 7(0.1)$). With a 5-day week there is an arrival, on average, every 2.5 days. So, unless there is more than one 'service point' or simultaneous service of several clients the queue length will expand indefinitely.

In the simulation outlined below we shall thus assume that *two* customers can be served simultaneously (this would take the physical form of two 'attendants' each serving one customer or the same attendant serving two—it does not matter which in this case). For the problem to be of any interest there had better be some random elements. We shall assume that the customers arrive Poisson-fashion at the mean rate of 2 per 5 days. We shall, however, assume that the 'service' times are fixed at 2, 5, or 7 days as implied by the question.

Now consider a possible format for the simulation. The queueing theory experiment of section 13.5 provides one arrangement. Getting the data on a daily basis, the mean rate of arrivals is $\lambda = 0.4$ per day, so that the inter-arrival time in days (T) is given by

$$f(T) = \lambda e^{-\lambda T} = 0.4 e^{-0.4T}$$

for which the cumulative distribution is

$$F(T) = 1 - e^{-0.4T}$$

Let us now use the first set of random digits

4 7 1 0 5 1 4 9 1 2 7 9 6 1 3 1 5 2 5 3 9 8 0 8 7 6 4 9 7 5

To generate values of T, use these in triplets (as before, although two at a time would be sufficiently accurate here). Thus the first value of T is the solution to

$$0.471 = 1 - e^{-0.4T}$$

which solves for $T = 1.59$ which we shall round to the nearest whole number, so $T = 2$. The next observation on inter-arrival time is given by

$$0.051 = 1 - e^{-0.4T}$$

giving $T = 0.13$, rounded to *zero*. The full list of values is contained in the following table:

Digits (D)	1—D	T	T (rounded)
0.471	0.529	1.59	2
0.051	0.949	0.13	0
0.491	0.509	1.69	2
0.279	0.721	0.82	1
0.613	0.387	2.37	2
0.152	0.848	0.41	0
0.539	0.461	1.93	2
0.808	0.192	4.12	4
0.764	0.236	3.61	4
0.975	0.025	9.22	9

Using the rounded T numbers in the table below, the urgent (u) or non-urgent (N) status of an arrival is determined (randomly) by the first of the digits in the triplets above. A zero would give a u classification—anything else would give an N classification. Thus the first arrival is N (from the 4 in the .471), the second is u (from the 0 in .051) and so on.

(1) Arrival no.	1	2	3	4	5	6	7	8	9	10
(2) Inter-time	2	0	2	1	2	0	2	4	4	9
(3) Type	N	u	N	N	N	N	N	N	N	N
(4) Arrival time	2	2	4	5	7	7	9	13	17	26
(5) Service time	5	2	5	5	5	5	5	5	5	5
(6) Into time	2	2	4	7	9	12	14	17	19	26
(7) From time	7	4	9	12	14	17	19	22	24	31 =total time
(8) Q time	0	0	0	2	2	5	5	4	2	0 Σ=20
(9) System time	5	2	5	7	7	10	10	9	7	5

It turns out that the one urgent case in this simulation can be dealt with at once. Arrival (1) goes straight into service at $t = 2$, arrival (2) (sometime later that same day) can be served at once (he goes 'into' at $t = 2$) since the service point can, by our assumption, handle two customers at once. Arrival (3) can be served as soon as *either* (1) or (2) emerges. This is at $t = 4$. And so on. Various system parameters can then be estimated. For instance, the average queueing time for non-urgent cases is 20/9 days (total time that N cases spend queueing divided by the number of N cases in the simulation). The ASPT (non-urgent) is 65/9 days. These values are low and reflect the fact that we started the exercise with an empty queue. Different initial conditions could have been employed. However, the queue length would (on average) reduce slowly as time goes on in the conditions assumed.

(b) Re-run the exercise with the non-urgent (b) cases now treated as urgent. Say 0 or 1 as the first digit in a triplet would now indicate an urgent case. More complex arrangements could also be tried involving different classes of urgency.

(c) If a very large number of runs are performed in each case (say several hundreds) there is little possibility of any significant chance differences remaining. Otherwise the same set of random numbers could be used in each alternative system, thus ensuring that comparisons are made under the same arrival conditions.

13-6 Certain features of the problem need to be defined more precisely before the simulation can begin. 'Slight variation' in the yearly total will be taken to mean that a 5 per cent shortfall would not be excessive, so it would be helpful if the simulation could give the probabilities of producing at least 950 000 units in each of the years. We should certainly want to obtain the probability of producing 3 000 000 units over the three-year period. Any contract would stipulate what the 'substantial penalty' was, so that the different probabilities of achieving the figure with the X equipment or the Y equipment could be used in an expected value calculation involving the initial costs.

The simulation would have to be performed by computer since 900 days are required per run and several runs would be required. The assignation of the random numbers would be as follows. For company X we should first need a two-digit table for the probability of breakdown on any day, viz.:

Random nos	Outcome
00–95	No breakdown
96–99	Breakdown

(once again we should point out that it does not matter *which* four two-digit numbers are used to correspond to breakdown). This table would be used for all three machines. For the downtime separate tables are required for each machine:

A	B	C	Downtime (days)
00–39	00–39	00–34	1
40–74	40–69	35–74	2
75–99	70–99	75–99	3

The simulation could then proceed for company X's machines. A possible layout is shown below.

Day	A	B	C	D_A	D_B	D_C	Downtime	Output
1	63	88	06	—	—	—	0	4500
2	24	51	79	—	—	—	0	4500
3	96	20	13	41	—	—	2	0
4								0
5	81	34	42	—	—	—	0	4500

On day (1) there are no breakdowns on any machines according to the random numbers turning up so that no random numbers are needed for the downtime (these would be shown in the columns headed D_A, D_B, D_C) and output is 4500. On day (2) there are no breakdowns and output is again 4500. On day (3), however, machine A breaks down (but B and C do not). Use of the downtime random number table shows that 41 falls in the two-day range for machine A. So there will be zero output on days (3) and (4). And so on. If two breakdowns occurred on one day the longer down time duration would apply. Output would be summed for days 1–300, 301–600, 601–900. Each sum would give the simulated observation on yearly output (for comparsion with 950 000). The sum for the whole 900 days would give one observation on three-yearly output. The simulation would then be repeated.

Similar procedures would then be followed for company Y's equipment. Note that a three-digit table would be required for the breakdowns. Comparisons between the machines could then be undertaken.

13-7 (a) Although they could be used in any order, the digits provided in the question will be used in groups of three pairs to indicate values of sales revenue, variable costs, overhead (one run) then sales revenue again, etc., for the required eleven runs. The results are (using Fig. 13-5)

Digit pairs	Revenue	Var. costs	Overhead	Profit
99|38|07	13 300	6 850	1 400	5 050
58|39|21	11 200	6 900	1 680	2 620
85|51|94	12 000	7 000	2 640	2 360
07|67|35	9 500	7 200	1 880	1 420
30|00|96	10 500	5 750	2 720	2 030
39|95|90	10 800	7 850	2 520	430
05|42|61	9 300	6 900	2 080	320
48|51|19	11 000	7 000	1 680	2 320
43|96|29	10 900	7 900	1 800	1 200
58|40|50	11 200	6 900	2 000	2 300
61|38|84	11 200	6 850	2 400	1 950
				$\Sigma = 22\ 000$

where, in the first 'run', the digits 99 in the table correspond to an observation for Revenue 2.3 standard deviations above its mean, i.e. $11\ 000 + 2.3\ (1000) = 13\ 300$. Similarly 38 represents an observation for variable costs 0.3 standard deviations below its mean, i.e. $7000 - 0.3(500) = 6850$. Finally in the first run the digits 07 give an observation for overhead 1.5 standard deviations below its mean, i.e. $2000 - 1.5(400) = 1400$. Since profit is Revenue $-$ (Costs $+$ Overhead) the first value of profit generated in the exercise is 5050. The remaining ten runs are carried out in a similar fashion with a total result of 22 000 over eleven runs—an average of 2000 per run. This is the point estimate of weekly profitability.

(b) The 95 per cent confidence interval for weekly profit is:

$$2000 \pm 1.96\sigma$$

where σ is the standard deviation of weekly profit. Letting profit be represented by x we have:

$$\sigma = \sqrt{\frac{\Sigma(x - \bar{x})^2}{n-1}}$$

where $\bar{x}$ is mean profit (2000) and n is the number of observations (runs). The workings for σ are as follows:

Profit (x)	$(x - \bar{x})$	$(x - \bar{x})^2$
5 050	3 050	9 302 500
2 620	620	384 400
2 360	360	129 600
1 420	-580	336 400
2 030	30	900
430	$-1 570$	2 464 900
320	$-1 680$	2 822 400
2 320	320	102 400
1 200	-800	640 000
2 300	300	90 000
1 950	-50	2 500
		$\Sigma = 16\ 276\ 000$

so that standard deviation of weekly profit is given by:

$$\sigma = \sqrt{\frac{16\ 276\ 000}{11-1}} = 1275.77$$

Thus the 95 per cent confidence interval as estimated by the simulation is:

$$2000 \pm 1.96(1275.77)$$

i.e.

$$-500 \text{ to } +4500$$

REFERENCES

Cook, T. M., and Russell, R. A. (1981), *Introduction to Management Science*, second edition, Prentice Hall.

Wilkes, F. M. (1983), *Capital Budgeting Techniques*, second edition, Wiley.
Wilkes, F. M. and Brayshaw, R. E. (1986), *Company Finance and its Management*, Van Nostrand Reinhold.

FURTHER READING

Anderson, D. R., Sweeney, D. J., and Williams, T. A. (1985), *An Introduction to Management Science*, fourth edition, West Publishing Co. Includes queueing theory and inventory illustrations.
Cohen, S. S. (1985), *Operational Research*, Edward Arnold. Includes stock control and queueing examples.
Littlechild, S. C. (1977), *Operational Research for Managers*, Philip Allan. Shows application of simulation to the design of engineering facilities.
Monks, J. G. (1982), *Operations Management*, second edition, McGraw-Hill. Contains product and process planning example and application to maintenance problems.

FOURTEEN

THE THEORY OF GAMES

14-1 INTRODUCTION

All the problems that we have so far described have involved one decision maker. In Game Theory, the value of the objective function of one decision maker will depend not only upon his own actions but also upon the actions of others. Game Theory is the study of such situations and in general both conflict and co-operation are involved.

In mathematical form, such situations often resemble parlour games of strategy. The theory has been applied at a variety of levels including international strategic situations, imperfect competition, social choice theory and marketing strategies.

The study of interest conflict in mathematical form—game theory—has its roots in the 1920s and 1930s with early work by von Neumann and Borel. It was not until 1944 that great interest was attracted to the subject when von Neumann (a mathematician) and Morgenstern (an economist) published *The Theory of Games and Economic Behaviour*. Game Theory was then caught up in the general rapid growth of operational research after the Second World War. A comprehensive review is contained in Luce and Raiffa (1957).

A *game* is a collection of rules, known to all participants, determining what players may do and the *pay-offs* that result from their choices of *courses of action* (the tactical alternatives). A *strategy* is a set of decisions formulated in advance of play specifying the choice, or the means of choice of courses of action in every contingency.

There is a large number of essentially distinct games and this chapter will introduce some of the simpler models from which general principles will be drawn. Games differ according to the *number of players*, the *number of courses of action* open to each player, the nature of the *pay-off function* (for example, if some players can gain only what other players lose this defines a *zero-sum* game) and the absence or presence of *co-operation* between players and the form that any such co-operation may take. We shall begin here with a look at two-person zero-sum games.

14-2 TWO-PERSON ZERO-SUM GAMES

Consider the following *pay-off matrix:*

		Action 1	Player B Action 2	Action 3
Player A	Action 1	+3	+1	+2
	Action 2	−4	0	+5

A has two courses of action, B has three. A *play* of the game consists of the *simultaneous* selection of courses of action by the two players. The entries in the pay-off matrix show the outcomes for the Row Player A. As the game is zero-sum, Player B gets *minus* these amounts—there are no overall gains or losses. The row player is a maximizer—seeking to arrive at high pay-off entries in the matrix. Obviously B, by contrast, is a minimizer seeking to make A's gain as small as possible.

What outcome will result? Consider a common-sense investigation. We shall make the important underlying presumption of rational and intelligent conduct of play by each participant. This being the case, Player B would decline ever to use Action 3. This is because no matter which action A chooses, B would be better off (have less to pay out to A) by playing his Action 2 rather than Action 3. Action 3 is said to be *dominated* by Action 2 for Player B. Player A, being rational, will know that B will never play the dominated action and A will consider only the first two columns of the pay-off matrix and will observe that what remains of row 1 (the pay-offs 3 and 1) dominate from his or her point of view what remains of row 2 (−4 and 0). Thus, a rational player A against a rational opponent would never use Action 2. Player B will, of course, draw the same conclusion and in what remains of the pay-off matrix (simply the elements 3 and 1) will see that Action 2 now dominates Action 1. The result of these considerations is that Player B plays Action 2 and Player A plays Action 1, the result being that B must pay A one unit.

This outcome can be arrived at in another way. Player A knows that Player B is a rational opponent and a minimizer. Consequently, for each of A's actions only the *minimum* pay-off is relevant—it is all that can be guaranteed. Player A then examines the row minima in the pay-off matrix. These are

	Action			Row minima
	1	2	3	
Action 1	+3	+1	+2	+1
2	−4	0	+5	−4
Column maxima	+3	+1	+5	+5

Figure 14-1

indicated in Fig. 14-1. Player B knows that A is rational and a maximizer, thus for each of B's columns, A will take the action that produces the *maximum* element. Player B accordingly examines the column maxima. Player A then selects the action corresponding to the greatest of the row minima while B selects the action corresponding to the least of the column maxima. These considerations give rise to the pay-off of +1 to A (hence −1 to B). This is known as the *maximin–minimax* solution. The outcome of +1 to Player A is known as the *value of the game*.

The pay-off +1, it will be observed, is both the minimum element in its own row and the maximum in its column. This defines a *saddle-point* in the pay-off matrix. It is an important property of such a point that there are *no gains to either player from a unilateral change of course of action*. It will be seen that, if switching from Action 2, B will be one or two units worse off, so long as A persists with Action 1. If A switches to Action 2, A will be one unit worse off so long as B persists with Action 2. Thus, if a saddle-point exists in a pay-off matrix in a two-person zero-sum game between rational opponents there is a watertight argument for the saddle-point outcome either in the case of a game played once or repeated a number of times. Choosing to play one course of action all the time represents the adoption of a *pure strategy*. The reader should now find the saddle-point and the corresponding pure strategy for each player with the following pay-off matrix:

$$
\begin{array}{rrrr}
-7 & 6 & 1 & -2 \\
0 & -5 & -1 & 4 \\
6 & 4 & 2 & 3 \\
3 & -3 & -7 & 5
\end{array}
$$

It will be noted that here the saddle-point cannot be arrived at by dominance considerations as in the earlier example. When approaching a two-person zero-sum game, the first step is always to examine the pay-off matrix for a possible saddle point.

Not all matrices have saddle-points. Consider the pay-off matrix:

$$
\begin{array}{rr}
2 & 4 \\
5 & 3
\end{array}
$$

Some inspection of this game soon makes obvious the conclusion that there is *always* a gain from a unilateral switch of action for one of the players. Also, should an opponent's course of action be known, advantage can be taken of this—this information has no value when the game has a saddle-point. What is a logical strategy for players when no saddle-point exists? Since the playing of a single course of action or a predictable sequence of actions will be exploited by the opponent, it is essential for a rational player to be *unpredictable*. This will imply the use of some or all of the actions with some degree of *probability*. This represents the adoption of a *mixed strategy*, the desired result of which for Player A is to maximize the minimum *expected* pay-off while B must determine probabilities to minimize the maximum expected pay-out.

To see how this situaton is worked out consider the non-saddle-point game above. Player A attaches probabilities p and $1-p$ to the choice of his actions 1 and 2 respectively. What is the best value of p from Player A's point of view? It is that value which gives him the largest expected pay-off. If B always played *his/her* Action 1, then A's pay-off would be (reading down the first column) E_1 where

$$E_1 = 2p + 5(1-p) = 5 - 3p$$

On the other hand if B played his/her Action 2 then A would expect E_2 where

$$E_2 = 4p + 3(1-p) = 3 + p$$

In repeated plays of the game, B might be expected to select the action that produced the *lower* of the E_1 and E_2 values. Consequently it is best for A to select the value of p that makes this least value *as large as possible*. The solution can be found by solving the equation

$$5 - 3p = 3 + p$$

$$\therefore \quad p = 0.5 \cdot \quad \text{and so} \quad (1-p) = 0.5$$

Thus A should make equiprobable his/her selection of actions—in this case. The situation is graphed in Fig. 14-2. As will be seen from Fig. 14-2, the best

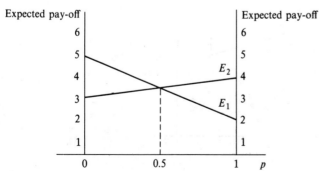

Figure 14-2

position for Player A is where the *lower envelope* of the E_1 and E_2 lines reaches its highest point and the value of the game $V = 3.5$. Note that, should Player A depart from the probabilities producing $E_1 = E_2$ then Player B will have an optimal *pure* strategy corresponding to the lower value of E_1 and E_2.

Similarly, optimal probabilities are determined for the column player. In order to minimize the expected payout, Player B should attach probabilities q and $1 - q$ to the selection of his actions so that:

$$2q + 4(1 - q) = 5q + 3(1 - q)$$

$$4 - 2q = 3 + 2q$$

$$q = \tfrac{1}{4}$$

$$(1 - q) = \tfrac{3}{4}$$

In which case B will keep A's gain *down* to 3.5. The situation for Player B is graphed in Fig. 14-3. In Fig. 14-3, it is the *upper* envelope—the highest of the two lines F_1 and F_2—that counts. Only when $q = \tfrac{1}{4}$ does B's expected payout get as low as 3.5. Again, if B departed from his or her optimal mixed strategy probabilities of $\tfrac{1}{4}$ and $\tfrac{3}{4}$ there would be an optimal *pure* strategy for A. For example, if B used both actions with equal probability, then A would play Action 2 alone and as a result would obtain $F_2 = 5(\tfrac{1}{2}) + 3(1 - \tfrac{1}{2}) = 4.$

In summary, B's problem is to minimize the maximum of F_1 and F_2 while A's was to maximize the minimum of E_1 and E_2. If both do this, a saddle-point in mixed strategies is obtained and the maximin-minimax philosophy is extended to games without a saddle-point in the original pay-off matrix. The distinction remains that where there is a saddle-point, A's gain is *guaranteed*,

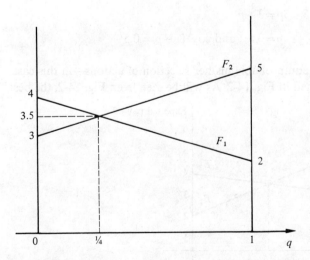

Figure 14-3

without a saddle-point it is *expected*. When there are more than two undominated actions for each player, and where there is no saddle-point, the calculation of optimal probabilities can involve extensive workings. There are a variety of solution techniques and also approximation methods. The problems can also be expressed as linear programming problems and solved via the simplex method. When the game is not zero-sum but the sum of the pay-offs to A and B in each case is constant, the game is said to be *constant sum*. Constant sum games can be easily reduced to zero-sum games and the same strategic considerations apply. In section 14-4, we shall consider an approximation procedure for the mixed strategy probabilities and section 14-5 will show how a solution via linear programming is possible. First, however, we shall consider games against nature.

14-3 GAMES AGAINST NATURE: A MARKETING EXERCISE

In a *game against nature* there is only *one* rational player or decision maker, but the outcomes depend not only upon the player's decisions but also upon the *state of nature*. The pay-off matrix has the same structure as in an ordinary two-person game but Player B is 'nature' and B's courses of action are the 'states'. These states are not selected on a known, rational criterion, but are determined by some unknown process. Obvious examples of games against nature are agricultural—where nature would represent factors such as weather, pests, etc. Less obviously, player A could be the firm and Player B 'the market'. In general, 'nature' consists of all the factors in the environment over which the decision maker has no control and about which uncertainty exists. The environment is then partitioned into the various states which reflect the combined effects of the uncontrollable and uncertain factors. The states of nature must be mutually exclusive and exhaustive.

Consider an example. A company is about to launch a new product and considers itself to have three essentially different possible actions.

1. To undertake a television-based advertising campaign which would bring rich rewards if successful, but big bills and poor rewards if the product is not well accepted (A_1).
2. To undertake a pilot study—a trial launch in a comparatively self-contained and representative community. This would be expected to give better prior knowledge of the product, so less widespread outcomes, but 'lack punch at the top end' (A_2).
3. Instead of the TV campaign, undertake a magazine- and poster-based programme of sales promotion. This might be expected to produce results somewhere between the other alternatives (A_3).

Market reaction to the product has been classified into three states, and estimated profits (in £10 000 units) are as given in the pay-off matrix below:

	Market reaction		
	Good	Moderate	Poor
A_1	110	45	−30
A_2	80	40	10
A_3	90	55	−10

How can a decision be arrived at? What course of action should be adopted?

In contrast to games between two rational and calculating players, in games against nature there is no definitive 'correct' strategy. A great deal depends on the particular outlook and current situation of the decision maker. Nevertheless, there are a number of distinct strategic possibilities to consider. At first, this in itself may be surprising as we assume *no information whatever* as to which state of nature will emerge. The strategies we shall review are as follows:

    (i) Maximin
    (ii) Maximax
    (iii) The Hurwicz criterion
    (iv) The Laplace criterion
    (v) Minimax regret.

The *maximin strategy* selects that course of action with the best of the worst outcomes—the minimum possible gain is maximized. Thus A_2 with a worst outcome of + 10 would be selected and the trial launch undertaken. However, unlike the two-player situation there is no compelling argument that this strategy must be adopted by a rational player. In games against nature, maximin is a suitable strategy for a decision maker of cautious disposition.

The *maximax strategy* selects that course of action which produces the best of the *best* outcomes. Thus, the maximax approach would identify A_1 in this case with an overall best possible outcome of + 110 and the TV campaign would get underway. Unlike the situation where there are two rational players, there is no compelling reason *against* this strategy. In games against a randomizer with unknown probabilities, the overall best outcome *could* occur and the adoption of a maximax strategy is logically defensible.

A common disadvantage of both maximin and maximax is that they take no explicit account of two thirds of the information in the pay-off matrix. In general, these strategies ignore a proportion $(n-1)/n$ of the available information when nature is partitioned into n states. This disadvantage can be overcome and greater generality achieved by adoption of the *Hurwicz criterion* which includes maximin and maximax as special cases and doubles the quantitative information used.

In the Hurwicz criterion approach, a number is determined for each course of action so that for each action the Hurwicz number is a proportion α of the best outcome plus a proportion $(1-\alpha)$ of the worst $(0 \leqslant \alpha \leqslant 1)$. Note that if $\alpha = 0$ we have the maximin strategy and if $\alpha = 1$ the maximax strategy results. The investor must choose α to best reflect his psychology. We shall see shortly that sensitivity analysis can help in this respect. For the moment set $\alpha = 0.3$. The Hurwicz numbers produced are:

$H(\alpha=0.3)$
12
31
20

In this event A_2 would be selected. On the other hand, if $\alpha = 0.7$

$H(\alpha=0.7)$
68
59
60

in which event the TV campaign would be indicated. A sensitivity analysis on α is strongly indicated since the action selected depends on the value of α used and an appropriate value of α is difficult to identify with precison. The simplest way to proceed is as follows. First each Hurwicz number must be expressed in terms of α.

For A_1 the Hurwicz number for arbitrary α will be H_1 where

$$H_1 = 110\alpha - 30(1-\alpha) = 140\alpha - 30$$

For A_2 we have

$$H_2 = 80\alpha + 10(1-\alpha) = 70\alpha + 10$$

and for A_3

$$H_3 = 90\alpha - 10(1-\alpha) = 100\alpha - 10$$

The values of H_1, H_2 and H_3 are shown plotted against α in Fig. 14-4. In Fig. 14-4, the relevant line for any value of α is the highest one and indicates the action to be preferred. For values of α up to $\frac{4}{7}$, Action 2 comes out best. For higher values of α, Action 1 is preferred. At no point does Action 3 emerge as

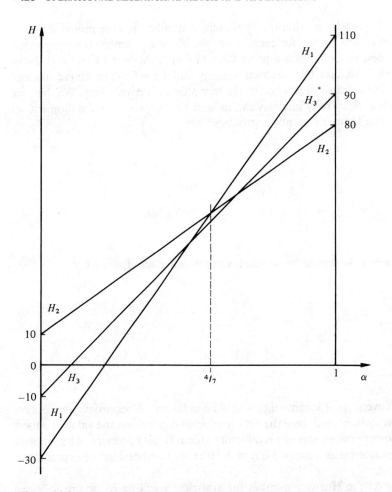

Figure 14-4

superior to both Action 1 and Action 2 and so would not be selected by the Hurwicz criterion on either of its special cases maximin and minimax. The sensitivity analysis also assists the decision maker in the problem of setting a value of α.

   Although the decision maker may not be able to pin down a precise value of α he may be able to make the statement: 'In my opinion no less emphasis should be placed on the worst result than on the best.' In other words $0 \leqslant \alpha \leqslant 0.5$. Throughout this range A_2 is preferred, so the trial launch is selected.

   The question arises as to whether there are any grounds on which Action 3 would be selected? When it is observed that the strategies examined so far have not taken the middle range outcomes into account, it is clear that since A_3

has the best of these, any criterion that gave sufficient emphasis to the moderate outcome would select A_3.

The *Laplace criterion* argues that since no information exists about how the states of nature are determined then there is no reason to think that any one state of nature is more probable than any other. The Laplace criterion, therefore, attaches a weight of $\frac{1}{3}$ to each pay-off that may result from a course of action and the products are summed. Called the results L_1, L_2, and L_3 the results are:

$$L_1 = 110/3 + 45/3 - 30/3 = 125/3$$
$$L_2 = 80/3 + 40/3 + 10/3 = 130/3$$
$$L_3 = 90/3 + 55/3 - 10/3 = 135/3$$

The action producing the highest L number is preferred—in this case Action 3. So the calculations proceed as if the weights were probabilities and the results expected values. The principle underlying the Laplace criterion is sometimes known as the *equiprobability of the unknown* or the *principle of insufficient reason* and the approach is also known as *Bayes criterion*. The main advantage of the Laplace criterion is that it takes all available information into account. In general, if there were n states of nature the weight attached to outcomes for each state would be $\frac{1}{n}$. The disadvantage of the approach is that the decision may be a function of the number of states into which it is decided to partition nature.

It would, in principle, be possible to extend the Hurwicz criterion to include all available information. The extended criterion would attach a weight of α_1 to the best outcome, α_2 to the second best, α_3 to the third best and so on down to α_n for the worst outcome of the n possibilities. The weights α would sum to unity. Thus A_3 could emerge if α_2 was sufficiently large relative to α_1 and α_3. It is important to note that the Laplace criterion can *not* be subsumed as a special case of the extended Hurwicz criterion with all α values set at $\frac{1}{n}$. In general the best, worst and middling outcomes will not, unlike the present example, be confined to their own columns. The Laplace criterion weights the states of nature. The Hurwicz approach weights outcomes according to their rank order of desirability.

Now consider the criterion of *minimax regret*.
This is in some ways the most subtle approach and is akin to the ideas of opportunity cost in economic theory. For each state of nature and payoffs are subtracted from the best payoff in that state (column). For the reaction 'Good'

	'Good'
A_1	0
A_2	30
A_3	20

The entries here can be thought of as 'regrets' in the following sense. *If* A_1 had been selected and *if* the market response was good, then the decision maker would have 'no regrets'. On the other hand if A_2 had been selected and the market response turned out to be good, then there would have been 30 less profit made than for the optimum decision in this state. There are regrets to the tune of 30. If A_3 had been selected then the regrets would have been $110 - 90 = 20$. Below is given the full regret matrix, where in the 'poor' state the regret of 40 for A_1 is $10 - (-30)$. Minimax regret then selects that action which has the *least maximum regret figure*. The maximum entry in the A_1 row is 40, in the A_2 row it is 30, and in the A_3 row it is 20. So with A_3 we guarantee that regrets are not excessive.

	Regret matrix		
	Good	Moderate	Poor
A_1	0	10	40
A_2	30	15	0
A_3	20	0	20

It is for decision makers to determine which of the strategies best suits their particular circumstances and psychology. Once the decision maker has selected the strategy, the strategy will identify the appropriate course of action.

14-4 PROBABILITY APPROXIMATION PROCEDURE

In two-person zero-sum games without a saddle-point, considerable work can be involved in identifying the optimal mixed strategy probabilities if there are several courses of action available to each player. There is an interesting procedure involving simulated play of the game which gives approximate value of the probabilities, a range within which the value of the game must lie and quite possibly precise values for both.

Consider the problem examined earlier with the pay-off matrix:

$$\begin{pmatrix} 2 & 4 \\ 5 & 3 \end{pmatrix}$$

The simulated play is begun, arbitrarily, with the Row Player A, selecting Action 1. In this case, the ideal choice of action for B would have been his or her Action 1 which keeps A's gain down to two units. A's selected action and B's ideal response are set down in a further row beneath the matrix thus:

$$\begin{pmatrix} 2 & 4 \\ 5 & 3 \end{pmatrix}$$

$$②\ 4$$

Number 2 is circled to indicate the selection of the corresponding action by B. If, however, B had selected his or her Action 2, A's best choice would have been Action 2. This is indicated by an additional column to the right of the pay-off matrix showing the pay-offs corresponding to B's Action 1 and in which:

$$\begin{pmatrix} 2 & 4 \\ 5 & 3 \end{pmatrix} \quad \begin{matrix} 2 \\ ⑤ \end{matrix}$$
$$② \quad 4$$

the number 5 is circled to indicate the consequent choice of Action 2 by A. The pay-offs that could result from A's choice of Action 2 are 5 units and 3 units. These are now added to the row beneath the pay-off to produce a second row representing totals for two plays. This is shown thus:

$$\begin{pmatrix} 2 & 4 \\ 5 & 3 \end{pmatrix} \quad \begin{matrix} 2 \\ ⑤ \end{matrix}$$
$$② \quad 4$$
$$⑦* \quad 7$$

B will choose the action giving rise to the lowest cumulative figure at any stage. In the present case, there is a tie which we shall resolve by selecting the lowest numbered course of action. Thus, B again selects Action 1. The star simply represents the resolution of a tied situation. Following Player B's selection of Action 1, these pay-offs are added to those in the additional column on the right of the matrix shown thus:

$$\begin{pmatrix} 2 & 4 \\ 5 & 3 \end{pmatrix} \quad \begin{matrix} 2 \\ ⑤ \end{matrix} \quad \begin{matrix} 4 \\ ⑩ \end{matrix}$$
$$② \quad 4$$
$$⑦* \quad 7$$

The number 10 is circled to indicate the maximizing player's preference for a total of 10 and the choice again of the second action by A. The corresponding pay-offs 5 and 3 are added to the second row beneath the matrix to produce:

$$\begin{pmatrix} 2 & 4 \\ 5 & 3 \end{pmatrix} \quad \begin{matrix} 2 \\ ⑤ \end{matrix} \quad \begin{matrix} 4 \\ ⑩ \end{matrix}$$
$$2 \quad 4$$
$$⑦* \quad 7$$
$$12 \quad ⑩$$

Again the circled number indicates the minimizing player's preference for a total of 10 rather than 12. This clearly identifies the choice of his second action the pay-offs in which are added to the second column to the right of the pay-off matrix.

This process continues for a given number of iterations—for example, 10 and the results are shown in Fig. 14-5. At the end of the 10 iterations, the number of times a given action has been selected by a player (as indicated by the circles) is divided by the number of iterations. This is the approximate value of the optimal mixed strategy probabilities. Thus A's probabilities are estimated as $p=0.3$ for the first action and $(1-p)=0.7$ for the second (true values $p=(1-p)=0.5$). For B the approximate values of $q=0.2$ and

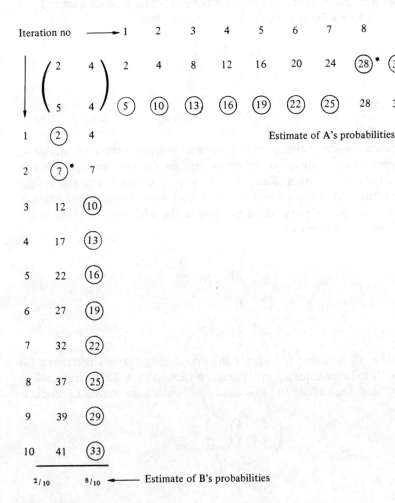

Figure 14-5

$(1-q)=0.8$ are closer to the true values of 0.25 and 0.75. Of course, the larger the number of iterations undertaken, the better the fit.

Intuitively, the procedure works because the iterations below the matrix list B's *optimal* selections given the choices made by A. Obviously B could not improve on this. To the right are A's optimal choices given the decisions made by B.

The totals after 10 iterations can be used to give a range for the value of the game (the expected pay-off to player A). Looking at the columns to the right, A's choices have resulted in a total of 36 after 10 iterations — an average of 3.6 per play. This represents an *upper bound* on the value of the game since in generating the columns optimal decisions for A were always made. Similarly, looking at the rows beneath the matrix, B manages to keep the pay-off total to A down to 33 after 10 iterations—an average of 3.3. This represents a lower bound on the value of the game V. Thus we can write:

$$3.3 \leqslant V \leqslant 3.6$$

However, it may be possible to set a narrower range than this. There was no particular reason to select 10 iterations. The *least upper bound* that can be produced from the exercise is found by looking across the columns and dividing the total at each stage by the number of iterations to that point. Thus after 8 iterations a total of no more than 28 was achieved. This is an average of 3.5. Examination of the rows produces a greatest lower bound of 3.5 at iteration 2. In this case, the value of the game is in fact identified since GLB = LUB = 3.5 = V.

14-5 LINEAR PROGRAMMING SOLUTION

The fact that two-player zero-zum games can be expressed as linear programming problems is at first sight surprising, since LP problems involve just one decision maker. But it should be recalled that with each maximizing LP problem (the *primal*) there is associated a minimizing problem—*the dual* which has the same optimal value of the objective function. The maximizing player's problem corresponds to the primal LP problem and the minimizing player's problem to the dual. Set out in linear programming form, A's problem is to:

$$
\left.
\begin{array}{ll}
\text{Maximize } V & \\
\text{subject to } 2p + 5(1-p) \geqslant V & \\
4p + 3(1-p) \geqslant V & \\
p \qquad \leqslant 1 & \\
p \geqslant 0 &
\end{array}
\right\} \qquad (14\text{-}1)
$$

where in (14-1) V represents the value of the game and p is the probability that A must determine for the selection of the first action. Consider the first of the constraints. $2p + 5(1-p)$ is A's expected gain if B plays his Action 1. This cannot be less than the value of the game because, if it was, B would always play Action 1 and keep A's pay-off down to this amount. Recall that V represents the amount that B can keep A's pay-off down to and that A can ensure for him or herself in expected terms. In general, V is not restricted in sign (as the value of the game may represent a loss to Player A) but this need not concern us here.

A more convenient arrangement for the simplex method is to bring all the

			V	p	s_1	s_2	s_3
0	s_1	5	1	3	1	0	0
0	s_2	3	1	-1	0	1	0
0	s_3	1	0	1	0	0	1
		0	-1	0	0	0	0

			V	p	s_1	s_2	s_3
0	s_1	2	0	4	1	-1	0
1	V	3	1	-1	0	1	0
0	s_3	1	0	1	0	0	1
		3	0	-1	0	1	0

			V	p	s_1	s_2	s_3
0	p	½	0	1	¼	-¼	0
1	V	3½	1	0	¼	¾	0
0	s_3	½	0	0	-¼	¼	1
		3½	0	0	¼	¾	0

Figure 14-6

variables in 14-1 over to the left-hand side and reverse the direction of the inequalities by multiplying by -1. The result is:

$$\left.\begin{aligned}
&\text{Maximize } V \\
&\text{subject to } V + 3p \leqslant 5 \\
&\qquad\quad V - \ \ p \leqslant 3 \\
&\qquad\qquad\quad p \leqslant 1 \\
&\qquad\qquad\quad p \geqslant 0
\end{aligned}\right\} \qquad (14\text{-}2)$$

Slack variables, s_1, s_2, and s_3 can now be added into the constraints of (14-2) and the problem solved via the simplex method. The workings are shown in Fig. 14-6. In Fig. 14-6, the optimal value of p is shown to be $\frac{1}{2}$ and V emerges as $3\frac{1}{2}$ as we had previously seen. Note that in the second tableau, p does not appear in the solution column so $p = 0$ and $1 - p = 1$. This situation corresponds to Player A adopting the pure strategy of always playing the second action. Consequently, B would employ his other Action 2, thus keeping A's gain down to 3. An advantage of using the simplex method to solve for the optimal mixed strategy probabilities is that both A and B's problems are solved at once—the optimal probabilities for B appear in the final index row.

The linear programming problem faced by A is graphed in Fig. 14-7. The feasible region (hatched) is OABCD with the optimum at B.

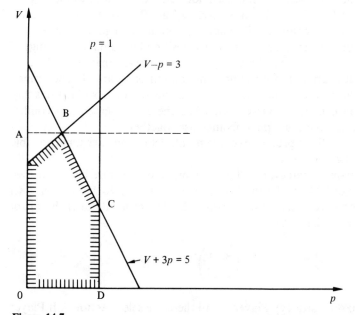

Figure 14-7.

14-6 NON-ZERO-SUM GAMES

Where the total pay-off to the players varies depending on the actions they choose, the possibility of co-operation enters the picture (zero-sum games are situations of pure conflict). Bargaining problems are of this form and much work has been done to address the theory to this area.

The pay-off matrix in non-zero-sum games has to state separately the gain to each player for each combination of actions. Figure 14-8 shows the structure of the 'prisoner's dilemma' game:

$$
\begin{array}{c}
\qquad\qquad\qquad \text{Player B} \\
\qquad\qquad \text{Action 1} \quad \text{Action 2} \\
\text{Player A} \left\{ \begin{array}{ccc} \text{Action 1} & (4,4) & (0,5) \\ \text{Action 2} & (5,0) & (2,2) \end{array} \right.
\end{array}
$$

Figure 14-8.

where the first element in any bracketed pair is A's gain and the second is B's gain.

We shall examine a number of *solution concepts* (rather than clear-cut solutions) in the context of the pay-off matrix above. First, however, it is worth examining the matrix to see if the combinations of actions produce points which are either *Pareto optima* or *equilibrium points*. A Pareto optimum point is one from which one player cannot be made better off without worsening the position of the other. Thus, all points *except* 2,2 are Pareto optima. The point 2,2, therefore, lacks economic efficiency. An equilibrium point is one from which *neither* player can improve his or her position by a unilateral change of course of action. The only equilibrium point in the pay-off matrix is 2,2 which means that if it is arrived at by some combination of separately determined strategies by the players, it may well 'stick'. The pay-off matrix illustrates that communication can be desirable even when there are elements of conflict provided that in *some* cases pay-offs increase together.

Having noted these properties of the points, let us consider some possible strategies for the players.

In the *max-min* strategy, the player attempts to maximize his or her own minimum pay-off. Thus, Player A having regard only to his or her own pay-offs will observe a matrix comprising the first elements of each pair of pay-offs in Fig. 14-8. This is:

$$
\begin{pmatrix} 4 & 0 \\ 5 & 2 \end{pmatrix}
$$

Under the max-min strategy Player A will therefore select Action 2. If Player B adopts a max-min approach he or she will observe a matrix consisting of the second elements of Fig. 14-8, specifically:

$$\begin{pmatrix} 4 & 5 \\ 0 & 2 \end{pmatrix}$$

and will accordingly select the second column. Thus, the outcome of the game when both players adopt the max-min strategy is (2, 2). Note (a) that this is likely to persist because (2, 2) is an equilibrium point and (b) that the outcome is inferior for both players compared with (4, 4).

In the *min-max* strategy the player seeks to minimize the other player's maximum pay-off. This is not the same as minimax in zero-sum games as the opponent's pay-off is not the other player's pay out. If Player A adopted this strategy for whatever reason, he or she would observe the second elements (B's gains) in the pay-off matrix of Fig. 14-8. Specifically A would see:

$$\begin{pmatrix} 4 & 5 \\ 0 & 2 \end{pmatrix}$$

and note that under A's Action 1, B might achieve a gain of 5 but under A's Action 2, B's maximum gain is limited to 2. Accordingly, A plays Action 2. If B also adopts this strategy in looking at A's pay-offs in Fig. 14-8, he or she will select Action 2. The outcome will again be (2, 2).

In the *max-diff* strategy the player attempts to maximize the difference between his or her own pay-off and that of the other player. A will thus observe:

$$\begin{pmatrix} 0 & -5 \\ 5 & 0 \end{pmatrix}$$

where clearly Action 2 dominates. If Player B also adopts this approach he or she will observe:

$$\begin{pmatrix} 0 & 5 \\ -5 & 0 \end{pmatrix}$$

and will select the second column. The outcome will be 2, 2 in which neither player succeeds in achieving a positive differential.

Under *altruism* the player attempts to maximize the other player's minimum or maximum pay-off. Thus, A will observe B's pay-offs, i.e.

$$\begin{pmatrix} 4 & 5 \\ 0 & 2 \end{pmatrix}$$

and will choose row 1, regardless of whether he is seeking to protect B against low outcomes or create the possibility of a maximal result for B. If B is also an altruist, he or she will observe A's gain, i.e.

$$\begin{pmatrix} 4 & 0 \\ 5 & 2 \end{pmatrix}$$

and so will select the first column. The outcome is (4, 4) which is a Pareto optimum. Also, given that each player continues to observe the other's gain, it is an equilibrium point and is likely to persist.

The final strategy we shall examine is *max-sum*. This is a *co-operative* stategy between the players with a prior agreement to play the actions that result in the (4, 4) outcome. It should be noted that since 4, 4 is not an equilibrium point there is an incentive to unilaterally renege on the agreement and take a profit of one. If both do so, the outcome (2, 2) would result.

In the above brief review, we have considered the outcome when both players have the same strategy. There is no reason why this should be the case in general. It is a useful exercise to confirm the following results for the given pay-off matrix by studying the outcomes when players adopt different strategies:

1. If both players adopt self-seeking/'vindictive' strategies, an economically inefficient 'social minimum' of (2, 2) results.
2. If one player adopts a self-seeking/vindictive strategy and the other is an altruist, an economically efficient (Pareto optimal) but, socially inequitable, result occurs.
3. If both players adopt selfless strategies an economically efficient and socially equitable result occurs.

In general, non-zero-sum games can be classified as either *co-operative* or *non-co-operative*. In non-co-operative games, players make independent decisions because enforcible agreements are either forbidden (as with anti-cartel legislation) or impossible. In non-co-operative games the equilibrium point concept extends to mixed strategy cases. Co-operative games divide into two types—with and without *side payments* (transferable pay-offs). The division of the pay-off presents the basic problem of these games and it is a major problem facing any profit-sharing cartel. Where side payments are possible, only the total pay-off to each group of players (*coalitions*) needs to be considered. An important concept here is the *core*. A core settlement is a set of pay-offs so that a coalition of players of any size can't do better by refusing the settlement and 'slogging it out' in the game. The core does not exist for zero-sum games but clearly it is an interesting point as to whether any given set of wages, dividends, subsidies, etc., in the economy as a whole (a non-zero-sum game) represents a core settlement.

14-7 MEASUREMENT OF PAY-OFFS

The theory of games depends on the possibility of attaching numerical values to outcomes. The mechanism by which this is done in particular cases can vary. Cash sums will often be the obvious units—crop yields or market shares are other possibilities. It is important, however, that whatever the units of pay-off are called they are measured by an appropriate *scale*.

In Game Theory in general, pay-offs must be measured on an *interval scale*. When such a scale (call it x) is used, any other scale, y, could be used so that $y = ax + b$ with $a > 0$. Such a *transformation* is said to be *order preserving* and *linear*. A good example is temperature measurement with degrees Fahrenheit being obtained from degrees Celsius by the transformation $F = 1.8C + 32$.

A *ratio scale* is a special, more restrictive, case of an interval scale. Here ratios are meaningful—unlike the interval case. For ratios to be preserved only a transformation $y = ax$ with $a > 0$ will suffice. This is said to be a *similarity transformation*. Money, weight and energy are measured on ratio scales. A ratio scale is more restrictive than necessary for Game Theory.

For most purposes in Game Theory, an *ordinal scale* is too weak. In an ordinal scale no significance can be attached to the magnitude of differences between pay-offs. On an ordinal scale if pay-offs were measured in units x any transformation $y = f(x)$ that is order preserving (i.e. $dy/dx > 0$) will do equally well. In games against nature some concepts such as minimax or minimax regret are valid on an ordinal scale.

It is generally assumed in Game Theory that the pay-off data are linear with respect to money (or, in general, with respect to the physical units involved; for example, crop yields).

14-8 CONCLUSIONS

In the context of business and economics, the theory of games has provided useful insight into bargaining situations, the nature of cartels, marketing problems and consideration of overall corporate strategy.

In theoretical terms, the theory of games provides a good analysis of situations involving one, two or a very large number of players. It does not provide uniquely satisfactory analysis of situations involving a limited number of three or more players. In this respect, a comparison has been drawn with mechanics which describes very well situations involving 1, 2 or 10^{23} bodies.

It is, however, always likely that in a situation that can be characterized as a game against nature (or where a number of participants interact in a situation with elements of conflict and co-operation) Game Theory will be able to provide the decision makers with useful strategic insight.

EXERCISES

14-1 Revision exercises
    (i) What characteristic distinguishes Game Theory from most other OR topics?
    (ii) Why is Game Theory so called?
    (iii) In what areas has Game Theory provided useful insight?
    (iv) With respect to what criteria do games differ?
    (v) Provide a rationale for the maximin strategy in two-person zero-sum games.
    (vi) What is the distinguishing feature of a saddle-point in a pay-off matrix?
    (vii) Distinguish between pure and mixed strategies.
    (viii) What is meant by a game against nature?
    (ix) What is the Hurwicz criterion?
    (x) Is maximax a reasonable strategy in a game against nature?
    (xi) What is the principle of insufficient reason?
    (xii) Explain the minimax regret strategy.
    (xiii) Set out a two-person zero-sum game with two actions per player in the form of a linear programming problem.
    (xiv) In non-zero sum-games what is meant by a Pareto optimal point?
    (xv) What is meant by an equilibrium point in a pay-off matrix? Why is such a point likely to have stability?
    (xvi) Briefly explain what is meant by max-min; min-max; max-diff and altruism.
    (xvii) What is meant by a side-payment? In what category of game are side payments important?
    (xviii) What is meant by an interval scale? Give an example.

14-2 Find the saddle points in the following pay-off matrix:

$$
\begin{pmatrix}
4 & -2 & -6 & 6 & -3 \\
7 & 5 & 3 & 4 & -1 \\
1 & -4 & 0 & 5 & 0 \\
-6 & 7 & 2 & -1 & -2 \\
2 & 6 & 4 & 3 & 0
\end{pmatrix}
$$

14-3 Find the optimal mixed strategy probabilities for Player A in the following game:

$$
\text{Player A} \begin{array}{c} \text{Player B} \\ \begin{pmatrix} -1 & 2 \\ 1 & 0 \end{pmatrix} \end{array}
$$

What is the value of the game of Player A?

14-4 An agricultural research station has estimated that for a 50-acre farm with standard soil conditions and husbandry, the annual profits to be obtained from planting the land solely with each of four varieties of wheat depend on rainfall in the following way:

		Rainfall	
	Low	Medium	High
Seed variety A	11 200	9 100	7000
B	10 100	14 000	5600
C	6 800	10 800	7300
D	9 900	13 500	5500

For a farmer with a standard 50 acres, and for *one season only*, ascertain which variety should be sown under each of the following decision rules:

  (a) maximax;
  (b) maximin;
  (c) Hurwicz and criterion for $\alpha = 0.6$;
  (d) the Laplace criterion;
  (e) minimax regret.

14-5 What is 'special' about the following game:

$$\begin{Bmatrix} 0 & -4 & 2 \\ 4 & 0 & -1 \\ -2 & 1 & 0 \end{Bmatrix}$$

What relationship will exist between the optimal probability vectors for the two players? (No need to solve for the actual values.)

14-6 Use the iterative procedure for twelve iterations to find approximate value of the players mixed strategy probabilities in the following game. From your workings also determine the greatest lower bound and least upper bound that may be placed on the value of the game.

$$\begin{Bmatrix} 5 & -4 & 2 \\ -2 & 3 & -1 \\ 1 & -1 & 3 \end{Bmatrix}$$

Notes: (i) Start with A playing action No. 1.
   (ii) In the case of ties select the lowest numbered course of action in each case.

14-7 Formulate the following game as a linear programming problem and solve it by the simplex method.

$$\begin{bmatrix} 1 & 4 \\ 3 & 2 \end{bmatrix}$$

14-8 For the following non-zero-sum two-player game:

		Player B	
		Action 1	Action 2
Player A	Action 1	(1, 1)	(4, −1)
	Action 2	(−1, 4)	(3, 3)

Find

  (i) the equilibrium point,
  (ii) the max-min solution,
  (iii) the min-max solution,
  (iv) the max-diff solution,
  (v) the max-sum solution,
  (vi) an altruistic solution.

Solution guides

14-2 Row two, column three (3); row five, column five (0).

14-3 A's probabilities must be such that no matter what B's actions A's expected gain is the same. If Player B plays the first column, A's expected gain is E_1 where

$$E_1 = -p + (1 - p)$$

This must be equated to the expected gain when B plays his second column

$$E_2 = 2p + 0(1-p)$$

Solving $\qquad E_1 = E_2$ gives $p = \frac{1}{4}$, $1 - p = \frac{3}{4}$

The value of the game to Player A is given by either E_1 or E_2 when the optimal value of p is inserted. Thus the value of the game is 0.5. This is what A can expect to gain on average.

14-4 Note that variety D is dominated by variety B, so that D can be omitted.

(i) (a) Variety B
   (b) Variety A
   (c) The Hurwicz numbers (H) will be 0.6 (best profit) +0.4 (worst profit) as shown below.

Variety	H
A	9 520
B	10 640
C	9 200

Thus variety B would be planted.

(d) In the Laplace criterion we assume that each of the rainfall patterns is equally likely and the Laplace number (L) for variety will be 1/3 (low rainfall profit) + 1/3 (medium rainfall profit) + 1/3 (high rainfall profit). So we obtain:

Variety	L
A	9100
B	9900
C	8300

Thus variety B would be selected in this case.

(e) The regret matrix is:

	Low	Medium	High
A	0	4900	300
B	1100	0	1700
C	4400	3200	0

Thus variety B with maximum 'regrets' of only 1700 is clearly indicated.

14-5 The unusual feature of this zero-sum game is that the same pay-offs are faced by each player. For this to occur, the pay-off matrix must be *skew symmetric* (the rows are the negation of the columns). For such a game the optimal mixed strategy probabilities are the same for each player. Also, the game is a *fair game*, that is the value of the game $V = 0$.

14-6 The calculations are as follows:

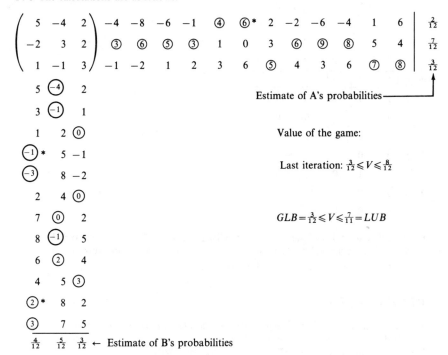

14-7 In linear programming form, the problem as seen by Player A is to:

Maximize V
subject to $p + 3(1-p) \geqslant V$
$4p + 2(1-p) \geqslant V$
$p \leqslant 1$

where $p \geqslant 0$.

After re-arrangement and inclusion of slack variables the problem becomes:

Maximize V

subject to $V + 2p + s_1 = 3$

$V - 2p + s_2 = 2$

$p + s_3 = 1$

where $p \geqslant 0,\ s_1 \geqslant 0,\ s_2 \geqslant 0,\ s_3 \geqslant 0$

The simplext workings are:

		1	0	0	0	0
		V	p	s_1	s_2	s_3
0	s_1	3	1	2	1	0	0
0	s_2	2	1	-2	0	1	0
0	s_3	1	0	1	0	0	1
		0	-1	0	0	0	0
0	s_1	1	0	4	1	-1	0
1	V	2	1	-2	0	1	0
0	s_3	1	0	1	0	0	1
		2	0	-2	0	1	0
0	p	$\frac{1}{4}$	0	1	$\frac{1}{4}$	$-\frac{1}{4}$	0
1	V	$\frac{10}{4}$	1	0	$\frac{1}{2}$	$\frac{1}{2}$	0
0	s_3	$\frac{3}{4}$	0	0	$-\frac{1}{4}$	$\frac{1}{4}$	1
		$\frac{10}{4}$	0	0	$\frac{1}{2}$	$\frac{1}{2}$	0

Player A should employ Action 1 with probability $\frac{1}{4}$ and Action 2 with probability $\frac{3}{4}$. As a result, the value of the game will be $\frac{10}{4}$. Player B's optimal mixed strategy probabilities are $\frac{1}{2}$ and $\frac{1}{2}$.

14-8 (i) (1, 1); (ii) (1, 1); (iii) (1, 1); (iv) (1, 1); (v) (3, 3); (vi) (3, 3)

REFERENCES

Von Neumann, J., and Morgenstern, O. (1953), *The Theory of Games and Economic Behaviour*, third edition, Princeton University Press.

Luce, R. D., and Raiffa, H. (1957), *Games and Decisions*, Wiley.

FURTHER READING

Duckworth, W. E., Gear, A. E., and Lockett, A. G. (1977), *A Guide to Operational Research*, third edition, Chapman & Hall. Includes production application of games against nature and wider consideration of operational gaming.

Hillier, F. S., and Lieberman, G. J. (1974), *Operational Research*, second edition, Holden Day. Includes graphical solution procedure and linear programming formulation.

Kim, C. (1975), *Quantitative Analysis for Managerial Decisions*, Addison-Wesley. Contains section on converting business conflict situations into games.

Rapoport, A. (1966), *Two-Person Game Theory: the essential ideas*. University of Michigan Press. Highly readable review of all you need to know about two-person games.

Taha, H. A. (1987), *Operational Research*, fourth edition, Collier Macmillan. Includes graphical solution procedure, linear programming formulation and Hurwicz criterion.

Young, O. R. (1975), *Bargaining-Formal Theories of Negotiation*, University of Illinois Press. An advanced text containing several chapters in game-theoretic models of bargaining.

FIFTEEN

SEQUENCING PROBLEMS

15-1 INTRODUCTION

The owner of a small printing business has one typesetting machine, two offset litho machines and one folding machine. He has a number of orders to produce leaflets and brochures. In what order should the leaflets be put through the machines to keep idle time to a minimum? A building firm has contracts at a number of sites all of which call for the use of excavators, mixers and other equipment in limited supply. How should the contracts be worked on in order to minimize overall completion time? A factory manager has a number of jobs that need to be worked on by several machines. In what order should the jobs be done?

The regularly encountered situations above are examples of *sequencing problems*. The difficult nature of these situations has long been recognized but they have only be subjected to scientific analysis since the advent of operational research. The principle difficulty is presented by the combinatorial nature of the—even comparatively small numbers of jobs and machines produce an astronomical number of alternatives. For example, if there are five jobs to be processed on each of six machines, there are no less than 2 985 984 000 000 ways in which this can be done! In general, if there are n jobs to be processed on m machines, the number of alternative sequences in $(n!)^m$. It is not surprising, therefore, that exact solutions cannot be computed for the larger problems of this kind—even on today's high-powered computers.

Sequencing problems can be formulated in a number of ways; for example, as integer linear programming problems, although this does not provide a practical method of solution. Here, we shall concentrate on problems with the objective of time minimization in mind. The cases we shall examine can be classified as follows:

Number of jobs	Number of machines	Method considered
(n)	(m)	
n	1	Enumeration
n	2	Johnson's method
n	3*	Johnson's method
2	m	Graphical method
n	m	Review of approximation procedures

*Subject to certain special conditions

15-2 A ONE-MACHINE PROBLEM

In section 15-1, we saw that where several machines and jobs are involved, the number of prima facie possible schedules soon becomes enormous. Clearly, however, if $m = 1$, this reduces the number of possible schedules to n! Provided n is not too lage, *complete enumeration* may be possible; that is, all sequences may be explicitly considered. Even in cases where n is too large for this to be possible, some groups of sequences may be ruled out by other considerations. For example, there may be some restrictions on the feasible sequences or the method may implicitly eliminate some sequences as clearly non-optimal. Here, we shall consider a scheduling problem involving five jobs but where the first and last jobs are specified in advance.

A firm makes a line of five tinned food-products. They are made in batches ('jobs') using one process ('machine'). When one job has been done the equipment must be cleaned and re-set for the next job. The 'set-up times' between each pair of jobs are shown below. For technical reasons job (2) *must* be done first and job (4) must be the last to be done. With these restrictions in mind the firms management wishes to answer the following questions:

(a) What sequence minimizes total set-up times?
(b) The processing times for each job (not given) are widely different—could this affect the answer?
(c) Although it is not essential, management would prefer job (1) to be done before job (3). Can this desire be accommodated without undue time penalty?
(d) As a result of a time and motion study it is found that the (2) to (1) set-up time could be substantially reduced. What size reduction would be needed to cause a change in the optimal sequence?

The set-up times (in minutes) are shown in Fig. 15-1. Consider now the

To job

	(1)	(2)	(3)	(4)	(5)
(1)	—	18	13	21	12
(2)	32	—	16	17	14
From job (3)	18	25	—	20	11
(4)	12	21	19	—	41
(5)	27	16	20	40	—

Figure 15-1

minimization of machine set-up times. This is one case where complete enumeration is possible. Since job (2) must come first and job (4) last, the possible sequences differ only in the ordering of jobs (1), (3), and (5). There are just $3! = 6$ different arrangements. Simply add up the times for each sequence, viz.:

$$(2)(1)(3)(5)(4) \qquad 32 + 13 + 11 + 40 = 96 \text{ min}$$

$$(2)(1)(5)(3)(4) \qquad 32 + 12 + 20 + 20 = 84 \text{ min}$$

$$(2)(3)(1)(5)(4) \qquad 16 + 18 + 12 + 40 = 86 \text{ min}$$

$$(2)(3)(5)(1)(4) \qquad 16 + 11 + 27 + 21 = 76 \text{ min}$$

$$(2)(5)(1)(3)(4) \qquad 14 + 27 + 13 + 20 = 74 \text{ min}$$

$$(2)(5)(3)(1)(4) \qquad 14 + 20 + 18 + 21 = 73 \text{ min}$$

Thus the sequence $(2)(5)(3)(1)(4)$ is optimal with total set-up times of 73 minutes.

Now consider the case of widely varying production times for the jobs once they are on the machines. In fact, the actual processing times would make no difference to the sequence that minimizes total time (processing + set-up) since the sum total of the processing times will be the same in any sequence (remember that it is a one-machine problem).

The possibility of accommodating a management preference for Job (1) to be carried out before Job (3) is easily considered simply by examining the above list for the best sequence in which Job (1) precedes Job (3). It is evident that only one minute would be lost by switching to the sequence $(2)(5)(1)(3)(4)$.

The necessary reduction in two-to-one set-up time required to bring about a change in the optimal sequence is found by taking the time difference between the best sequence involving (2) and (1) consecutively (84 minutes) and the current optimum. Thus the saving would need to be at least 12 minutes ($32 \rightarrow 20$) to make a change positively worth while. This time saving could come down to 11 minutes if the (1) before (3) preference is adopted. While 'one machine' problems can yield to enumeration, and, as we have seen, reveal useful management information, a more sophisticated method is required to address problems involving two machines.

15-3 JOHNSON'S METHOD

The method developed by S. M. Johnson was originally designed to work with any number of jobs but only two machines. It was later extended to the three-machine case (still any number of jobs) provided that there is no bottleneck on the middle machine. This procedure will be described later on. Johnson's original method is best illustrated by example.

A firm has seven jobs which must be processed by two machines, a cutting machine and a polishing machine. For all jobs, cutting precedes polishing. The jobs differ in specification and the times taken by each job on each machine are as shown in Fig. 15-2. In what sequence should the jobs be put through the two machines so as to minimize the total time taken to complete all of the jobs? Suppose that numerical order was used to determine the sequencing, i.e., Job (1) first, Job (2) second, and so on. The results are shown in Fig. 15-3.

Job (1) goes onto the cutting machine at time $t = 0$ and is finished at time $t = 8$. It goes straight onto the polishing machine and is finished after $8 + 14 = 22$ minutes. Meanwhile the cutter became free at $t = 8$ and Job (2) can go on at that time. Cutting is finished at $t = 17$ but Job (2) now has to wait until $t = 22$ for the polishing machine to be free. Again, Job (3) can be started on cutting a $t = 17$ and, since it is not finished until $t = 31$ it can go straight onto the polisher (Job (2) has finished polishing at $t = 28$). And so on. The time out of polishing for the last job is the total time of the problem. Thus the arrangement takes 74 minutes.

Now let us find the optimal sequence. Johnson's method, which is

	Job						
	(1)	(2)	(3)	(4)	(5)	(6)	(7)
Cutting m/c (min)	8	9	14	12	6	10	7
Polishing m/c (min)	14	6	6	9	5	7	8

Figure 15-2

Job	Cutting m/c		Polishing m/c	
	Time in	Time out	Time in	Time out
(1)	0	8	8	22
(2)	8	17	22	28
(3)	17	31	31	37
(4)	31	43	43	52
(5)	43	49	52	57
(6)	49	59	59	66
(7)	59	66	66	74

Figure 15-3

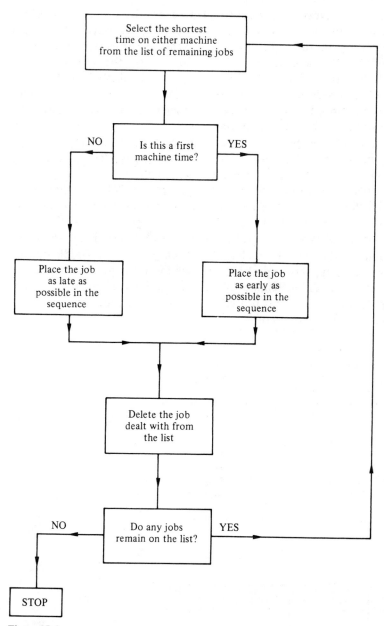

Figure 15-4

guaranteed to produce an optimal sequence, can be presented as a flow diagram as shown in Fig. 15-4. In applying the procedure as shown in Fig. 15-4, (5) crops up first of all from the complete original job list, having the shortest overall time of 5 minutes. This is a second-machine time so (5) goes to the end of the list. Next come Jobs (2) and (3) each with six minutes' polishing time. We shall put Job (3) in next to last place and Job (2) above it. The reader should verify that the same total time is arrived at if the order of Jobs (3) and (2) is reversed. This is true in general, 'ties' do not matter—they can be resolved arbitrarily. This is true for ties of all kinds, e.g., if a job takes the same time on both machines it does not matter whether the job is treated as a first-machine case or a second-machine case. The two resulting sequences will usually differ but both will have the same total time.

Continuing with the sequencing, next are Jobs (7) and (6) each with a seven-minute time. Job (7) goes to the top of the list and (6) goes above (2). Then comes Job (1) which goes beneath (7) and finally Job (4) goes in the last remaining place. The sequence is then: (7), (1), (4), (6), (2), (3), (5) and the times in and out are shown in Fig. 15-5. Thus the completion time has been reduced to 71 minutes total. The result of Fig. 15-5 can also be presented as a bar chart with the horizontal axis being time in minutes. This is done in Fig. 15-6. In Fig. 15-6, the initial idle time on Machine 2 (polishing) and the final idle time on Machine 1 (cutting) show up clearly. In this form, the necessity of having short-time jobs at the extremities of the sequence is evident. We can now consider an extension of this procedure: to cases involving three machines which meet a special provision.

Job	Cutting m/c		Polishing m/c	
---	Time in	Time out	Time in	Time out
(7)	0	7	7	15
(1)	7	15	15	29
(4)	15	27	29	36
(6)	27	37	37	44
(2)	37	46	46	52
(3)	46	60	60	66
(5)	60	66	66	71

Figure 15-5

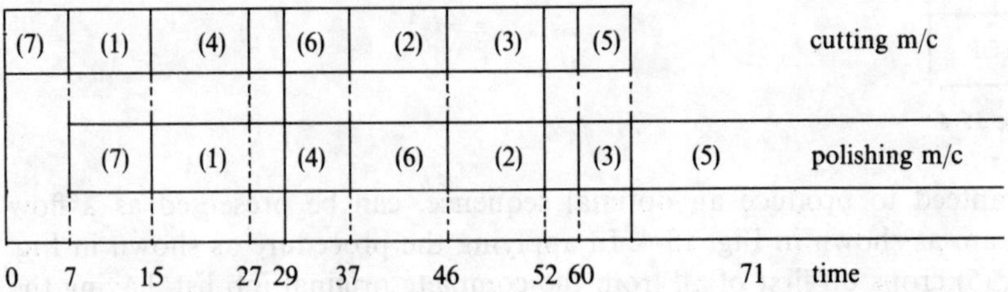

Figure 15-6

15-4 THREE MACHINES: USE OF JOHNSON'S METHOD

While there is no solution for the *general* three-machine case, we mentioned that Johnson's method can be extended to the three-machine, *n*-job case if there was no bottleneck on the middle machine. To be more specific if the three machines are A, B, and C, Johnson's method can be used if one or both of the following conditions are satisfied: (a) the lowest job time for machine A is at least as large as the largest job time for machine B; and (b) the lowest job time for machine C is at least as large as the largest job time for machine B.

The extension is quite simple. Let the individual job times by A_i, B_i, and C_i for the jobs $i = 1, \ldots, n$. Reduce the problem to a *two*-machine case by defining new times D_i and E_i where

$$D_i = A_i + B_i$$
$$E_i = B_i + C_i$$

and apply Johnson's method as if there were only two machines D and E.

Consider an example where there are six jobs to be sequenced through the three machines A, B, and C. The job times are given in Fig. 15-7(the units are minutes). It will be seen that condition (a) above is satisfied since the least of the times on machine A is eight and the greatest of the machine B times is also eight. The D_i and E_i values produced are shown in Fig. 15-8. The application of Johnson's, method to the composite data of Fig. 15-8 produces the 'in-out

Job	A_i	B_i	C_i
(1)	13	8	14
(2)	8	6	11
(3)	12	8	10
(4)	8	5	10
(5)	10	8	7
(6)	11	8	4

Rule (a) applies.

Figure 15-7

Job	D_i	E_i	
(1)	21	22	3
(2)	14	17	2
(3)	20	18	4
(4)	13	15	1
(5)	18	15	5
(6)	19	12	6

Figure 15-8

$= 4, 2, 1, 3, 5, 6$

Job	A		B		C	
	In	Out	In	Out	In	Out
④	0	8	8	13	13	23
②	8	16	16	22	23	34
①	16	29	29	37	37	51
③	29	41	41	49	51	61
⑤	41	51	51	59	61	68
⑥	51	62	62	70	70	74

Figure 15-9

table' shown in Fig. 15-9. The optimal sequence of jobs ④, ②, ①, ③, ⑤, ⑥ produces an overall minimum time of 74 minutes. In the case of Machine 3, the 'in' time of a job is the later of its 'out' time from Machine B and the out time of the proceeding job from Machine C. The latter situation is the case for Jobs (2), (3), and (5). Total idle time on Machine B is 19 minutes between jobs or 31 minutes out of the total of 74. This idle time figure can be calculated directly from Fig. 15-9 or the total of job times on Machine B subtracted from the 74 minutes completion time for the problem. As an exercise, the reader may confirm that the effect of a requirement that Job (6) precede Job (5) would be a 3 minute addition to total time.

15-5 TWO JOBS, *m* MACHINES

Consider a situation in which two jobs are to be processed by m machines. As we saw in section 15-1, there are $(2!)^m$ alternative arrangements for whether each machine will work first on Job (1) or on Job (2). However, if there is a prescribed sequence for each job in which it must go through the machines (for technological reasons), many of the 2^m arrangements will not be consistent with these orderings. A procedure for weeding out these technically infeasible arrangements was developed by Akers and Friedman (see Sasieni, Yaspan and Friedman, 1959). The remaining feasible arrangements are then enumerated to find the one which takes the least time. Gantt charts can be used in this stage of the procedure and the method is described as *reduced enumeration.*

There is also a graphical means by which the prescribed ordering through the machines can be ensured and clashes of the two jobs on any particular machine avoided. The method also provides a visual means of obtaining 'good' solutions. We shall explain the graphical method in the context of an example.

Suppose that two jobs are to be processed on each of five machines A—E. The necessary technological ordering for the two jobs is given as:

Job 1	A	B	C	D	E
Job 2	E	C	A	D	B

The time taken by each job on each of the machines is as follows (the units are minutes):

Machine	A	B	C	D	E	Total machine time
Job 1 time	3	5	6	2	3	17 mins
Job 2 time	4	3	2	4	5	18 mins

The machine orderings and the times taken by each job are now set out along the axes of a diagram—each axis corresponding to one job. This is done in Fig. 15-10. The hatched areas in the figure are *infeasible* regions representing the simultaneous use of a machine by both jobs. The point with co-ordinates given by the total machine time for the two jobs represents the completion of both.

Optimization is achieved by constructing the shortest line from the start

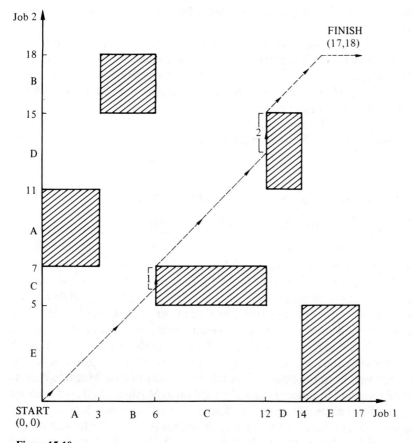

Figure 15-10.

(of both jobs) at the origin to the finish point. Movement along this line must be at 45° (representing a situation where both jobs are being worked on) or vertically (Job (2) progressing, Job (1) not progressing) or horizontally (only Job (1) being worked on). Clearly, diagonal travel is superior to vertical or horizontal travel and a 'good' line is indicated.

With any such line from start to finish, the total time taken by Job (1) will be the 17 minutes machine time plus the number of minutes during which the job was not on any machine. This will be the sum of the vertical distances, V. The total time taken to complete Job (2) will be the 18 minutes machine time plus any horizontal travel, h). The objective is to minimize the time required for *both* jobs to be completed. This will be whichever is the greatest of $17 + V$ or $18 + h$. In general, the objective will be to:

$$\text{Minimize } [\text{Maximum}[T_1 + V, T_2 + h]] \qquad (15\text{-}1)$$

where in (15-1) T_1 is total machine time for Job (1) and T_2 is total on machine time for Job (2).

The graphical method does not provide a formal means of optimizing 15-1 but seeks to arrive at a good solution. The dashed line in Fig. 15-10 does, in fact, produce an optimal solution. The conflict over Machine C usage results in one minute of idle time for Job (1). The conflict over Machine D usage results in two minutes of idle time for Job (1).

Thus, total idle time for Job (1) is $V = 1 + 2 = 3$ mins while Job (2) experiences no delays between machines. The total times taken for the jobs are then:

$$\text{Job (1):} \qquad T_1 + V = 17 + 3 = 20 \text{ mins}$$

$$\text{Job (2):} \qquad T_2 + h = 18 + 0 = 18 \text{ mins}$$

The two jobs can thus be completed in 20 minutes overall.

It should be noted from Fig. 15-10, that there are alternative ways in which the result of 20 minutes overall time can be arrived at. Initial delays of 1, 2 or 3 minutes in Job (1), represented by movement up the vertical axis by these amounts, would produce the same overall result—eliminating the 1 minute delay on Machine C and reducing or eliminating the delay on Machine D.

Following the line shown in Fig. 15-10, the work on the jobs can be read off as follows. Both jobs start at $t = 0$. Job (1) is finished on Machine A at an elapsed time $t = 3$ minutes and goes straight on to Machine B. At $t = 5$ minutes, Job (2) is finished on Machine E and goes straight on to Machine C. At $t = 6$ minutes Job (1) is finished on Machine B but has to stand idle for one minute waiting for Job (2) to come off Machine C at $t = 7$. Both jobs then proceed, Job

2 on Machine A and Job (1) on Machine C. At $t = 11$, Job (2) is finished on Machine A and goes straight on to Machine D. At $t = 13$, Job (1) is finished on Machine C but must wait 2 minutes for Job (2) to come off Machine D. At $t = 15$ Job (2) is complete on Machine D and goes straight on to Machine B, while Job (1) goes on to Machine D. At $t = 17$, Job (1) comes off Machine D and goes straight on to Machine E. At $t = 18$, Job (2) is complete. At $t = 20$, Job (1) comes off Machine E and both are finished.

The graphical approach is useful, therefore, when there are predetermined orders in which an individual job must be worked on by the machines. Blocking off areas of simultaneous usage makes it easy to see where clashes can occur.

15-6 n JOBS, m MACHINES

There is no general solution procedure that will produce global optimum solutions in the n jobs, m machine case. Although there are a number of mathematical programming formulations (linear, dynamic and integer), it is not usually practicable to employ programming methods as exact solution procedures.

One approach to the n job, m machine case is that of *sampling*. A number of feasible schedules are selected at random and the schedule giving the shortest time is adopted. The larger the sample size, the greater is the probability of having included an optimal schedule. There is, of course, a trade-off here as computation time and costs will rise with the size of sample. A balance has to be struck between the benefits of more effective schedules and the costs of more expensive computing.

The problems we have considered are *static* problems. Many scheduling situations in practice have new jobs arriving daily with specified latest completion dates. This defines a *dispatching problem*. Practicable approaches employ *heuristic methods*—empirically tested rules and practices that result from accumulated experience with scheduling problems. *Priority decision rules* are an example of this type of approach. For instance, jobs with the shortest on-machine times or those with the earliest late start times might be prioritized. Several examples are listed in Wild (1989). Priority rules have been tested using simulation methods and combinations of two or more priority rules can prove to be effective.

In this brief look at scheduling techniques, we have considered problems in which time taken was the measure of effectiveness. In general, while effectiveness will be a function of the order in which the jobs are carried out it may be machine *set-up costs* which are minimized rather than time. The set-up costs involved in getting a machine ready for a job will depend upon the job last done by the machine. In this case, an optimal sequence minimizes these costs overall. In the 'one machine' example of section 15-2, the data of Fig. 15-1 could have referred to set-up costs and the procedure used in a similar fashion.

EXERCISES

15-1 Revision exercise

    (i) Give examples of sequencing problems that can arise in practice.

    (ii) Explain how the number of possible orderings of jobs expands with the number of machines and jobs involved.

    (iii) Explain Johnson's Method for sequencing n jobs through two machines.

    (iv) Under what circumstances can Johnson's Method be used in three machine problems?

    (v) Explain the graphical procedure in the m machine, two job case where there are prescribed technological orderings for the jobs.

    (vi) What is the essence of the sampling approach to the n job, m machine, sequencing problem?

    (vii) Give an example of a priority decision rule.

15-2 A company makes a range of five products in batches. It has to decide in what order to run off the batches. Machine re-set times (hours) between manufacture of each pair of products are:

	To product				
	(1)	(2)	(3)	(4)	(5)
From product (1)	—	5.8	3.8	3.4	3.5
(2)	5.9	—	3.7	3.9	3.0
(3)	2.9	3.8	—	4.3	3.6
(4)	3.2	3.5	3.4	—	5.0
(5)	3.0	3.9	3.1	3.6	—

It is necessary that Job (5) is the last to be done. Because of tight delivery schedules Job (4) must not be later than second to be done and Job (3) must be no later than third.

    (i) Find a time minimizing sequence. Is it unique?

    (ii) What would be the time penalty involved in starting with product three?

15-3 A company has 10 jobs which must each be processed on two machines. For all jobs the Machine A operation precedes the Machine B operation. The times required by each job are shown below. In what sequence should the jobs be put through the two machines so as to minimize the total time taken to complete all of the jobs?

	Job									
	(1)	(2)	(3)	(4)	(5)	(6)	(7)	(8)	(9)	(10)
Machine A (min)	23	21	15	19	16	17	17	24	18	17
Machine B (min)	14	16	17	22	20	13	20	18	17	23

15-4 Eight jobs are to be sequenced through three machines: A, B, and C. The job times on each machine are given below. Find an optimal sequence.

Job	Time required on machine A	B	C
(1)	25	17	20
(2)	17	17	18
(3)	20	16	23
(4)	15	18	24
(5)	13	14	21
(6)	21	15	19
(7)	22	13	25
(8)	12	18	26

15-5 Two jobs are to be sequenced through five machines A–E with the following technological orderings and job times in minutes:

Job 1	A	B	C	D	E
Time	2	4	3	2	3
Job 2	A	D	B	C	E
Time	2	3	2	4	3

Use the graphical method to obtain the minimum completion time for both jobs.

Solution guides

15-2 (i) Given the conditions stated, there are only eight alternative arrangements. The total times are given in the table

Arrangement	Time (hours)
4 3 1 2 5	15.1
4 3 2 1 5	16.6
4 1 3 2 5	13.8
4 2 3 1 5	13.6
1 4 3 2 5	13.6
2 4 3 1 5	13.7
3 4 1 2 5	16.3
3 4 2 1 5	17.2

Thus there are two optimal sequences: 42315 and 14325
    (ii) 2.7 hours ($= 16.3 - 13.6$).
15-3 (ii) 3, 5, 10, 7, 4, 8, 9, 2, 1, 6. The solution is non-unique as the positions of Jobs 10 and 7 could be interchanged.
15-4 (ii) Reducing the problem to a two-machine case (as condition (b) for Johnson's method is

satisfied). Let D_i be the combined machine A and B times and let E_i be the combined times on machines B and C. We obtain:

Job	D_i	E_i
(1)	42	37
(2)	34	35
(3)	36	39
(4)	33	42
(5)	27	35
(6)	36	34
(7)	35	38
(8)	30	44

which leads to the optimal sequence:

$$5, 8, 4, 2, 7, 3, 1, 6.$$

15-5 The optimal arrangement is shown in Fig. 15-11. Job (1) goes first on Machine A, giving rise to 2 minutes idle time for Job (2). Subsequently, there is a further 1 minute idle time for Job (2)

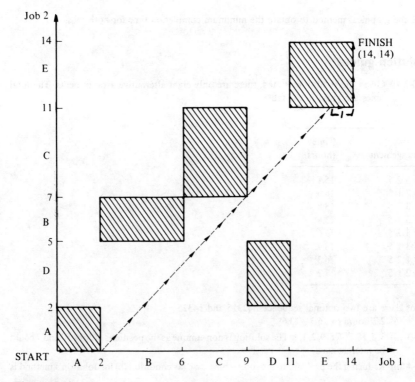

Figure 15-11

waiting for Job (1) to come off Machine E. Total time taken for Job (2) is then:

$$T_2 + h = 14 + 3 = 17 \text{ minutes}$$

Job (1) has a uninterrupted run and is completed after 14 minutes. Minimum time to complete the jobs is therefore 17 minutes.

REFERENCES

Sasieni, M., Yaspan, A., and Friedman, L. (1959), *Operations Research: methods and problems*, Wiley.

Wild, R. (1989), *Production and Operations Management*, fourth edition, Cassell.

FURTHER READING

Monks, J. G. (1982), *Operations Management: theory and problems*, second edition, McGraw-Hill. Contains sections on priority decision rules and the use of Gantt charts.

Taha, H. A. (1987), *Operations Research: An Introduction*, fourth edition, Collier Macmillan. Shows integer programming formulation of scheduling problems.

DYNAMIC PROGRAMMING

16-1 INTRODUCTION

Where a decision problem can be structured to take the form of a number of sequentially related stages, *dynamic programming* will be a possible solution procedure. Dynamic programming is an enumerative method but, as we shall see, a good deal of the enumeration is implicit. Where non-linear objective functions are involved, the case for a dynamic programming approach is strengthened. The central notion is to break a complex problem down into more manageable sequentially linked sub-problems. Under certain conditions (multiple stages, non-linearities), dynamic programming is likely to be the method of choice if not the only option. In other circumstances, dynamic programming will be one of a number of alternative approaches.

Dynamic programming developed mainly as the work of Richard Bellman in the 1950s. It is structurally related to *control theory* and has found many engineering applications. In operations research proper it has found application in network flows, capital budgeting, stock control, scheduling, and integer programming problems. Dynamic programming overlaps virtually all types of mathematical programming areas and is not easily compartmentalized.

Advanced work in the area is, naturally, not easy to grasp, but even the elementary material has been rendered obscure by a rather opaque notation. As far as is possible we shall avoid the use of symbols in this presentation and attempt to convey the essential notions by way of examples drawn from various parts of operational research.

16-2 THE ROUTING PROBLEM

One of the best illustrations of the value of dynamic programming is in *routing problems*, in physical terms relating to electrical power transmission or to the construction of gas or oil pipelines. Figure 16-1 represents a pipeline routing problem. From a storage reservoir, S, a pipeline is to be routed through intermediate stations to a delivery point or terminal, T. Five intermediate stations are required (for pumping, inspection, etc.) but there are a number of alternative locations for each station. Costs of constructing links between possible stations are shown. The only feasible linkages are as illustrated. What is the cheapest route for the pipeline? We shall solve the problem by the

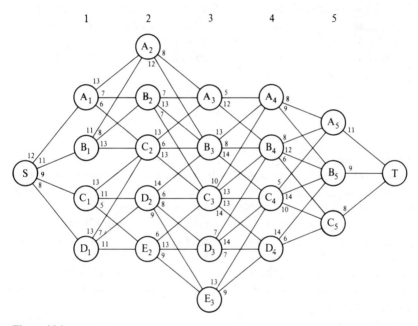

Figure 16-1

backward solution. The reader will already be familiar with the notion of a backward pass through a network from the process of obtaining late start or late event times in critical path method. Consider first the choice of location for station (5). There are three possibilities: A_5, B_5, or C_5. In each of the circles enter the *least cost* of getting to the terminus, T, from that location. In fact there is no choice. It costs 11 from A_5, 9 from B_5, and 8 from C_5. We would put this as in Fig. 16-2 nothing having been decided so far. Now consider the choice of location for station (4). There are four possibilities: A_4, B_4, C_4, and D_4. For *each* of these stations we want to determine the least cost of completing the journey to T. Consider A_4. From here we can go, at a cost of 8,

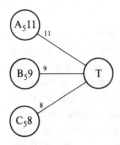

Figure 16-2

to A_5 and from there we know it costs 11 to get to T. Thus the cost would be 19. But there is another possibility. We can go from A_4 to B_5 and thence to T. This means of completing the journey from A_4 would cost 9 (from A_4 to B_5) + 9 (from B_5 to T), a total of 18. These are the only possibilities. Enter the *lower* figure in the circle for A_4 thus:

Now do the same for B_4, C_4, and D_4. From B_4 there are three choices: via A_5 costing $8 + 11 = 19$; via B_5 costing $12 + 9 = 21$; or via C_5 costing $6 + 8 = 14$. So in the B_4 circle enter 14. Applying the same simple procedure to C_4 and D_4 gives the picture as in Fig. 16-3. Now apply the same ideas to the station three locations as shown in Fig. 16-4. And similarly for stations (2) and (1).

The complete picture is shown in Fig. 16-5. The first thing that is found is that the cheapest pipeline would cost 44. The actual route is then 'unrolled' quite simply since it was D_1 that gave rise to the 44 at S, it was D_2 that gave rise to the 36 at D_1 and so on. It will be seen that there are *two* optimal routes

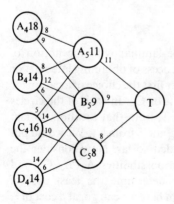

Figure 16-3

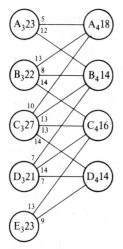

Figure 16-4

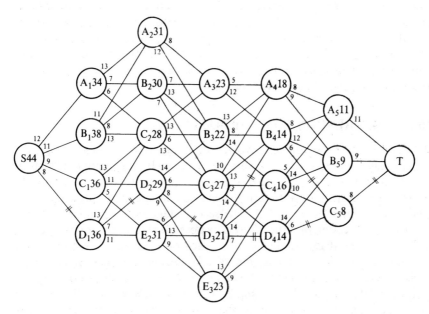

Figure 16-5

marked ——‖——. They diverge at D_3 and consist of

$$D_1, D_2, D_3, B_4, C_5 \text{ and } D_1, D_2, D_3, D_4, C_5$$

This *non-uniqueness* is usually welcomed in practice as some flexibility is introduced, although it is minimal here.

The reader may confirm that the solution is correct by repeating the exercise going *forwards* from S. The principle is the same. At first glance, the methods may seem rather close to a complete enumeration of all possibilities— but this is far from being the case. As will have been noted, once the structure was given, it took only a few minutes to solve the problem. Explicit evaluation of every route would take far longer. As the number of connections increases and the number of choices at each stage increases, the total number of possible routes rises *combinatorially*. Even in the present, small example, there are 272 routes. By complete explicit enumeration each path would have to be (a) identified, (b) recorded, and (c) evaluated by adding up six figures. If we allowed 20 seconds or so to do each path, over $1\frac{1}{2}$ hours of intense effort would be required to solve the problem by complete enumeration. There would also be much greater likelihood or error. The reader might like to verify that there are 272 paths through the network. This can be done by a method not dissimilar to the one we have just used. Go through the network but at each station enter not the least cost to that point, but the *number of paths to that point*. The number of paths to A_3 (from S) for instance is the *sum* of the number of paths to A_2, B_2, and C_2. This result can be confirmed by a backward pass.

If you have understood the workings of the pipeline example and have grasped the idea of why it works, then you have all that is needed to solve numerical examples. In the next section we spell out what has been involved and what the general principles are.

16-3 THE PRINCIPLE OF OPTIMALITY

We have seen that the problem involves five *stages*. At each of these stages the system may be on any one of a number of *states*. In our example a 'state' is a choice of location. For instance at the *first* stage we are concerned with the choice of location for the fifth station. The states possible here are 'being at A_5', 'being at B_5', and 'being at C_5'. The *second* stage in the problem solution relates to the location of station four. The possible states here are being at A_4, at B_4, at C_4, or at D_4. And so on. For each of these states we need a *state description*. This is a presentation of all relevant information for future decision. Here, we are concerned with costs. The state description at A_4, for instance, is the cost of 18. Working back from T we have seen that 18 is the lowest cost that we can arrive at. Put another way, 18 is the least cost of completing the journey from A_4. The sequence of states that gave rise to the optimal cost of 18 was A_4, B_5, T—this sequence of states constitutes an optimal *sub-policy*. In the system as a whole we look for the optimal *policy* which is a sequence of states from start to finish. Now the fundamental concept in dynamic programming is the *principle of optimality*. This can be stated in numerous ways. In respect of a least-cost routing problem we can express it thus:

> *Principle of optimality:* 'The overall least cost route from origin to destination (i.e., from S to T) contains the least-cost route between any two stations on the overall least-cost route.'

By 'station' here we intend to include both S and T. So that the overall least-cost route gives, for example, the cheapest route between B_4 and T, or between S and D_3, or between D_1 and C_5.

In all the workings we had no idea which stations would figure in the optimum. We did not know whether A_3 or D_3 would be part of the optimal sequence. The full sequence—and hence the optimal states of which it is comprised—is only revealed at the 'unrolling'. All the bridges have to be properly built: we do not know, when we are building them, which ones the army will pass over.

The method of solving a problem in stages with the result of a (usually simple) calculation at one stage being used to perform a subsequent calculation of another stage is known as *recursion*. The principle of recursive or *serial optimization* is fundamental to dynamic programming. The various stages are linked through the recursive relationship so that a solution to all the sub-problems leads to a solution of the problem as a whole.

16-4 THE WAREHOUSING PROBLEM

We have already studied one well-known problem in dynamic programming—the routing problem. Now we consider another famous case—the *warehousing problem*. This is a simplified and stylized version of the wholesaler's situation in which it is desired to decide on purchases and sales of a single commodity to take best advantage of known price variations.

A wholesaler stocks a single item. The ex-factory price (c_t) at which he buys and the wholesale price (p_t) at which he sells vary from month to month. Lead time on his purchases is 14 days, i.e., an order placed on 18 March arrives in stock on 1 April. Each month he buys an amount, q_t, around mid-month so that it arrives in stock on the first day of the following month. Sales volume in any month, v_t, will not exceed the stock available at the start of that month. Total storage capacity is K. Ignore storage and transactions costs. The prices are expected to be:

Month (t)	Ex-factory price (c_t)	Wholesale price (p_t)
Jan. $(t=1)$	70	90
Feb. $(t=2)$	64	82
Mar. $(t=3)$	72	70
Apr. $(t=4)$	70	85
May $(t=5)$	65	90
June $(t=6)$	65	85

The wholesaler holds an initial stock of 300 units on 1 January. What should be the pattern of purchases and sales to maximize profit over the six-month period?

Again a backward working method will be employed. Consider the situation in June. Let this be stage one. Profit in this stage, Π_1, is revenue from sales less cost of purchases. Namely:

$$\Pi_1 = p_6 v_6 - c_6 q_6$$

which we wish to maximize with respect to v_6 and q_6; the June sales and purchases. Clearly:

$$v_6 \leqslant I_6$$

since by the specification of the problem sales in any month cannot exceed the inventory at the start of the month. Now purchases in June are limited by storage capacity:

$$q_6 \leqslant K - I_6 + v_6$$

i.e., storage capacity is K; there are already I_6 in stock to start with but v_6 have already been sold. Naturally v_6 and q_6 cannot be negative. So what we are faced with is a linear programming problem! In full, it is to

$$\text{Maximize } \Pi_1 = p_6 v_6 - c_6 q_6$$

$$\text{subject to} \qquad v_6 \leqslant I_6$$

$$q_6 \leqslant K - I_6 + v_6$$

$$\text{where} \qquad q_6 \geqslant 0, v_6 \geqslant 0$$

Now this problem is trivial. We shall assume that no terminal stocks are required (this *could* be incorporated) and June is the last month being considered; thus it is pointless making purchases, so $q_6 = 0$. Also v_6 is made as large as possible (all stock is sold) so $v_6 = I_6$. Thus:

$$\text{Maximum } \Pi_1 = p_6 I_6$$

and we should note, for use in a moment, that:

$$I_6 = I_5 + q_5 - v_5$$

Now consider transactions in May. This is stage two. In keeping with the principle of optimality we want the profit *from here on* (i.e., May *plus* June's) to be as large as possible. So we write the profit function at stage (2) as:

$$\Pi_2 = p_5 v_5 - c_5 q_5 + \Pi_1$$

in which the *maximum* value of Π_1 would be used, i.e., $p_6 I_6$. But if we now substitute for I_6 we get:

$$\text{Maximum}\quad \Pi_1 = p_6 I_6 = p_6 I_5 + p_6 q_5 - p_6 v_5$$

and substituting into Π_2 gives:

$$\Pi_2 = p_5 v_5 - c_5 q_5 + p_6 I_5 + p_6 q_5 - p_6 v_5$$
$$\therefore \Pi_2 = (p_5 - p_6)v_5 + (p_6 - c_5)q_5 + p_6 I_5$$

which is the expression to be maximized with respect to the two variables v_5 and q_5. The constraints are:

$$v_5 \leqslant I_5$$
$$q_5 \leqslant K - I_5 + v_5$$

so that the linear programming problem is:

$$\text{Maximize } \Pi_2 = (p_5 - p_6)v_5 + (p_6 - c_5)q_5 + p_6 I_5$$
$$\text{subject to} \qquad v_5 \leqslant I_5$$
$$q_5 \leqslant K - I_5 + v_5$$
$$v_5 \geqslant 0, q_5 \geqslant 0$$

Figure 16-6 graphs the feasible region (shaded). The optimum will be at one of the corners OABC depending on the slope of the objective function contours.

This whole procedure is repeated for each month until January (stage (6)).

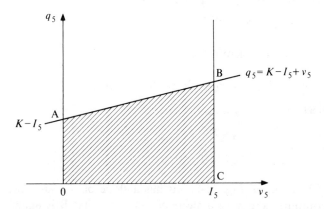

Figure 16-6

The solution is then unrolled. Let us now use the actual figures and carry out the workings.

For stage (1) we can straightaway write:

$$\text{Maximum} \quad \Pi_1 = p_6 I_6 = \boxed{85 I_6}$$

Now the LP problem for stage (2) is:

$$\text{Maximize} \quad \Pi_2 = (90 - 85) v_5 + (85 - 65) q_5 + 85 I_5$$

$$\text{subject to} \quad v_5 \leqslant I_5$$

$$q_5 \leqslant K - I_5 + v_5$$

Now thinking in terms of Fig. 16-6 the objective function contours have negative slope $(= -5/20)$ so B will be the optimal point. Thus $v_5 = I_5$ and $q_5 = K$. So that:

$$\text{Maximum} \quad \Pi_2 = 5 v_5 + 20 q_5 + 85 I_5$$

$$= 5 I_5 + 20 K + 85 I_5$$

$$= \boxed{90 I_5 + 20 K}$$

Now for April (stage (3), $t = 4$) we must maximize Π_3, that is:

$$\text{Maximize} \quad \Pi_3 = p_4 v_4 - c_4 q_4 + \text{maximum } \Pi_2$$

$$= 85 v_4 + 70 q_4 + 90 I_5 + 20 K$$

but $I_5 = I_4 + q_4 - v_4$ so that:

$$\Pi_3 = 85 v_4 - 70 q_4 + 90 (I_4 + q_4 - v_4) + 20 K$$

$$= -5 v_4 + 20 q_4 + 90 I_4 + 20 K$$

and the linear programming problem is to:

$$\text{Maximize} \quad \Pi_3 = -5 v_4 + 20 q_4 + 90 I_4 + 20 K$$

$$\text{subject to} \quad v_4 \leqslant I_4$$

$$q_4 \leqslant K - I_4 + v_4$$

$$v_4 \geqslant 0, q_4 \geqslant 0$$

Now again thinking in terms of Fig. 11-8, AB has a slope of $+1$ and the objective function contours here have a slope of $+1/4$. So that B is again optimal. Thus:

$$v_4 = I_4 \quad \text{and} \quad q_4 = K$$

and maximum $\quad \Pi_3 = -5I_4 + 20K + 90I_4 + 20K$

so maximum $\quad \Pi_3 = \boxed{85I_5 + 40K}$

Now for the fourth stage (March):

$$\Pi_4 = p_3 v_3 - c_3 q_3 + \max \Pi_3$$

So:

$$\Pi_4 = 70v_3 - 72q_3 + 85I_4 + 40K$$
$$= -15v_3 + 13q_3 + 85I_3 + 40K$$

and in this case the objective function contours (slope $= 15/13$) are steeper than the constraint line AB so that point A is optimal. At this point $v_3 = 0$ and $q_3 = K - I_3$. This results in:

$$\text{Maximum} \quad \Pi_4 = 72I_3 + 53K$$

By similar processes we obtain:

$$\text{Maximum} \quad \Pi_5 = 82I_2 + 61K \quad (v_2 = I_2, q_2 = K)$$

and

$$\text{Maximum} \quad \Pi_6 = 90I_1 + 73K \quad (v_1 = I_1, q_1 = K)$$

and the fully unrolled results sequence (recalling that $I_1 = 300$) and setting $K = 1000$) is:

$$v_1 = 300$$
$$q_1 = 1000$$
$$\text{So} \quad I_2 = 1000$$
$$\therefore \quad v_2 = 1000$$
$$q_2 = 1000$$
$$I_3 = 1000$$
$$v_3 = 0$$
$$q_3 = 0$$

$$I_4 = 1000$$
$$v_4 = 1000$$
$$q_4 = 1000$$
$$I_5 = 1000$$
$$v_5 = 1000$$
$$q_5 = 1000$$
$$I_6 = 1000$$
$$v_6 = 1000$$
$$q_6 = 0$$

and the total profit made is:

$$\Pi_6 = 90I_1 + 73K = 27\,000 + 73\,000 = 100\,000$$

In retrospect the optimal policy is fairly obvious but we have gained a little more than this. For instance we have seen that the optimal level of profit (the 100 000) is a *linear* function of initial stock and warehouse capacity (the coefficients 90 and 73 depend upon the pattern of prices) and various further results can be proved. The main point of the exercise was to illustrate a classic dynamic programming problem which turns out to be a sequence of simple linear programming problems.

16-5 MARKETING APPLICATION

It is sometimes the case that a problem may present itself which does not at first appear to be of a suitable structure for dynamic programming. However, as the following example illustrates, when formulated appropriately, the problem can be expressed in stages and dynamic programming may turn out to be a good solution procedure.

The marketing manager of a chain of retail chemists is faced with the following problem. The company is thinking of introducing its own brand of shampoos. There would be three types: Gold (dry air), Silver (greasy hair) and Green (medicated). The maximum sales promotion (sp) budget is £45 000 and the relationship between the various possible sp levels and subsequent contributions is

	\multicolumn{13}{c	}{Type}
	\multicolumn{4}{l}{Gold}	\multicolumn{4}{l}{Silver}	\multicolumn{5}{l}{Green}
Sp expenditure (£000's)	10	15	20	30	10	15	20	30	10	15	20	25	30
Contribution (£000's)	25	35	40	48	25	28	30	48	30	35	38	40	48

It is necessary that each product receive some expenditure and the alternatives above represent distinct 'packages' and are neither divisible nor repeatable. The entire budget need not be spent. What should be the level of sales promotion expenditure on each product in order to maximize total contribution? How does dynamic programming improve on complete enumeration in this type of problem?

As is the case in many operational research problems, it is, as a rule, a good idea to spend a few moments checking for any obvious simplifications or reductions in problem size that can be made at once. A little reflection reveals that the most expensive alternative (sp = 30) can be ruled out in each case since even if the cheapest package was used in the other cases (10 each) the budget limit would be exceeded.

This done, we come to the questions of stages and states. There is a fairly obvious sequence of stages. The first stage will be the consideration of *one product alone*. Stage (2) will be the joint consideration of two products and stage (3) will incorporate all three products. We shall see that it does not matter which product is taken first. The process is like the consideration of the months in the warehousing problem: first June, then May and June together, and so on.

But what are we to mean by 'state' in this problem? As Taha (1987) points out, 'The definition of "state" is usually the most subtle concept in dynamic programming formulations.' Taha goes on to suggest two helpful questions:

1. What relationships bind the stages together?
2. What information is needed to make feasible decisions at the current stage without checking the feasibility of decisions made at previous stages?

These questions point very strongly towards 'sp expenditure so far' as the 'state'. This links the stages and is one of the two feasibility considerations.

Now for the workings. Let stage (1) be consideration of Green expenditures (states). So, in tabular form we have:

Stage (1): (Green)

State	Π_1
10	30
15	35
20	38
25	40

That is all that is done for the moment in this stage—no more than a recording of the possibilities. The objective function Π_1 simply records the contributions from Green alone. There is no way of telling at the moment which 'state' will be selected. This will become clear only at the unrolling phase. Now for stage (2). Here we shall consider Green and Silver *taken together*. The function Π_2 will consist of Silver *and* Green returns. Now there are only four distinct states (representing total sp expenditure on Green and Silver) made up as shown below. But for the states 25, 30, and 35 these can be made up in different ways and, of course, only the *best* value of Π_2 for these states could ever be relevant.

Stage (2): (Green + Silver)

State	Silver sp		Stage (1) state	Π_2
		Compositon		
20	10	+	10	55
25	15	+	10	58
	10	+	15	60*
30	20	+	10	60
	15	+	15	63*
	10	+	20	63*
35	20	+	15	65
	15	+	20	66*
	10	+	25	65

Figure 16-7

Details are shown in Fig. 16-7. This completes stage (2) at the moment. Again, there is no indication as to what the best decision is. The asterisk indicates the best value of Π where there is more than one possibility. Now on to stage (3). This brings in Gold as well, so that Π_3 will represent the total contributions from all three products. Details are shown in Fig. 16-8. Now the solution can be unrolled. Obviously the best value of Π_3 is 100. This is the greatest total contribution from all three products. As in the warehousing problem the value of the objective at the last stage represents the total position, not just what is added at that stage. The 100 corresponded to 20 for Gold and the state of 25

Stage (3): (Green + Silver + Gold)

State	Gold sp		Stage (2) state	Π_3
		Composition		
30	10	+	20	80
35	15	+	20	90*
	10	+	25	85
40	20	+	20	95
	15	+	25	95
	10	+	30	98*
45	20	+	25	100*
	15	+	30	98
	10	+	35	91

Figure 16-8

from stage (2). Referring to the stage (2) workings we see that the 25 is best made up by 10 from Silver and the state of 15 from stage (1). This completes the solution.

To demonstrate that the same optimum would be arrived at if the (a, b and c) products had been brought together in a different order, Fig. 16-9 (a, b and c) gives the workings when Gold is taken first and then Green

(a) Stage (1): Gold

State	Π_1
10	25
15	35
20	40

(b) Stage (2): (Gold + Green)

State	Composition			Π_2
	Green sp		Stage (1) state	
20	10	+	10	55
25	15	+	10	60
	10	+	15	65*
30	20	+	10	63
	15	+	15	70*
	10	+	20	70*
35	25	+	10	65
	20	+	15	73
	15	+	20	75*

(c) Stage (3): (Gold + Green + Silver)

State	Composition			Π_3
	Silver sp		Stage (2) state	
30	10	+	20	80
35	15	+	20	83
	10	+	25	90*
40	20	+	20	85
	15	+	25	93
	10	+	30	95*
45	20	+	25	95
	15	+	30	98
	10	+	35	100*

Figure 16-9

introduced at the second stage. Thus all products are included in a different order to the original workings. The optimal decision (choice of state) at each stage has been boxed. There are three important points to note when comparing the workings. The first is that the *best* value of Π_3 for each state of stage (3) in either set of workings is the same. But some of the inferior values may not be (examine state (40)). Why? Since the best values are the same this must include the optimal state. The best values of states at pre-final stages may be quite different between the two sets of workings (why?). Finally the list of possible states for the final stage must be the same in any workings, but the list of states at earlier stages may differ between workings.

How does the procedure improve on complete enumeration? We see that in other sets of workings (as it happens) we have evaluated 21 combinations of three, two, or one product sp expenditures. Excluding the sp levels of 30 there are 36 $(= 3 \times 3 \times 4)$ combinations of the remaining possibilities (three at a time). Thus we got away with (roughly) $[100 \times \frac{21}{36}]$ per cent = 58 per cent of the work involved in enumeration calculations. This is quite a high percentage, but this would rapidly drop as problem size becomes more realistic (consider the routing problem again in this respect). It could easily turn out that dynamic programming workings occupy less than 1 per cent, or less than one-tenth of 1 per cent, or less than one-hundredth part of 1 per cent, of the time needed for complete enumeration.

16-6 CONCLUSIONS

We have illustrated the dynamic programming style of approach with three fairly representative problems from one side of the subject. Of course, in so doing we have by no means exhausted the possible range of problems. All the cases we examined were *discrete* examples in which the state variable took on integral values and a tabular (or equivalent) method could be employed. There is also *continuous-state dynamic programming* where the state variable can take any value in an allowable range. There are also *multiple-state dynamic programming* problems in which there is more than one state variable.

Various areas of application were mentioned in the introduction. We would only add here that the shampoo marketing problem has a *capital budgeting* structure. Taha gives the following example of a capital budgeting problem with the same structure. A company has a number of factors each of which could be expanded. The number of expansion alternatives differs between factories. The cost of plan i for factory j is c_{ij} and the present value of return from this plan is n_{ij}. The total budget is k. Which plan should be adopted at each factory so as to maximize NPV overall?

Problems also frequently arise in operational research (for example, in production management) that have the structure of a *knapsack problem*. In the archetypal knapsack problem, a variety of items of differing weight and value are to be placed into a container so as to maximize the value of the items packed, subject to a restriction on overal weight. This problem can be solved (amongst other ways) by dynamic programming.

In principle then, dynamic programming has a broad range of potential applications and uses. But this advantage of dynamic programming gives rise to some relative disadvantages. Notable amongst these is the fact that each type of problem addressed by dynamic programming must be individually modelled—there being no all-purpose dynamic programming algorithm.

However, in some problem areas (for example, control theory) the dynamic programming approach is the only one available. More generally, in problems with non-linear objective functions, dynamic programming can be amongst the more attractive alternatives.

In such cases where the problem structure requires three or less state variables, dynamic programming is seen at its best and can achieve substantial computational savings (see Phillips, Ravindran and Solberg, 1976). Although, as yet, dynamic programming is not one of the more widely used operational research methods, its use should be seriously considered when the problem structure is appropriate.

EXERCISES

16-1 Revision exercise.
   (i) What characteristic of a problem may make dynamic programming a possible solution procedure?
   (ii) Explain what is meant by a routing problem and how dynamic programming can be used as a solution procedure.
   (iii) What is the principle of optimality?
   (iv) Explain how the principle of optimality means that when an optimal policy has been identified at a late problem stage, that policy remains best irrespective of the way in which that stage is entered.
   (v) Outline the nature of the warehousing problem and its suitability for solution by dynamic programming.
   (vi) In the context of a routing problem explain how dynamic programming improves on a procedure of explicitly evaluating each possible route.
   (vii) Set out some of the operational research problem areas in which dynamic programming could in principle be used.
   (viii) What are the main advantages and disadvantages of dynamic programming and under what circumstances is its use likely to be relatively advantageous?

16-2 A routing problem is set out in Fig. 16-10 below:

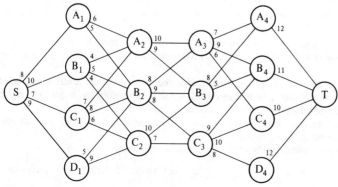

Figure 16-10.

(i) Find the cheapest route using a backward pass.

(ii) How many different routes are there through the system?

16-3 A wholesaler stocks a single item. The ex-factory price (at which the wholesaler buys) and the wholesale price (at which the wholesaler sells) both vary from one month to the next, but all prices are constant within the month. The lead time on the wholesaler's purchases is two weeks. Each month an order is placed 13 days before the last day of the month. The wholesaler's sales take place around mid-month. The maximum warehouse capacity is 500 units and the warehouse is half full at the beginning of January. With the prices given below, what should be the pattern of purchases and sales to maximize profits over the six-month period?

Month	Ex-factory price	Wholesale price
Jan. ($t=1$)	35	45
Feb. ($t=2$)	37	35
Mar. ($t=3$)	36	41
Apr. ($t=4$)	38	36
May ($t=5$)	34	46
June ($t=6$)	39	43

(i) What is the maximum profit attainable in the six-month period?

(ii) Identify the month-by-month cash flows.

16-4 The Gassington Mineral Water Company is an old-established firm with modern ideas. At this moment three new product proposals are being investigated by the company's market research department. Under the working titles of Perraigne, Top-Pop, and Slim Fizz these materials are to be promoted as high-class non-alcoholic party drink, teenage jet-set refresher, and slimming aid beverage respectively. Having an extensive knowledge of rival ventures in all three fields as well as long experience of its own, the department has compiled a comprehensive table relating each product's expected contribution before advertising to three different levels of expenditure on advertising as follows:

Product	Perraigne			Top-Pop			Slim Fizz			
Advertising (£000's)	1.0	1.5	2.0	1.0	2.0	3.0	1.0	1.5	2.0	2.5
Expected contribution (£000's)	15	25	30	15	20	35	20	25	27.5	30

Current controls on promotional expenditure are particularly stringent, however, and the company will allocate no more than £4500 to the total advertising budget for Perraigne, Top-Pop, and Slim Fizz.

Assuming that the short-term aim is to maximize the total expected contribution before advertising of the three products, use a three-stage dynamic programming technique to determine the initial expenditure on advertising to be devoted to each.

(*Note:* Only the expenditure given in the table should be considered and each product must receive some promotional expenditure.)

To what extent is your method shorter than a complete enumeration method?

(Chartered Association of Certified Accountants)

Solution guides

16-2 (i) The network with cost calculations is:

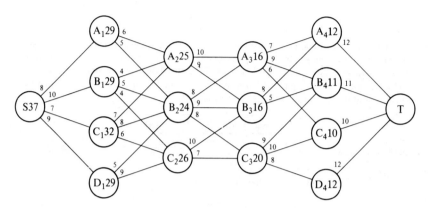

The lowest overall cost is 37 and the cheapest is S, A_1, B_2, A_3, C_4, T.

(ii) The number of paths from S to each 'station' is shown in the circles below. There are 62 paths all told.

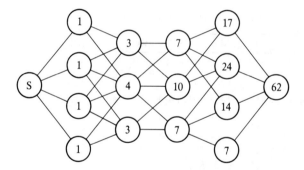

16-3 Let v_t = sales, month t; q_t = purchases, month t; I_t = stock at start of month t, then:
$I_t = I_{t-1} + q_{t-1} - v_{t-1}$. The first stage concerns June ($t = 6$) and the problem is to:

$$\text{Maximize } \Pi_1 = 43v_6 - 39q_6$$

$$\text{subject to } v_6 \leqslant I_6$$

$$q_6 \leqslant 500 - I_6 + v_6$$

$$q_6 \geqslant 0, v_6 \geqslant 0$$

Clearly $q_6 = 0$, $v_6 = I_6$ and maximum $\Pi_1 = 43I_6$. Now in stage two we:

$$\text{Maximize } \Pi_2 = 46v_5 - 34q_5 + \text{Max } \Pi_1$$

$$= 46v_5 - 34q_5 + 43I_6$$

$$= 46v_5 - 34q_5 + 43(I_5 + q_5 - v_5)$$

$$= 3v_5 + 9q_5 + 43I_5$$

$$\text{subject to} \quad v_5 \leqslant I_5$$

$$q_5 \leqslant 500 - I_5 + v_5$$

$$q_5 \geqslant 0, v_5 \geqslant 0$$

As will be apparent from a diagram, in the linear programming problem at each stage, the basic solution that will be optimal will be either $v_t = 0$, $q_t = 500 - I_t$ if the objective function contours (q_t on vertical axis) have slope $> +1$ or $v_t = I_t$, $q = 500$ if the objective function contours have slope $< +1$. The solution is non-unique if the contours have slope $+1$. In the case of the stage two problem the contours have negative slope $(-3/9)$ so that:

$$\boxed{v_5 = I_5, q_5 = 500, \text{ Max } \Pi_2 = 46I_5 + 4500}$$

In stage three we have:

$$\text{Maximize} \quad \Pi_3 = 36v_4 - 38q_4 + \text{Max } \Pi_2$$

$$= 36v_4 - 38q_4 + 46I_5 + 4500$$

$$= 36v_4 - 38q_4 + 46(I_4 + q_4 - v_4) + 4500$$

$$= -10v_4 + 8q_4 + 46I_4 + 4500$$

The slope of the contours is $+1.25$ ($= 10/8$) so that:

$$\boxed{v_4 = 0, q_4 = 500 - I_4, \text{ Max } \Pi_3 = 38I_4 + 8500}$$

In stage four:

$$\text{Maximize} \quad \Pi_4 = 41v_3 - 36q_3 + 38(I_3 + q_3 - v_3) + 8500$$

$$= 3v_3 + 2q_3 + 38I_3 + 8500$$

The slope of the contours is $-\frac{3}{2}$, so $\boxed{\begin{array}{l} v_3 = I_3, q_3 = 500, \\ \text{Max } \Pi_4 = 41I_3 + 9500 \end{array}}$

In stage five:

$$\text{Maximize} \quad \Pi_5 = -6v_2 + 4q_2 + 41I_2 + 9500$$

so that: $\boxed{v_2 = 0, q_2 = 500 - I_2, \text{ Max } \Pi_5 = 37I_2 + 11\,500}$

In stage six:

$$\text{Maximize} \quad \Pi_6 = 8v_1 + 2q_1 + 37I_1 + 11\,500$$

so: $\boxed{v_1 = I_1, q_1 = 500, \text{ Max } \Pi_6 = 45I_1 + 12\,500}$

Now since I_1 (January stocks) $= 250$ we have $v_1 = 250$ and Max $\Pi_6 = 23\,750$. This is the maximum overall profit that can be attained. Now, beginning the unrolling process, in stage five since

$$I_2 = I_1 + q_1 - v_1 \text{ so } I_2 = 250 + 500 - 250 = 500, \quad \therefore q_2 = 0.$$

And so on. The fully unrolled outcome is:

$$v_1 = 250$$

$$q_1 = 500$$

$$I_2 = 500$$

$$v_2 = 0$$

$$q_2 = 0$$

$$I_3 = 500$$

$$v_3 = 500$$

$$q_3 = 500$$

$$I_4 = 500$$

$$v_4 = 0$$

$$q_4 = 0$$

$$I_5 = 500$$

$$v_5 = 500$$

$$q_5 = 500$$

$$I_6 = 500$$

$$v_6 = 500$$

$$q_6 = 0$$

Although the total profit is 23 750, it varies greatly between the months. The cash flow is:

January	− 6 250
February	0
March	+ 2 500
April	0
May	+ 6 000
June	+ 21 500
	23 750

16-4 First note that the £3000 expenditure alternative on Top-Pop is not feasible given the budget and the necessity to promote each product. Let stage (1) consider only Slim-Fizz expenditures. We have:

State	Π_1
1.0	20
1.5	25
2.0	27.5
2.5	30

For stage (2) consider Slim-Fizz and Top-Pop together:

	Composition		
State	Top-Pop	Stage 1 stage	Π_2
2.0	1.0	1.0	35
2.5	1.0	1.5	40
3.0	2.0	1.0	40
	1.0	2.0	42.5
3.5	2.0	1.5	45
	1.0	2.5	45

Note that no decision has yet been taken—all is revealed at the unrolling stage. Now for stage (3) (Slim-Fizz + Top-Pop + Perraigne):

	Composition		
State	Perraigne	State 2 stage	Π_3
3.0	1.0	2.0	50
3.5	1.5	2.0	60
	1.0	2.5	55
4.0	2.0	2.0	65
	1.5	2.5	65
	1.0	3.0	57.5
4.5	2.0	2.5	70
	1.5	3.0	67.5
	1.0	3.5	60

The best entry in the Π_3 column is 70 which means that the Perraigne investment must be 2.0 and the stage (2) state must be 2.5. So, returning to the stage (2) table the only form of the 2.5 state is for Top-Pop to be 1.0 and for the state of 1.5 to hold at stage one. This means an investment of 1.5 in Slim-Fizz. In the present example we have considered 19 combinations of 3-, 2-, and 1-product expenditures. After deleting the 3.0 Top-Pop alternative there are only 24 combinations of expenditures remaining (some of which are unfeasible). Thus the method is not a great improvement on enumeration in this case. However, as the number of possibilities increases, dynamic programming evaluates a decreasing percentage of the number of possible combinations and can work well on problems for which complete explicit enumeration is totally unfeasible.

REFERENCES

Phillips, D. T., Ravindran, A., and Solberg, J. (1976). *Operations Research: Principles and Practice*, Wiley.

Taha, H. A. (1987), *Operations Research: an introduction*, fourth edition, Collier Macmillan.

FURTHER READING

Anderson, D. R., Sweeney, D. J., and Williams, T. A. (1985), *An Introduction to Management Science*, fourth edition, West Publishing Company. Shows use of dynamic programming in production and inventory problems, the 'knapsack' problem and an application by the United States Environmental Protection Agency.

Cook, T. A., and Russell, R. A. (1981), *Introduction to Management Science*, second edition. Shows the application of dynamic programming to a purchasing-inventory problem and reliability problems.

Sasieni, M., Yaspan, A., and Friedman, L. (1959), *Operations Research*, Wiley. Contains description of warehousing problem and shows extension of dynamic programming to problems with an indefinite number of consecutive decisions.

Wagner, H. M. (1969), *Principles of Operations Research*, Prentice-Hall. Shows application of dynamic programming to inventory and replacement problems and outlines recursive approach to other types of problem.

APPENDIX: TABLES

Table 1

Amount of 1 at compound interest: $(1+r)^n$

Periods interest rates (r)

(n)	1	2	3	4	5	6	7	8	9	10	11	12	13	14	15
1	1.0100	1.0200	1.0300	1.0400	1.0500	1.0600	1.0700	1.0800	1.0900	1.1000	1.1100	1.1200	1.1300	1.1400	1.1500
2	1.0201	1.0404	1.0609	1.0816	1.1025	1.1236	1.1449	1.1664	1.1881	1.2100	1.2321	1.2544	1.2769	1.2996	1.3225
3	1.0303	1.0612	1.0927	1.1249	1.1576	1.1910	1.2250	1.2597	1.2950	1.3310	1.3676	1.4049	1.4429	1.4815	1.5209
4	1.0406	1.0824	1.1255	1.1699	1.2155	1.2625	1.3108	1.3605	1.4116	1.4641	1.5181	1.5735	1.6305	1.6890	1.7490
5	1.0510	1.1041	1.1593	1.2167	1.2763	1.3382	1.4026	1.4693	1.5386	1.6105	1.6851	1.7623	1.8424	1.9254	2.0114
6	1.0615	1.1262	1.1941	1.2653	1.3401	1.4185	1.5007	1.5869	1.6771	1.7716	1.8704	1.9738	2.0820	2.1950	2.3131
7	1.0721	1.1487	1.2299	1.3159	1.4071	1.5036	1.6058	1.7138	1.8280	1.9487	2.0762	2.2107	2.3526	2.5023	2.6600
8	1.0829	1.1717	1.2668	1.3686	1.4775	1.5938	1.7182	1.8509	1.9926	2.1436	2.3045	2.4760	2.6584	2.8526	3.0590
9	1.0937	1.1951	1.3048	1.4233	1.5513	1.6895	1.8385	1.9990	2.1719	2.3579	2.5580	2.7731	3.0040	3.2519	3.5179
10	1.1046	1.2190	1.3439	1.4802	1.6289	1.7908	1.9672	2.1589	2.3674	2.5937	2.8394	3.1058	3.3946	3.7072	4.0456
11	1.1157	1.2434	1.3842	1.5395	1.7103	1.8983	2.1049	2.3316	2.5804	2.8531	3.1518	3.4785	3.8359	4.2262	4.6524
12	1.1268	1.2682	1.4258	1.6010	1.7959	2.0122	2.2522	2.5182	2.8127	3.1384	3.4985	3.8960	4.3345	4.8179	5.3503
13	1.1381	1.2936	1.4685	1.6651	1.8856	2.1329	2.4098	2.7196	3.0658	3.4523	3.8833	4.3635	4.8980	5.4924	6.1528
14	1.1495	1.3195	1.5126	1.7317	1.9799	2.2609	2.5785	2.9372	3.3417	3.7975	4.3104	4.8871	5.5348	6.2613	7.0757
15	1.1610	1.3459	1.5580	1.8009	2.0789	2.3966	2.7590	3.1722	3.6425	4.1772	4.7846	5.4736	6.2543	7.1379	8.1371
16	1.1726	1.3728	1.6047	1.8730	2.1829	2.5404	2.9522	3.4259	3.9703	4.5950	5.3109	6.1304	7.0673	8.1372	9.3576
17	1.1843	1.4002	1.6528	1.9479	2.2920	2.6928	3.1588	3.7000	4.3276	5.0545	5.8951	6.8660	7.9861	9.2765	10.7613
18	1.1961	1.4282	1.7024	2.0258	2.4066	2.8543	3.3799	3.9960	4.7171	5.5599	6.5436	7.6900	9.0243	10.5752	12.3755
19	1.2081	1.4568	1.7535	2.1068	2.5270	3.0256	3.6165	4.3157	5.1417	6.1159	7.2633	8.6128	10.1974	12.0557	14.2318
20	1.2202	1.4859	1.8061	2.1911	2.6533	3.2071	3.8697	4.6610	5.6044	6.7275	8.0623	9.6463	11.5231	13.7435	16.3665
25	1.2824	1.6406	2.0938	2.6658	3.3864	4.2919	5.4274	6.8485	8.6231	10.8347	13.5855	17.0001	21.2305	26.4619	32.9190

(n)	16	17	18	19	20	21	22	23	24	25	26	27	28	29	30
1	1.1600	1.1700	1.1800	1.1900	1.2000	1.2100	1.2200	1.2300	1.2400	1.2500	1.2600	1.2700	1.2800	1.2900	1.3000
2	1.3456	1.3689	1.3924	1.4161	1.4400	1.4641	1.4884	1.5129	1.5376	1.5625	1.5876	1.6129	1.6384	1.6641	1.6900
3	1.5609	1.6016	1.6430	1.6852	1.7280	1.7716	1.8158	1.8609	1.9066	1.9531	2.0004	2.0484	2.0972	2.1467	2.1970
4	1.8106	1.8739	1.9388	2.0053	2.0736	2.1436	2.2153	2.2889	2.3642	2.4414	2.5205	2.6014	2.6844	2.7692	2.8561
5	2.1003	2.1924	2.2878	2.3864	2.4883	2.5937	2.7027	2.8153	2.9316	3.0518	3.1758	3.3038	3.4360	3.5723	3.7129
6	2.4364	2.5652	2.6996	2.8398	2.9860	3.1384	3.2973	3.4628	3.6352	3.8147	4.0015	4.1959	4.3980	4.6083	4.8268
7	2.8262	3.0012	3.1855	3.3793	3.5832	3.7975	4.0227	4.2593	4.5077	4.7684	5.0419	5.3288	5.6295	5.9447	6.2749
8	3.2784	3.5115	3.7589	4.0214	4.2998	4.5950	4.9077	5.2389	5.5895	5.9605	6.3528	6.7675	7.2058	7.6686	8.1573
9	3.8030	4.1084	4.4355	4.7854	5.1598	5.5599	5.9874	6.4439	6.9310	7.4506	8.0045	8.5946	9.2234	9.8925	10.6045
10	4.4114	4.8068	5.2338	5.6947	6.1917	6.7275	7.3046	7.9259	8.5944	9.3132	10.0857	10.9153	11.8059	12.7614	13.7858
11	5.1173	5.6240	6.1759	6.7767	7.4301	8.1403	8.9117	9.7489	10.6571	11.6415	12.7080	13.8625	15.1116	16.4622	17.9216
12	5.9360	6.5801	7.2876	8.0642	8.9161	9.8497	10.8722	11.9912	13.2148	14.5519	16.0120	17.6053	19.3428	21.2362	23.2981
13	6.8858	7.6987	8.5994	9.5964	10.6993	11.9182	13.2641	14.7491	16.3863	18.1899	20.1752	22.3588	24.7588	27.3947	30.2875
14	7.9875	9.0075	10.1472	11.4198	12.8392	14.4210	16.1822	18.1414	20.3191	22.7374	25.4207	28.3957	31.6913	35.3391	39.3738
15	9.2655	10.5387	11.9737	13.5896	15.4070	17.4494	19.7423	22.3140	25.1956	28.4217	32.0301	36.0625	40.5648	45.5875	51.1859
16	10.7480	12.3303	14.1290	16.1715	18.4884	21.1138	24.0856	27.4462	31.2426	35.5271	40.3579	45.7994	51.9230	58.8079	66.5042
17	12.4677	14.4265	16.6722	19.2441	22.1861	25.5477	29.3844	33.7588	38.7408	44.4089	50.8510	58.1652	66.4614	75.8821	86.5042
18	14.4625	16.8790	19.6733	22.9005	26.6233	30.9127	35.8490	41.5233	48.0386	55.5112	64.0722	73.8698	85.0706	97.8822	112.4554
19	16.7765	19.7484	23.2144	27.2516	31.9480	37.4043	43.7358	51.0737	59.5679	69.3889	80.7310	93.8147	108.8904	126.2422	146.1920
20	19.4608	23.1056	27.3930	32.4294	38.3376	45.2593	53.3576	62.8206	73.8641	86.7362	101.7211	119.1446	139.3797	162.8524	190.0496
25	40.8742	50.6578	62.6686	77.3881	95.3962	117.3909	144.2101	176.8593	216.5420	264.6978	323.0454	393.6344	478.9049	581.7585	705.6410

Table 2

Present value of 1 at compound interest: $(1+r)^{-n}$

Periods Interest rates (%)

(n)	1	2	3	4	5	6	7	8	9	10	11	12	13	14	15
1	0.9901	0.9804	0.9709	0.9615	0.9524	0.9434	0.9346	0.9259	0.9174	0.9091	0.9009	0.8929	0.8850	0.8772	0.8696
2	0.9803	0.9612	0.9426	0.9246	0.9070	0.8900	0.8734	0.8573	0.8417	0.8264	0.8116	0.7972	0.7831	0.7695	0.7561
3	0.9706	0.9423	0.9151	0.8890	0.8638	0.8396	0.8163	0.7938	0.7722	0.7513	0.7312	0.7118	0.6931	0.6750	0.6575
4	0.9610	0.9238	0.8885	0.8548	0.8227	0.7921	0.7629	0.7350	0.7084	0.6830	0.6587	0.6355	0.6133	0.5921	0.5718
5	0.9515	0.9057	0.8626	0.8219	0.7835	0.7473	0.7130	0.6806	0.6499	0.6209	0.5935	0.5674	0.5428	0.5194	0.4972
6	0.9420	0.8880	0.8375	0.7903	0.7462	0.7050	0.6663	0.6302	0.5963	0.5645	0.5346	0.5066	0.4803	0.4556	0.4323
7	0.9327	0.8706	0.8131	0.7599	0.7107	0.6651	0.6227	0.5835	0.5470	0.5132	0.4817	0.4523	0.4251	0.3996	0.3759
8	0.9235	0.8535	0.7894	0.7307	0.6768	0.6274	0.5820	0.5403	0.5019	0.4665	0.4339	0.4039	0.3762	0.3506	0.3269
9	0.9143	0.8368	0.7664	0.7026	0.6446	0.5919	0.5439	0.5002	0.4604	0.4241	0.3909	0.3606	0.3329	0.3075	0.2843
10	0.9053	0.8203	0.7441	0.6756	0.6139	0.5584	0.5083	0.4632	0.4224	0.3855	0.3522	0.3220	0.2946	0.2697	0.2472
11	0.8963	0.8043	0.7224	0.6496	0.5847	0.5268	0.4751	0.4289	0.3875	0.3505	0.3173	0.2875	0.2607	0.2366	0.2149
12	0.8874	0.7885	0.7014	0.6246	0.5568	0.4970	0.4440	0.3971	0.3555	0.3186	0.2858	0.2567	0.2307	0.2076	0.1869
13	0.8787	0.7730	0.6810	0.6006	0.5303	0.4688	0.4150	0.3677	0.3262	0.2897	0.2575	0.2292	0.2042	0.1821	0.1625
14	0.8700	0.7579	0.6611	0.5775	0.5051	0.4423	0.3878	0.3405	0.2992	0.2633	0.2320	0.2046	0.1807	0.1597	0.1413
15	0.8613	0.7430	0.6419	0.5553	0.4810	0.4173	0.3624	0.3152	0.2745	0.2394	0.2090	0.1827	0.1599	0.1401	0.1229
16	0.8528	0.7284	0.6232	0.5339	0.4581	0.3936	0.3387	0.2919	0.2519	0.2176	0.1883	0.1631	0.1415	0.1229	0.1069
17	0.8444	0.7142	0.6050	0.5134	0.4363	0.3714	0.3166	0.2703	0.2311	0.1978	0.1696	0.1456	0.1252	0.1078	0.0929
18	0.8360	0.7002	0.5874	0.4936	0.4155	0.3503	0.2959	0.2502	0.2120	0.1799	0.1528	0.1300	0.1108	0.0946	0.0808
19	0.8277	0.6864	0.5703	0.4746	0.3957	0.3305	0.2765	0.2317	0.1945	0.1635	0.1377	0.1161	0.0981	0.0829	0.0703
20	0.8195	0.6730	0.5537	0.4564	0.3769	0.3118	0.2584	0.2145	0.1784	0.1486	0.1240	0.1037	0.0868	0.0728	0.0611
25	0.7798	0.6095	0.4776	0.3751	0.2953	0.2330	0.1842	0.1460	0.1160	0.0923	0.0736	0.0588	0.0471	0.0378	0.0304
30	0.7419	0.5521	0.4120	0.3083	0.2314	0.1741	0.1314	0.0994	0.0754	0.0573	0.0437	0.0334	0.0256	0.0196	0.0151
35	0.7059	0.5000	0.3554	0.2534	0.1813	0.1301	0.0937	0.0676	0.0490	0.0356	0.0259	0.0189	0.0139	0.0102	0.0075
40	0.6717	0.4529	0.3066	0.2083	0.1420	0.0972	0.0668	0.0460	0.0318	0.0221	0.0154	0.0107	0.0075	0.0053	0.0037
45	0.6391	0.4102	0.2644	0.1712	0.1113	0.0727	0.0476	0.0313	0.0207	0.0137	0.0091	0.0061	0.0041	0.0027	0.0019
50	0.6080	0.3715	0.2281	0.1407	0.0872	0.0543	0.0339	0.0213	0.0134	0.0085	0.0054	0.0035	0.0020	0.0014	0.0009

	16	17	18	19	20	21	22	23	24	25	26	27	28	29	30
1	0.8621	0.8547	0.8475	0.8403	0.8333	0.8264	0.8197	0.8130	0.8065	0.8000	0.7937	0.7874	0.7812	0.7752	0.7692
2	0.7432	0.7305	0.7182	0.7062	0.6944	0.6830	0.6719	0.6610	0.6504	0.6400	0.6299	0.6200	0.6104	0.6009	0.5917
3	0.6407	0.6244	0.6086	0.5934	0.5787	0.5645	0.5507	0.5374	0.5245	0.5120	0.4999	0.4882	0.4768	0.4658	0.4552
4	0.5523	0.5337	0.5158	0.4987	0.4823	0.4665	0.4514	0.4369	0.4230	0.4096	0.3968	0.3844	0.3725	0.3611	0.3501
5	0.4761	0.4561	0.4371	0.4190	0.4019	0.3855	0.3700	0.3552	0.3411	0.3277	0.3149	0.3027	0.2910	0.2799	0.2693
6	0.4104	0.3898	0.3704	0.3521	0.3349	0.3186	0.3033	0.2888	0.2751	0.2621	0.2499	0.2383	0.2274	0.2170	0.2072
7	0.3538	0.3332	0.3139	0.2959	0.2791	0.2633	0.2486	0.2348	0.2218	0.2097	0.1983	0.1877	0.1776	0.1682	0.1594
8	0.3050	0.2848	0.2660	0.2487	0.2326	0.2176	0.2038	0.1909	0.1789	0.1678	0.1574	0.1478	0.1388	0.1304	0.1226
9	0.2630	0.2434	0.2255	0.2090	0.1938	0.1799	0.1670	0.1552	0.1443	0.1342	0.1249	0.1164	0.1084	0.1011	0.0943
10	0.2267	0.2080	0.1911	0.1756	0.1615	0.1486	0.1369	0.1262	0.1164	0.1074	0.0992	0.0916	0.0847	0.0784	0.0725
11	0.1954	0.1778	0.1619	0.1476	0.1346	0.1228	0.1122	0.1026	0.0938	0.0859	0.0787	0.0721	0.0662	0.0607	0.0558
12	0.1685	0.1520	0.1372	0.1240	0.1122	0.1015	0.0920	0.0834	0.0757	0.0687	0.0625	0.0568	0.0517	0.0471	0.0429
13	0.1452	0.1299	0.1163	0.1042	0.0935	0.0839	0.0754	0.0678	0.0610	0.0550	0.0496	0.0447	0.0404	0.0365	0.0330
14	0.1252	0.1110	0.0985	0.0876	0.0779	0.0693	0.0618	0.0551	0.0492	0.0440	0.0393	0.0352	0.0316	0.0283	0.0254
15	0.1079	0.0949	0.0835	0.0736	0.0649	0.0573	0.0507	0.0448	0.0397	0.0352	0.0312	0.0277	0.0247	0.0219	0.0195
16	0.0930	0.0811	0.0708	0.0618	0.0541	0.0474	0.0415	0.0364	0.0320	0.0281	0.0248	0.0218	0.0193	0.0170	0.0150
17	0.0802	0.0693	0.0600	0.0520	0.0451	0.0391	0.0340	0.0296	0.0258	0.0225	0.0197	0.0172	0.0150	0.0132	0.0116
18	0.0691	0.0592	0.0508	0.0437	0.0376	0.0323	0.0279	0.0241	0.0208	0.0180	0.0156	0.0135	0.0118	0.0102	0.0089
19	0.0596	0.0506	0.0431	0.0367	0.0313	0.0267	0.0229	0.0196	0.0168	0.0144	0.0124	0.0107	0.0092	0.0079	0.0068
20	0.0514	0.0433	0.0365	0.0308	0.0261	0.0221	0.0187	0.0159	0.0135	0.0115	0.0098	0.0084	0.0072	0.0061	0.0053
25	0.0245	0.0197	0.0160	0.0129	0.0105	0.0085	0.0069	0.0057	0.0046	0.0038	0.0031	0.0025	0.0021	0.0017	0.0014
30	0.0116	0.0090	0.0070	0.0054	0.0042	0.0033	0.0026	0.0020	0.0016	0.0012	0.0010	0.0008	0.0006	0.0005	0.0004
35	0.0055	0.0041	0.0030	0.0023	0.0017	0.0013	0.0009	0.0007	0.0005	0.0004	0.0003	0.0002	0.0002	0.0001	0.0001
40	0.0026	0.0019	0.0013	0.0010	0.0007	0.0005	0.0004	0.0003	0.0002	0.0001	0.0001	0.0001	0.0001	0.0000	0.0000
45	0.0013	0.0009	0.0006	0.0004	0.0003	0.0002	0.0001	0.0001	0.0001	0.0000	0.0000	0.0000	0.0000	0.0000	0.0000
50	0.0006	0.0004	0.0003	0.0002	0.0001	0.0001	0.0000	0.0000	0.0000	0.0000	0.0000	0.0000	0.0000	0.0000	0.0000

Table 3

Present value of an annuity of 1: $\dfrac{1-(1+r)^{-n}}{r}$

Periods Interest rates (%)

(n)	1	2	3	4	5	6	7	8	9	10	11	12	13	14	15
1	0.9901	0.9804	0.9709	0.9615	0.9524	0.9434	0.9346	0.9259	0.9174	0.9091	0.9009	0.8929	0.8850	0.8772	0.8696
2	1.9704	1.9416	1.9135	1.8861	1.8594	1.8334	1.8080	1.7833	1.7591	1.7355	1.7125	1.6901	1.6681	1.6467	1.6257
3	2.9410	2.8839	2.8286	2.7751	2.7232	2.6730	2.6243	2.5771	2.5313	2.4869	2.4437	2.4018	2.3612	2.3216	2.2832
4	3.9020	3.8077	3.7171	3.6299	3.5460	3.4651	3.3872	3.3121	3.2397	3.1699	3.1024	3.0373	2.9745	2.9137	2.8550
5	4.8534	4.7135	4.5797	4.4518	4.3295	4.2124	4.1002	3.9927	3.8897	3.7908	3.6959	3.6048	3.5172	3.4331	3.3522
6	5.7955	5.6014	5.4172	5.2421	5.0757	4.9173	4.7665	4.6229	4.4859	4.3553	4.2305	4.1114	3.9975	3.8887	3.7845
7	6.7282	6.4720	6.2303	6.0021	5.7864	5.5824	5.3893	5.2064	5.0330	4.8684	4.7122	4.5638	4.4226	4.2883	4.1604
8	7.6517	7.3255	7.0197	6.7327	6.4632	6.2098	5.9713	5.7466	5.5348	5.3349	5.1461	4.9676	4.7988	4.6389	4.4873
9	8.5660	8.1622	7.7861	7.4353	7.1078	6.8017	6.5152	6.2469	5.9952	5.7590	5.5370	5.3282	5.1317	4.9464	4.7716
10	9.4713	8.9826	8.5302	8.1109	7.7217	7.3601	7.0236	6.7101	6.4177	6.1446	5.8892	5.6502	5.4262	5.2161	5.0188
11	10.3676	9.7868	9.2526	8.7605	8.3064	7.8869	7.4987	7.1390	6.8052	6.4951	6.2065	5.9377	5.6869	5.4527	5.2337
12	11.2551	10.5753	9.9540	9.3851	8.8633	8.3836	7.9427	7.5361	7.1607	6.8137	6.4924	6.1944	5.9176	5.6603	5.4206
13	12.1337	11.3484	10.6350	9.9856	9.3936	8.8527	8.3577	7.9038	7.4869	7.1034	6.7499	6.4235	6.1218	5.8424	5.5831
14	13.0037	12.1062	11.2961	10.5631	9.8986	9.2950	8.7455	8.2442	7.7862	7.3667	6.9819	6.6282	6.3025	6.0021	5.7245
15	13.8651	12.8493	11.9379	11.1184	10.3797	9.7122	9.1079	8.5595	8.0607	7.6061	7.1909	6.8109	6.4624	6.1422	5.8474
16	14.7179	13.5777	12.5611	11.6523	10.8378	10.1059	9.4466	8.8514	8.3126	7.8237	7.3792	6.9740	6.6039	6.2651	5.9542
17	15.5623	14.2919	13.1661	12.1657	11.2741	10.4773	9.7632	9.1216	8.5436	8.0216	7.5488	7.1196	6.7291	6.3729	6.0472
18	16.3983	14.9920	13.7535	12.6593	11.6896	10.8276	10.0591	9.3719	8.7556	8.2014	7.7016	7.2497	6.8399	6.4674	6.1280
19	17.2260	15.6785	14.3238	13.1339	12.0853	11.1581	10.3356	9.6036	8.9501	8.3649	7.8393	7.3658	6.9380	6.5504	6.1982
20	18.0456	16.3514	14.8775	13.5903	12.4622	11.4699	10.5940	9.8181	9.1285	8.5136	7.9633	7.4694	7.0248	6.6231	6.2593
25	22.0232	19.5235	17.4131	15.6221	14.0939	12.7834	11.6536	10.6748	9.8226	9.0770	8.4217	7.8431	7.3300	6.8729	6.4641
30	25.8077	22.3965	19.6004	17.2920	15.3725	13.7648	12.4090	11.2578	10.2737	9.4269	8.6938	8.0552	7.4957	7.0027	6.5660
35	29.4086	24.9986	21.4872	18.6646	16.3742	14.4982	12.9477	11.6546	10.5668	9.6442	8.8552	8.1755	7.5856	7.0700	6.6166
40	32.8347	27.3555	23.1148	19.7928	17.1591	15.0463	13.3317	11.9246	10.7574	9.7791	8.9511	8.2438	7.6344	7.1050	6.6418
45	36.0945	29.4902	24.5187	20.7200	17.7741	15.4558	13.6055	12.1084	10.8812	9.8628	9.0079	8.2825	7.6609	7.1232	6.6543
50	39.1961	31.4236	25.7298	21.4822	18.2559	15.7619	13.8007	12.2335	10.9617	9.9148	9.0417	8.3045	7.6752	7.1327	6.6605

n	16	17	18	19	20	21	22	23	24	25	26	27	28	29	30
1	0.8621	0.8547	0.8475	0.8403	0.8333	0.8264	0.8197	0.8130	0.8065	0.8000	0.7937	0.7874	0.7812	0.7752	0.7692
2	1.6052	1.5852	1.5656	1.5466	1.5278	1.5095	1.4915	1.4740	1.4568	1.4400	1.4235	1.4074	1.3916	1.3761	1.3609
3	2.2459	2.2096	2.1743	2.1399	2.1065	2.0739	2.0422	2.0114	1.9813	1.9520	1.9234	1.8956	1.8684	1.8420	1.8161
4	2.7982	2.7432	2.6901	2.6386	2.5887	2.5404	2.4936	2.4483	2.4043	2.3616	2.3202	2.2800	2.2410	2.2031	2.1662
5	3.2743	3.1993	3.1272	3.0576	2.9906	2.9260	2.8636	2.8035	2.7454	2.6893	2.6351	2.5827	2.5320	2.4830	2.4356
6	3.6847	3.5892	3.4976	3.4098	3.3255	3.2446	3.1669	3.0923	3.0205	2.9514	2.8850	2.8210	2.7594	2.7000	2.6427
7	4.0386	3.9224	3.8115	3.7057	3.6046	3.5079	3.4155	3.3270	3.2423	3.1611	3.0833	3.0087	2.9370	2.8682	2.8021
8	4.3436	4.2072	4.0776	3.9544	3.8372	3.7256	3.6193	3.5179	3.4212	3.3289	3.2407	3.1564	3.0758	2.9986	2.9247
9	4.6065	4.4506	4.3030	4.1633	4.0310	3.9054	3.7863	3.6731	3.5655	3.4631	3.3657	3.2728	3.1842	3.0997	3.0190
10	4.8332	4.6586	4.4941	4.3389	4.1925	4.0541	3.9232	3.7993	3.6819	3.5705	3.4648	3.3644	3.2689	3.1781	3.0915
11	5.0286	4.8364	4.6560	4.4865	4.3271	4.1769	4.0354	3.9018	3.7757	3.6564	3.5435	3.4365	3.3351	3.2388	3.1473
12	5.1971	4.9884	4.7932	4.6105	4.4392	4.2784	4.1274	3.9852	3.8514	3.7251	3.6059	3.4933	3.3868	3.2859	3.1903
13	5.3423	5.1183	4.9095	4.7147	4.5327	4.3624	4.2028	4.0530	3.9124	3.7801	3.6555	3.5381	3.4272	3.3224	3.2233
14	5.4675	5.2293	5.0081	4.8023	4.6106	4.4317	4.2646	4.1082	3.9616	3.8241	3.6949	3.5733	3.4587	3.3507	3.2487
15	5.5755	5.3242	5.0916	4.8759	4.6755	4.4890	4.3152	4.1530	4.0013	3.8593	3.7261	3.6010	3.4834	3.3726	3.2682
16	5.6685	5.4053	5.1624	4.9377	4.7296	4.5364	4.3567	4.1894	4.0333	3.8874	3.7509	3.6228	3.5026	3.3896	3.2832
17	5.7487	5.4746	5.2223	4.9897	4.7746	4.5755	4.3908	4.2190	4.0591	3.9099	3.7705	3.6400	3.5177	3.4028	3.2948
18	5.8178	5.5339	5.2732	5.0333	4.8122	4.6079	4.4187	4.2431	4.0799	3.9279	3.7861	3.6536	3.5294	3.4130	3.3037
19	5.8775	5.5845	5.3162	5.0700	4.8435	4.6346	4.4415	4.2627	4.0967	3.9424	3.7985	3.6642	3.5486	3.4210	3.3105
20	5.9288	5.6278	5.3527	5.1009	4.8696	4.6567	4.4603	4.2786	4.1103	3.9539	3.8083	3.6726	3.5458	3.4271	3.3158
25	6.0971	5.7662	5.4669	5.1951	4.9476	4.7213	4.5139	4.3232	4.1474	3.9849	3.8342	3.6943	3.5640	3.4423	3.3286
30	6.1772	5.8294	5.5168	5.2347	4.9789	4.7463	4.5338	4.3391	4.1601	3.9950	3.8424	3.7009	3.5693	3.4466	3.3321
35	6.2153	5.8582	5.5386	5.2512	4.9915	4.7559	4.5411	4.3447	4.1644	3.9984	3.8450	3.7028	3.5708	3.4478	3.3330
40	6.2335	5.8713	5.5482	5.2582	4.9966	4.7596	4.5439	4.3467	4.1659	3.9995	3.8458	3.7034	3.5712	3.4481	3.3332
45	6.2421	5.8773	5.5523	5.2611	4.9986	4.7610	4.5449	4.3474	4.1664	3.9998	3.8460	3.7036	3.5714	3.4483	3.3333
50	6.2463	5.8801	5.5541	5.2623	4.9995	4.7616	4.5452	4.3477	4.1666	3.9999	3.8461	3.7037	3.5714	3.4483	3.333

Table 4

Sinking Fund: $\dfrac{r}{(1+r)^n-1}$

Periods Interest rates (%)

(n)	1	2	3	4	5	6	7	8	9	10	11	12	13	14	15	N
1	1.0000	1.0000	1.0000	1.0000	1.0000	1.0000	1.0000	1.0000	1.0000	1.0000	1.0000	1.0000	1.0000	1.0000	1.0000	1
2	0.4975	0.4950	0.4926	0.4902	0.4878	0.4854	0.4831	0.4808	0.4785	0.4762	0.4739	0.4717	0.4695	0.4673	0.4651	2
3	0.3300	0.3268	0.3235	0.3203	0.3172	0.3140	0.3111	0.3080	0.3051	0.3021	0.2992	0.2963	0.2935	0.2907	0.2880	3
4	0.2463	0.2426	0.2390	0.2355	0.2320	0.2286	0.2252	0.2219	0.2187	0.2155	0.2123	0.2092	0.2062	0.2032	0.2003	4
5	0.1960	0.1922	0.1884	0.1846	0.1810	0.1774	0.1739	0.1705	0.1671	0.1638	0.1606	0.1574	0.1543	0.1513	0.1483	5
6	0.1625	0.1585	0.1546	0.1508	0.1470	0.1434	0.1398	0.1363	0.1329	0.1296	0.1264	0.1232	0.1202	0.1172	0.1142	6
7	0.1386	0.1345	0.1305	0.1266	0.1228	0.1191	0.1156	0.1121	0.1087	0.1054	0.1022	0.0991	0.0961	0.0932	0.0904	7
8	0.1207	0.1165	0.1125	0.1085	0.1047	0.1010	0.0975	0.0940	0.0907	0.0874	0.0843	0.0813	0.0784	0.0756	0.0729	8
9	0.1067	0.1025	0.0984	0.0945	0.0907	0.0870	0.0835	0.0801	0.0768	0.0736	0.0706	0.0677	0.0649	0.0622	0.0596	9
10	0.0956	0.0913	0.0872	0.0833	0.0795	0.0759	0.0724	0.0690	0.0658	0.0627	0.0598	0.0570	0.0543	0.0517	0.0490	10
11	0.0865	0.0822	0.0781	0.0741	0.0704	0.0668	0.0634	0.0601	0.0569	0.0540	0.0511	0.0484	0.0458	0.0434	0.0411	11
12	0.0788	0.0746	0.0705	0.0666	0.0628	0.0593	0.0559	0.0527	0.0497	0.0468	0.0440	0.0414	0.0390	0.0367	0.0345	12
13	0.0724	0.0681	0.0640	0.0601	0.0565	0.0530	0.0497	0.0465	0.0436	0.0408	0.0382	0.0357	0.0334	0.0312	0.0291	13
14	0.0669	0.0626	0.0585	0.0547	0.0510	0.0476	0.0443	0.0413	0.0384	0.0357	0.0332	0.0309	0.0287	0.0266	0.0247	14
15	0.0621	0.0578	0.0538	0.0499	0.0463	0.0430	0.0398	0.0368	0.0341	0.0315	0.0291	0.0268	0.0247	0.0228	0.0210	15
16	0.0579	0.0537	0.0496	0.0458	0.0423	0.0390	0.0359	0.0330	0.0303	0.0278	0.0255	0.0234	0.0214	0.0196	0.0179	16
17	0.0543	0.0500	0.0460	0.0422	0.0387	0.0354	0.0324	0.0296	0.0270	0.0247	0.0225	0.0205	0.0186	0.0169	0.0154	17
18	0.0510	0.0467	0.0427	0.0390	0.0355	0.0324	0.0294	0.0267	0.0242	0.0219	0.0198	0.0179	0.0162	0.0146	0.0132	18
19	0.0481	0.0438	0.0398	0.0361	0.0327	0.0296	0.0268	0.0241	0.0217	0.0195	0.0176	0.0158	0.0141	0.0127	0.0113	19
20	0.0454	0.0412	0.0372	0.0334	0.0302	0.0272	0.0244	0.0219	0.0195	0.0175	0.0156	0.0139	0.0124	0.0110	0.0098	20
21	0.0430	0.0388	0.0349	0.0313	0.0280	0.0250	0.0223	0.0198	0.0176	0.0156	0.0138	0.0122	0.0108	0.0095	0.0084	21
22	0.0409	0.0366	0.0327	0.0292	0.0260	0.0230	0.0204	0.0180	0.0159	0.0140	0.0123	0.0108	0.0095	0.0083	0.0073	22
23	0.0389	0.0347	0.0308	0.0273	0.0241	0.0213	0.0187	0.0164	0.0144	0.0126	0.0110	0.0096	0.0083	0.0072	0.0063	23
24	0.0371	0.0329	0.0290	0.0256	0.0225	0.0197	0.0172	0.0150	0.0130	0.0113	0.0098	0.0085	0.0073	0.0063	0.0054	24
25	0.0354	0.0312	0.0274	0.0240	0.0210	0.0182	0.0158	0.0137	0.0118	0.0102	0.0087	0.0075	0.0064	0.0055	0.0047	25

	16	17	18	19	20	21	22	23	24	25	26	27	28	29	30	
1	1.0000	1.0000	1.0000	1.0000	1.0000	1.0000	1.0000	1.0000	1.0000	1.0000	1.0000	1.0000	1.0000	1.0000	1.0000	1
2	0.4630	0.4608	0.4587	0.4566	0.4545	0.4525	0.4505	0.4484	0.4464	0.4444	0.4425	0.4405	0.4386	0.4367	0.4348	2
3	0.2853	0.2826	0.2799	0.2773	0.2747	0.2722	0.2697	0.2672	0.2647	0.2623	0.2599	0.2575	0.2552	0.2529	0.2506	3
4	0.1974	0.1945	0.1917	0.1890	0.1863	0.1836	0.1810	0.1785	0.1759	0.1734	0.1710	0.1686	0.1662	0.1639	0.1616	4
5	0.1454	0.1426	0.1398	0.1371	0.1344	0.1318	0.1292	0.1267	0.1242	0.1218	0.1195	0.1172	0.1149	0.1127	0.1106	5
6	0.1114	0.1086	0.1059	0.1033	0.1007	0.0982	0.0958	0.0934	0.0911	0.0888	0.0866	0.0845	0.0824	0.0804	0.0784	6
7	0.0876	0.0849	0.0824	0.0799	0.0774	0.0751	0.0728	0.0706	0.0684	0.0663	0.0643	0.0624	0.0605	0.0586	0.0567	7
8	0.0702	0.0677	0.0652	0.0629	0.0606	0.0584	0.0563	0.0543	0.0523	0.0504	0.0486	0.0468	0.0451	0.0435	0.0419	8
9	0.0571	0.0547	0.0524	0.0502	0.0481	0.0461	0.0441	0.0422	0.0405	0.0388	0.0371	0.0356	0.0340	0.0326	0.0312	9
10	0.0469	0.0447	0.0425	0.0405	0.0385	0.0367	0.0349	0.0332	0.0316	0.0301	0.0286	0.0272	0.0259	0.0247	0.0236	10
11	0.0389	0.0368	0.0348	0.0329	0.0311	0.0294	0.0278	0.0263	0.0249	0.0235	0.0222	0.0210	0.0198	0.0188	0.0177	11
12	0.0324	0.0305	0.0286	0.0269	0.0253	0.0237	0.0223	0.0209	0.0196	0.0184	0.0173	0.0163	0.0153	0.0143	0.0135	12
13	0.0272	0.0254	0.0237	0.0221	0.0206	0.0192	0.0179	0.0167	0.0156	0.0145	0.0136	0.0126	0.0118	0.0110	0.0102	13
14	0.0229	0.0212	0.0197	0.0182	0.0169	0.0156	0.0145	0.0134	0.0124	0.0115	0.0106	0.0099	0.0091	0.0084	0.0078	14
15	0.0194	0.0178	0.0164	0.0151	0.0139	0.0128	0.0117	0.0108	0.0099	0.0091	0.0084	0.0077	0.0071	0.0066	0.0060	15
16	0.0164	0.0150	0.0137	0.0125	0.0114	0.0104	0.0095	0.0087	0.0079	0.0072	0.0066	0.0060	0.0056	0.0051	0.0046	16
17	0.0140	0.0127	0.0115	0.0104	0.0094	0.0086	0.0078	0.0070	0.0064	0.0058	0.0052	0.0047	0.0043	0.0039	0.0035	17
18	0.0119	0.0107	0.0096	0.0087	0.0078	0.0070	0.0063	0.0057	0.0051	0.0046	0.0041	0.0037	0.0033	0.0030	0.0027	18
19	0.0101	0.0091	0.0081	0.0072	0.0065	0.0058	0.0051	0.0046	0.0041	0.0037	0.0033	0.0029	0.0026	0.0023	0.0021	19
20	0.0087	0.0077	0.0068	0.0060	0.0054	0.0047	0.0042	0.0037	0.0033	0.0029	0.0026	0.0023	0.0020	0.0018	0.0016	20
21	0.0074	0.0065	0.0057	0.0051	0.0044	0.0039	0.0034	0.0030	0.0026	0.0023	0.0020	0.0018	0.0016	0.0014	0.0012	21
22	0.0064	0.0056	0.0048	0.0042	0.0037	0.0032	0.0028	0.0024	0.0021	0.0019	0.0016	0.0014	0.0012	0.0011	0.0009	22
23	0.0054	0.0047	0.0041	0.0035	0.0031	0.0027	0.0023	0.0020	0.0017	0.0015	0.0013	0.0011	0.0010	0.0008	0.0007	23
24	0.0047	0.0040	0.0035	0.0030	0.0025	0.0022	0.0019	0.0016	0.0014	0.0012	0.0010	0.0009	0.0008	0.0007	0.0006	24
25	0.0040	0.0034	0.0029	0.0025	0.0021	0.0018	0.0015	0.0013	0.0011	0.0009	0.0008	0.0007	0.0006	0.0005	0.0004	25

Table 5

Annual equivalent annuity $r/[1-(1+r)^{-n}]$

Years Interest rates (%)

(n)	1	2	3	4	5	6	7	8	9	10	11	12	13	14	15
1	1.0100	1.0200	1.0300	1.0400	1.0500	1.0600	1.0700	1.0800	1.0900	1.1000	1.1100	1.1200	1.1300	1.1400	1.1500
2	0.5075	0.5150	0.5226	0.5302	0.5378	0.5454	0.5531	0.5608	0.5685	0.5762	0.5839	0.5917	0.5995	0.6073	0.6151
3	0.3400	0.3468	0.3535	0.3603	0.3672	0.3741	0.3811	0.3880	0.3951	0.4021	0.4092	0.4163	0.4235	0.4307	0.4380
4	0.2563	0.2626	0.2690	0.2755	0.2820	0.2886	0.2952	0.3019	0.3087	0.3155	0.3223	0.3292	0.3362	0.3432	0.3503
5	0.2060	0.2122	0.2184	0.2246	0.2310	0.2374	0.2439	0.2505	0.2571	0.2638	0.2706	0.2774	0.2843	0.2913	0.2983
6	0.1735	0.1785	0.1846	0.1908	0.1970	0.2034	0.2098	0.2163	0.2229	0.2296	0.2364	0.2432	0.2502	0.2572	0.2642
7	0.1486	0.1545	0.1605	0.1666	0.1728	0.1791	0.1856	0.1921	0.1987	0.2054	0.2122	0.2191	0.2261	0.2332	0.2404
8	0.1307	0.1365	0.1425	0.1485	0.1547	0.1610	0.1675	0.1740	0.1807	0.1874	0.1943	0.2013	0.2084	0.2156	0.2229
9	0.1167	0.1225	0.1284	0.1345	0.1407	0.1470	0.1535	0.1601	0.1668	0.1736	0.1806	0.1877	0.1949	0.2022	0.2096
10	0.1056	0.1113	0.1172	0.1233	0.1295	0.1359	0.1424	0.1490	0.1558	0.1627	0.1698	0.1770	0.1843	0.1917	0.1993
11	0.0965	0.1022	0.1081	0.1141	0.1204	0.1268	0.1334	0.1401	0.1469	0.1540	0.1611	0.1684	0.1758	0.1834	0.1911
12	0.0888	0.0946	0.1005	0.1066	0.1128	0.1193	0.1259	0.1327	0.1397	0.1468	0.1540	0.1614	0.1690	0.1767	0.1845
13	0.0824	0.0881	0.0940	0.1001	0.1065	0.1130	0.1197	0.1265	0.1336	0.1408	0.1482	0.1557	0.1634	0.1712	0.1791
14	0.0769	0.0826	0.0885	0.0947	0.1010	0.1076	0.1143	0.1213	0.1284	0.1357	0.1432	0.1509	0.1587	0.1666	0.1747
15	0.0721	0.0778	0.0838	0.0899	0.0963	0.1030	0.1098	0.1168	0.1241	0.1315	0.1391	0.1468	0.1547	0.1628	0.1710
16	0.0679	0.0737	0.0796	0.0858	0.0923	0.0990	0.1059	0.1130	0.1203	0.1278	0.1355	0.1434	0.1514	0.1596	0.1679
17	0.0643	0.0700	0.0760	0.0822	0.0887	0.0954	0.1024	0.1096	0.1170	0.1247	0.1325	0.1405	0.1486	0.1569	0.1654
18	0.0610	0.0667	0.0727	0.0790	0.0855	0.0924	0.0994	0.1067	0.1142	0.1219	0.1298	0.1379	0.1462	0.1546	0.1632
19	0.0581	0.0638	0.0698	0.0761	0.0827	0.0896	0.0968	0.1041	0.1117	0.1195	0.1276	0.1358	0.1441	0.1527	0.1613
20	0.0554	0.0612	0.0672	0.0736	0.0802	0.0872	0.0944	0.1019	0.1095	0.1175	0.1256	0.1339	0.1424	0.1510	0.1598
21	0.0530	0.0588	0.0649	0.0713	0.0780	0.0854	0.0923	0.0998	0.1076	0.1156	0.1238	0.1322	0.1408	0.1495	0.1584
22	0.0509	0.0566	0.0627	0.0692	0.0760	0.0830	0.0904	0.0980	0.1059	0.1140	0.1223	0.1308	0.1395	0.1483	0.1573
23	0.0489	0.0547	0.0608	0.0673	0.0741	0.0813	0.0887	0.0964	0.1044	0.1126	0.1210	0.1296	0.1383	0.1472	0.1563
24	0.0471	0.0529	0.0590	0.0656	0.0725	0.0797	0.0872	0.0950	0.1030	0.1113	0.1198	0.1285	0.1373	0.1463	0.1554
25	0.0454	0.0512	0.0574	0.0640	0.0710	0.0782	0.0858	0.0937	0.1018	0.1102	0.1187	0.1275	0.1364	0.1455	0.1547

	16	17	18	19	20	21	22	23	24	25	26	27	28	29	30	
1	1.1600	1.1700	1.1800	1.1900	1.2000	1.2100	1.2200	1.2300	1.2400	1.2500	1.2600	1.2700	1.2800	1.2900	1.3000	1
2	0.6230	0.6300	0.6387	0.6466	0.6545	0.6625	0.6705	0.6784	0.6864	0.6944	0.7025	0.7105	0.7185	0.7267	0.7348	2
3	0.4453	0.4526	0.4599	0.4673	0.4747	0.4822	0.4897	0.4972	0.5047	0.5123	0.5199	0.5275	0.5352	0.5429	0.5506	3
4	0.3574	0.3645	0.3717	0.3790	0.3863	0.3936	0.4010	0.4085	0.4159	0.4234	0.4310	0.4386	0.4462	0.4539	0.4616	4
5	0.3054	0.3126	0.3198	0.3271	0.3344	0.3418	0.3492	0.3567	0.3642	0.3718	0.3795	0.3872	0.3949	0.4027	0.4106	5
6	0.2714	0.2786	0.2859	0.2933	0.3007	0.3082	0.3158	0.3234	0.3311	0.3388	0.3466	0.3545	0.3624	0.3704	0.3784	6
7	0.2476	0.2549	0.2624	0.2699	0.2774	0.2851	0.2928	0.3006	0.3084	0.3163	0.3246	0.3324	0.3405	0.3486	0.3569	7
8	0.2302	0.2377	0.2452	0.2529	0.2606	0.2684	0.2763	0.2843	0.2923	0.3004	0.3086	0.3168	0.3251	0.3335	0.3419	8
9	0.2171	0.2247	0.2324	0.2402	0.2481	0.2561	0.2641	0.2722	0.2805	0.2888	0.2971	0.3056	0.3140	0.3226	0.3312	9
10	0.2069	0.2147	0.2225	0.2305	0.2385	0.2467	0.2549	0.2632	0.2716	0.2801	0.2886	0.2972	0.3059	0.3147	0.3235	10
11	0.1989	0.2068	0.2148	0.2229	0.2311	0.2394	0.2478	0.2563	0.2649	0.2736	0.2822	0.2910	0.2998	0.3088	0.3177	11
12	0.1924	0.2005	0.2086	0.2169	0.2253	0.2337	0.2433	0.2509	0.2596	0.2684	0.2773	0.2863	0.2953	0.3043	0.3135	12
13	0.1872	0.1954	0.2037	0.2121	0.2206	0.2292	0.2379	0.2467	0.2556	0.2645	0.2736	0.2826	0.2918	0.3010	0.3102	13
14	0.1829	0.1912	0.1997	0.2082	0.2169	0.2256	0.2345	0.2434	0.2524	0.2615	0.2706	0.2799	0.2891	0.2984	0.3078	14
15	0.1794	0.1878	0.1964	0.2051	0.2139	0.2228	0.2317	0.2408	0.2499	0.2591	0.2684	0.2777	0.2871	0.2965	0.3060	15
16	0.1764	0.1850	0.1937	0.2025	0.2114	0.2204	0.2295	0.2387	0.2479	0.2572	0.2666	0.2760	0.2855	0.2950	0.3046	16
17	0.1740	0.1827	0.1915	0.2004	0.2094	0.2186	0.2278	0.2370	0.2464	0.2558	0.2652	0.2747	0.2843	0.2939	0.3035	17
18	0.1719	0.1807	0.1896	0.1987	0.2078	0.2170	0.2263	0.2357	0.2451	0.2546	0.2641	0.2737	0.2833	0.2930	0.3027	18
19	0.1701	0.1791	0.1881	0.1972	0.2065	0.2158	0.2251	0.2346	0.2441	0.2537	0.2633	0.2729	0.2826	0.2923	0.3021	19
20	0.1687	0.1777	0.1868	0.1960	0.2054	0.2147	0.2242	0.2337	0.2433	0.2529	0.2626	0.2723	0.2820	0.2918	0.3016	20
21	0.1674	0.1765	0.1857	0.1951	0.2044	0.2139	0.2234	0.2330	0.2426	0.2523	0.2620	0.2718	0.2816	0.2914	0.3012	21
22	0.1664	0.1756	0.1848	0.1942	0.2037	0.2132	0.2228	0.2324	0.2421	0.2519	0.2616	0.2717	0.2812	0.2911	0.3009	22
23	0.1654	0.1747	0.1841	0.1935	0.2031	0.2127	0.2223	0.2320	0.2417	0.2515	0.2613	0.2711	0.2810	0.2908	0.3007	23
24	0.1647	0.1740	0.1835	0.1930	0.2025	0.2122	0.2219	0.2316	0.2414	0.2512	0.2610	0.2709	0.2808	0.2906	0.3006	24
25	0.1640	0.1734	0.1829	0.1925	0.2021	0.2118	0.2215	0.2313	0.2411	0.2509	0.2608	0.2707	0.2806	0.2905	0.3004	25

Table 6 Area under the standard normal curve up to z standard units above the mean

z	0.00	0.01	0.02	0.03	0.04	0.05	0.06	0.07	0.08	0.09
0.0	0.5000	0.5040	0.5080	0.5120	0.5160	0.5199	0.5239	0.5279	0.5319	0.5359
0.1	0.5398	0.5438	0.5478	0.5517	0.5557	0.5596	0.5636	0.5675	0.5714	0.5753
0.2	0.5793	0.5832	0.5871	0.5910	0.5948	0.5987	0.6026	0.6064	0.6103	0.6141
0.3	0.6179	0.6217	0.6255	0.6293	0.6331	0.6368	0.6406	0.6443	0.6480	0.6517
0.4	0.6554	0.6591	0.6628	0.6664	0.6700	0.6736	0.6772	0.6808	0.6844	0.6879
0.5	0.6915	0.6950	0.6985	0.7019	0.7054	0.7088	0.7123	0.7157	0.7190	0.7224
0.6	0.7257	0.7291	0.7324	0.7357	0.7389	0.7422	0.7454	0.7486	0.7517	0.7549
0.7	0.7580	0.7611	0.7642	0.7673	0.7704	0.7734	0.7764	0.7794	0.7823	0.7852
0.8	0.7881	0.7910	0.7939	0.7967	0.7995	0.8023	0.8051	0.8078	0.8106	0.8133
0.9	0.8159	0.8186	0.8212	0.8238	0.8264	0.8289	0.8315	0.8340	0.8365	0.8389
1.0	0.8413	0.8438	0.8461	0.8485	0.8508	0.8531	0.8554	0.8577	0.8599	0.8621
1.1	0.8643	0.8665	0.8686	0.8708	0.8729	0.8749	0.8770	0.8790	0.8810	0.8830
1.2	0.8849	0.8869	0.8888	0.8907	0.8925	0.8944	0.8962	0.8980	0.8997	0.9015
1.3	0.9032	0.9049	0.9066	0.9082	0.9099	0.9115	0.9131	0.9147	0.9162	0.9177
1.4	0.9192	0.9207	0.9222	0.9236	0.9251	0.9265	0.9279	0.9292	0.9306	0.9319
1.5	0.9332	0.9345	0.9357	0.9370	0.9382	0.9394	0.9406	0.9418	0.9429	0.9441
1.6	0.9452	0.9463	0.9474	0.9484	0.9495	0.9505	0.9515	0.9525	0.9535	0.9545
1.7	0.9554	0.9564	0.9573	0.9582	0.9591	0.9599	0.9608	0.9616	0.9625	0.9633
1.8	0.9641	0.9649	0.9656	0.9664	0.9671	0.9678	0.9686	0.9693	0.9699	0.9706
1.9	0.9713	0.9719	0.9726	0.9732	0.9738	0.9744	0.9750	0.9756	0.9761	0.9767
2.0	0.9772	0.9778	0.9783	0.9788	0.9793	0.9798	0.9803	0.9808	0.9812	0.9817
2.1	0.9821	0.9826	0.9830	0.9834	0.9838	0.9842	0.9846	0.9850	0.9854	0.9857
2.2	0.9861	0.9864	0.9868	0.9871	0.9875	0.9878	0.9881	0.9884	0.9887	0.9890
2.3	0.9893	0.9896	0.9898	0.9901	0.9904	0.9906	0.9909	0.9911	0.9913	0.9916
2.4	0.9918	0.9920	0.9922	0.9925	0.9927	0.9929	0.9931	0.9932	0.9934	0.9936
2.5	0.9938	0.9940	0.9941	0.9943	0.9945	0.9946	0.9948	0.9949	0.9951	0.9952
2.6	0.9953	0.9955	0.9956	0.9957	0.9959	0.9960	0.9961	0.9962	0.9963	0.9964
2.7	0.9965	0.9966	0.9967	0.9968	0.9969	0.9970	0.9971	0.9972	0.9973	0.9974
2.8	0.9974	0.9975	0.9976	0.9977	0.9977	0.9978	0.9979	0.9979	0.9980	0.9981
2.9	0.9981	0.9982	0.9982	0.9983	0.9984	0.9984	0.9985	0.9985	0.9986	0.9986
3.0	0.9987	0.9987	0.9987	0.9988	0.9988	0.9989	0.9989	0.9989	0.9990	0.9990
3.1	0.9990	0.9991	0.9991	0.9991	0.9992	0.9992	0.9992	0.9992	0.9993	0.9993
3.2	0.9993	0.9993	0.9994	0.9994	0.9994	0.9994	0.9994	0.9995	0.9995	0.9995
3.3	0.9995	0.9995	0.9995	0.9996	0.9996	0.9996	0.9996	0.9996	0.9996	0.9997
3.4	0.9997	0.9997	0.9997	0.9997	0.9997	0.9997	0.9997	0.9997	0.9997	0.9998
3.5	0.9998	0.9998	0.9998	0.9998	0.9998	0.9998	0.9998	0.9998	0.9998	0.9998
3.6	0.9998	0.9998	0.9999	0.9999	0.9999	0.9999	0.9999	0.9999	0.9999	0.9999

Table 7 Poisson probabilities $(T = 1)$; $\lambda^n e^{-\lambda}/n!$

λ \ n	0	1	2	3	4	5	6	7	8	9	10	11	12
0.1	0.9048	0.0905	0.0045	0.0002	0.0000								
0.2	0.8187	0.1637	0.0164	0.0011	0.0001								
0.3	0.7408	0.2222	0.0333	0.0033	0.0002								
0.4	0.6703	0.2681	0.0536	0.0072	0.0007	0.0001							
0.5	0.6065	0.3033	0.0758	0.0126	0.0016	0.0002							
0.6	0.5488	0.3293	0.0988	0.0198	0.0030	0.0004	0.0000						
0.7	0.4966	0.3476	0.1217	0.0284	0.0050	0.0007	0.0001	0.0000					
0.8	0.4493	0.3595	0.1438	0.0383	0.0077	0.0012	0.0002	0.0000					
0.9	0.4066	0.3659	0.1647	0.0494	0.0111	0.0020	0.0003	0.0000					
1.0	0.3679	0.3679	0.1839	0.0613	0.0153	0.0031	0.0005	0.0001	0.0000				
1.1	0.3329	0.3662	0.2014	0.0738	0.0203	0.0045	0.0008	0.0001	0.0000				
1.2	0.3012	0.3614	0.2169	0.0867	0.0260	0.0062	0.0012	0.0002	0.0000				
1.3	0.2725	0.3543	0.2303	0.0998	0.0324	0.0084	0.0018	0.0003	0.0001	0.0000			
1.4	0.2466	0.3452	0.2417	0.1128	0.0395	0.0111	0.0026	0.0005	0.0001	0.0000			
1.5	0.2231	0.3347	0.2510	0.1255	0.0471	0.0141	0.0035	0.0008	0.0001	0.0000			
1.6	0.2019	0.3230	0.2584	0.1378	0.0551	0.0176	0.0047	0.0011	0.0002	0.0000	0.0000		
1.7	0.1827	0.3106	0.2640	0.1496	0.0636	0.0216	0.0061	0.0015	0.0003	0.0001	0.0000		
1.8	0.1653	0.2975	0.2678	0.1607	0.0723	0.0260	0.0078	0.0020	0.0005	0.0001	0.0000		
1.9	0.1496	0.2842	0.2700	0.1710	0.0812	0.0309	0.0098	0.0027	0.0006	0.0001	0.0000		
2.0	0.1353	0.2707	0.2707	0.1804	0.0902	0.0361	0.0120	0.0034	0.0009	0.0002	0.0000		
2.2	0.1108	0.2438	0.2681	0.1966	0.1082	0.0476	0.0174	0.0055	0.0015	0.0004	0.0001	0.0000	
2.4	0.0907	0.2177	0.2613	0.2090	0.1254	0.0602	0.0241	0.0083	0.0025	0.0007	0.0002	0.0000	
2.6	0.0743	0.1931	0.2510	0.2176	0.1414	0.0735	0.0319	0.0118	0.0038	0.0011	0.0003	0.0001	0.0000
2.8	0.0608	0.1703	0.2384	0.2225	0.1557	0.0872	0.0407	0.0163	0.0057	0.0018	0.0005	0.0001	0.0000
3.0	0.0498	0.1494	0.2240	0.2240	0.1680	0.1008	0.0504	0.0216	0.0081	0.0027	0.0008	0.0002	0.0001

n / λ	0	1	2	3	4	5	6	7	8	9	10	11	12
3.2	0.0408	0.1304	0.2087	0.2226	0.1781	0.1140	0.0608	0.0278	0.0111	0.0040	0.0013	0.0004	0.0001
3.4	0.0334	0.1135	0.1929	0.2186	0.1858	0.1264	0.0716	0.0348	0.0148	0.0056	0.0019	0.0006	0.0002
3.6	0.0273	0.0984	0.1771	0.2125	0.1912	0.1377	0.0826	0.0425	0.0191	0.0076	0.0028	0.0009	0.0003
3.8	0.0224	0.0850	0.1615	0.2046	0.1944	0.1477	0.0936	0.0508	0.0241	0.0102	0.0039	0.0013	0.0004
4.0	0.0183	0.0733	0.1465	0.1954	0.1954	0.1563	0.1042	0.0595	0.0298	0.0132	0.0053	0.0019	0.0006
5.0	0.0067	0.0337	0.0842	0.1404	0.1755	0.1755	0.1462	0.1044	0.0653	0.0363	0.0181	0.0082	0.0034
6.0	0.0025	0.0149	0.0446	0.0892	0.1339	0.1606	0.1606	0.1377	0.1033	0.0688	0.0413	0.0225	0.0113
7.0	0.0009	0.0064	0.0223	0.0521	0.0912	0.1277	0.1490	0.1490	0.1304	0.1014	0.0710	0.0452	0.0263
8.0	0.0003	0.0027	0.0107	0.0286	0.0573	0.0916	0.1221	0.1396	0.1396	0.1241	0.0993	0.0722	0.0481
9.0	0.0001	0.0011	0.0050	0.0150	0.0337	0.0607	0.0911	0.1171	0.1318	0.1318	0.1186	0.0970	0.0728
10.0	0.0000	0.0005	0.0023	0.0076	0.0189	0.0378	0.0631	0.0901	0.1126	0.1251	0.1251	0.1137	0.0948

INDEX